## PROJECT MATHS

G000060076

# Text & Tests 3

## LEAVING CERTIFICATE
## ORDINARY LEVEL
## STRANDS 1 & 2

## O. D. MORRIS

 The Celtic Press

*Acknowledgements*
I would like to express my deep gratitude to Paul Cooke and Paul Behan for the enormous contributions they have made to the contents and design of this book.

First Published in 2010 by
The Celtic Press
Educational Publishers,
Goldenbridge, Dublin 8.

Reprinted with corrections August 2010

ISBN: 978-1-907705-05-2

*Design*: Philip Ryan
*Layout and artwork*: Tech-Set Limited
*Photography*: Simon Wakefield, David Iliff, Mila Zinkova
whose work has been reproduced herein under
Creative Commons Attribution-Share Alike licenses.

Printed and bound in Ireland by
Colour Books Limited,
Baldoyle,
Dublin 13.

# Table of Contents

# Introduction

This book was compiled and written for ***Project Maths – Strands 1 and 2*** of the Leaving Certificate, Ordinary Level. The book reflects the overall approach to the teaching of maths as envisaged in *Project Maths*. It encourages the development of not only the students' mathematical knowledge and skills but also the understanding needed for continuing their learning of maths.

There is an excellent range of imaginatively written and probing questions on each topic which will help students to understand what they are doing and to develop their problem solving skills. A sufficient number of questions in varying degrees of difficulty have been provided to satisfy the needs of the vast majority of students at this level.

The motivating and stimulating full-colour design together with the large number of well constructed diagrams should help the student's understanding of the topic being studied. At the beginning of each chapter there is a list of ***Key Words*** that students are expected to know and understand when the chapter is completed. Each chapter concludes with a blue coloured ***Test Yourself*** section which provides comprehensive consolidation and revision. The ***Summary of Key Points*** page in each chapter will remind the student of key facts and important formulae.

The chapters in each of the two Strands are kept together in this book. However, it is left to the teachers to select chapters from these Strands based on the progress and requirements of their classes. The intention and aims of the new strands are to build on the students' Junior Certificate experience. It is hoped that their greater understanding of what they are doing will encourage and motivate them in their learning of maths at this level.

O. D. Morris, April 2010

# Collecting Data and Sampling

# chapter 1

## Key Words

| | | | | |
|---|---|---|---|---|
| data | numerical | discrete | continuous | categorical data |
| ordinal | univariate | bivariate | primary data | secondary data |
| survey | experiment | data capture sheet | | questionnaire |
| respondent | bias | population | simple random sample | |

## Introduction

The charts and diagrams below can be seen regularly in newspapers, magazines and on television.

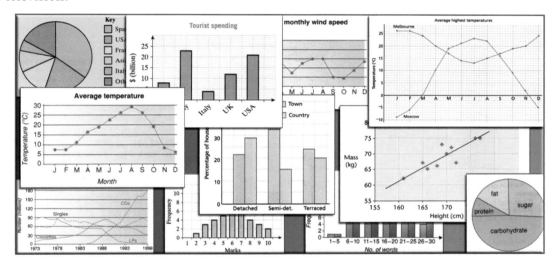

They are an attempt to present facts, figures and information in a way that is easy to understand. The information that is gathered is generally called **data**. The branch of mathematics that deals with collecting, presenting and analysing data is called **statistics**.

Statistics is generally concerned with
- collecting and recording data
- sorting and organising the data
- representing data in the form of charts and diagrams
- making calculations and choosing a suitable average
- interpreting the results and drawing conclusions from them.

This chapter introduces us to the different types of data and discusses some of the methods

# SECTION 1.1  Types of data

Consider these questions:

- 'What is the most common shoe size in our class?'
- 'How many cars are there in the car park?'
- 'What were the times taken by a group of people to complete a crossword puzzle?'

To answer these questions we must either count or measure.

The answers to all three questions will be a number, e.g.,

> size 40 shoe;        134 cars;        26 minutes.

Data which can be counted or measured is called **numerical** data because the answer is a number. Numerical data can be either **discrete** or **continuous**.

## Discrete data

Data which can take only certain individual values is called **discrete data**.

Here are some examples of **discrete data**:

- The number of goals scored by football teams on a Saturday
- The numbers of desks in the classrooms of the school
- The marks achieved in a test.

## Continuous data

**Continuous data** is measured on some scale and can take any value on that scale.

Here are some examples of **continuous data**:

- The heights of students in your class
- The speeds of cars passing a certain point on a road
- The time taken to complete a 100-metre sprint

### Example 1

For each of these types of data, write down whether it is discrete or continuous.

- (i)   the number of coins in your pocket
- (ii)  the number of tickets sold for a concert
- (iii) the time taken to complete a puzzle
- (iv)  the weights of students in your class
- (v)   dress sizes.

| (i) discrete | (ii) discrete | (iii) continuous |
|---|---|---|
| (iv) continuous | (v) discrete | |

## Exercise 1.1

1. State if each of the following data is discrete or continuous:
   - (i)   The number of rooms in each of the houses on a road
   - (ii)  The number of CDs that have been sold
   - (iii) The weights of the eggs in a carton
   - (iv)  Shoe sizes
   - (v)   The number of kilometres travelled on one litre of petrol.

2. Amy takes 22 minutes to complete a maths problem.
   Is the 22 minutes a discrete or continuous variable?
   Explain your answer.

> A variable is something that is measured or observed.

3. A mechanic counts the number of spanners in his toolbox.
   Is this discrete or continuous data?
   Explain your answer.

4. Derek is examining a second-hand car.
   He is interested in
   (i)   the number of doors
   (ii)  the year of manufacture
   (iii) the number of kilometres travelled.
   State if each of these three variables is discrete or continuous.

5. Sonia recorded how long it took her to run a cross-country race and the race-number on her bib.
   Say if each of these variables is discrete or continuous.

6. For each of these types of data, write down whether it is discrete or continuous.
   (i)    The number of coins collected by a street performer.
   (ii)   The length of a road.
   (iii)  Shirt sizes.
   (iv)   The midday temperature for each day in July.
   (v)    The marks given by judges in a competition.
   (vi)   The area of a field.
   (vii)  The numbers of buttons on a selection of shirts.

July Midday Temperatures

| JULY | | | | | | 2008 |
|------|------|------|------|------|------|------|
| SUN | MON | TUE | WED | THU | FRI | SAT |
|  | 1 17 | 2 16 | 3 18 | 4 18 | 5 18 | 6 17 |
| 7 19 | 8 20 | 9 22 | 10 22 | 11 21 | 12 21 | 13 22 |
| 14 22 | 15 23 | 16 24 | 17 23 | 18 23 | 19 23 | 20 24 |
| 21 24 | 22 23 | 23 23 | 24 24 | 25 25 | 26 23 | 27 23 |
| 28 25 | 29 25 | 30 24 | 31 25 | | | |

7. Emma says she is 16 years of age.
   Explain why this response is actually *continuous* but may appear to be *discrete*.

## SECTION 1.2 Categorical data

The answer to the question, 'What colour is your car?' will not be a numerical value.
Rather, it will fit into a group or category such as blue, red, black, white, ...

Data which fits into a group or category is called **categorical data**.

Here are some examples of categorical data:

- gender (male, female)
- country of birth (Ireland, France, Spain, Nigeria,...)
- favourite sport (soccer, hurling, tennis, basketball...)

Categorical data in which the categories have an obvious order such as first division, second division, third division, etc, is called **ordinal data**.

Other examples of ordinal data are:

- type of house (1-bedroomed, 2-bedroomed, 3-bedroomed)
- attendance at football matches (never, sometimes, very often)
- opinion scales (strongly disagree, disagree, neutral, agree, strongly agree).

## Univariate data

When **one item** of information is collected, for example, from each member of a group of people, the data collected is called **univariate data**.

Examples of univariate data include:

- colour of eyes
- distance from school
- height in centimetres.

## Bivariate data

Data that contains **two items** of information such as the height and weight of a person is generally called **paired data** or **bivariate data**.

Examples of bivariate data are:

- hours of study per week and marks scored in an examination
- the age of a car and the price of that car
- the engine sizes of cars and the number of kilometres travelled on a litre of petrol.

Colour of hair and gender is an example of **bivariate categorical data**.

The number of rooms in a house and the number of children in the house is an example of **bivariate discrete data**.

---

### Example 1

For each of these sets of data, write down whether it is numerical or categorical:
- (i) the sizes of shoes sold in a shop
- (ii) the colours of shoes sold in a shop
- (iii) the subjects offered to Leaving Certificate students
- (iv) the marks given by judges in a debating competition
- (v) the crops grown on a village farm
- (vi) the area of your classroom.

|   |   |   |
|---|---|---|
| (i) numerical | (ii) categorical | (iii) categorical |
| (iv) numerical | (v) categorical | (vi) numerical. |

## Exercise 1.2

1.  State whether each of the following is categorical or numerical data:
    (i)   The number of bicycles sold by a shop in a particular week
    (ii)  The colours of cars sold by a garage last month
    (iii) The numbers of horses in the six races at a meeting
    (iv)  The favourite sports of all the students in a school.

2.  Imelda bought a new dress.
    She wrote down     (i)    the colour of the dress
                           (ii)    the number of buttons on the dress
                           (iii)    the length of the dress.
    For each of these data types, write down whether it is numerical or categorical.
    Which of the three is discrete data?

3.  State if each of the following is paired data:
    (i)   The colours of shirts on a stand
    (ii)  The ages and the heights of a group of students
    (iii) The number of brothers and their ages that each pupil in a class has.
    (iv)  The ages of all the people living on my street.

4.  *The number of desks in the classroom and the number of children in the class.*
    This is an example of discrete paired data.
    Write down two more examples of this type of data.

5.  *The amount of flour and the number of eggs needed to make a cake.*
    (i)   Explain why this is paired data.
    (ii)  Which part of the data is discrete?
    (iii) Which part of the data is continuous?

6.  All the football players in the premier league of a European country were categorised
    according to their ages and country of birth.
    Copy and complete this sentence:
    This is paired data; the first part is ......... data and the second part is ......... data.

7.  A doctor records information about her patients.
    The variables that she uses are described below:
    (i)   the colour of the patient's eyes
    (ii)  the patient's weight and height
    (iii) the patient's shoe size
    (iv)  the patient's blood group.
    State if each variable is    (a)   categorical     (b)   numerical.
    Which of the four data types is discrete?
    Describe in full the data type given in part (ii).

8. State whether each of the following statements is true or false.
   Give a reason for your answer in each case.
   (i)   The number of pockets on a jacket is discrete data.
   (ii)  The types of trees in a forest is categorical data.
   (iii) The countries in which people like to holiday is numerical data.
   (iv)  The number of bedrooms in each house on my street is categorical data.
   (v)   The age of a tree and the height of the tree is bivariate data.
   (vi)  The birth month of the students in your class is categorical data.
   (vii) The number of matches played and the number of goals scored is bivariate and discrete data.
   (viii) The weights of horses in a race and the times taken by the horses to complete the race is bivariate and continuous data.

9. Cars are often categorised as small, economy, family, executive and luxury.
   This is an example of **ordinal data**.
   Give three more examples of ordinal data.

# SECTION 1.3  Collecting data

Data is collected for a variety of reasons and from a variety of sources.

Companies do market research to find out what customers like or dislike about their products and to see whether or not they would like new products. The government carries out a census of every person in the country every five years. Local government, education authorities and other organisations use the information obtained for further planning.

Data can be collected by carrying out a survey, doing an experiment or by doing interviews and completing questionnaires.

Before you collect data, you need to have a clear aim in mind. You then need to decide what sort of data to collect and the most suitable and efficient method of collecting it.

The data you collect can be divided into two broad categories, namely, **primary data** and **secondary data**.

## Primary data

Data that is collected by an organisation or an individual who is going to use it is called **primary data**.

Primary data is generally obtained
- by using a questionnaire
- by carrying out an experiment
- by investigations
- by making observations and recording the results.

## Secondary data

Data which is already available or has been collected by somebody else for a different purpose is called **secondary data**.

Secondary data is obtained

- from the internet
- from published statistics and databases
- from tables and charts in newspapers and magazines.

The advantages and disadvantages of both types of data are given below.

| Data | Advantages | Disadvantages |
|---|---|---|
| Primary data | • It is possible to collect exactly what your require<br>• You know how it was collected<br>• You know from whom it was collected | • Expensive<br>• Time consuming |
| Secondary data | • Cheap to obtain<br>• Easy to obtain | • Method of collection unknown<br>• May be out of date<br>• May not be exactly what is required |

## Surveys

Surveys are particularly useful for collecting data that is likely to be personal.

The main survey methods are:

- postal surveys in which people are asked questions
- personal interviews in which people are asked questions; this type of survey is very widely used in market research.
- telephone surveys; here the interview is conducted by phone
- **observation**, which involves monitoring behaviour or information

| Survey method | Advantages | Disadvantages |
|---|---|---|
| Observation | Systematic and mechanical | Results are prone to chance |
| Personal interview and telephone survey | Many questions can be asked<br>High response rate | Expensive<br>Interviewer may influence responses |
| Postal survey | Relatively cheap<br>Large amounts of data can be collected | Limited in the type of data that can be collected<br>Poor response rate |

### Example 1

A businessman is considering building a leisure centre in the town centre. Which method of collecting primary data should he use to help him decide whether or not to build the leisure centre?

Data could be collected by using personal interviews or by doing a postal survey. The question 'Would you use a leisure centre if it was available?' should be included in any method used.

## Experiments

Experiments are particularly useful for collecting scientific data. Drug companies carry out experiments to check if a new drug has any benefits or side-effects.

When you carry out an experiment you can use a **data capture sheet** to record your results.

The following example illustrates Derek's experiment to test whether or not a dice is fair:

### Example 2

Derek has a six-sided dice. He throws it 60 times and records his results in a data capture sheet.

Derek 'expects' that each number on the dice should appear 10 times. He concludes that the dice is fair as all the frequencies are close enough to 10.

| Score | Tally | Frequency |
|-------|-------|-----------|
| 1 | JHT IIII | 9 |
| 2 | JHT JHT I | 11 |
| 3 | JHT JHT II | 12 |
| 4 | JHT IIII | 9 |
| 5 | JHT JHT | 10 |
| 6 | JHT IIII | 9 |

## Exercise 1.3

1. Write down whether each of the following is an example of primary data or secondary data:
   (i) Alan counted the number of red cars passing the school gate.
   (ii) Helen examined records at a maternity hospital to find out how many babies were born each day in December.
   (iii) Robbie threw a dice 100 times and recorded the results to investigate if the dice was fair.
   (iv) Niamh used the internet to check the number of gold medals won by each competing country at the Beijing Olympics.

2. Roy and Damien want to predict next season's football league champions.
   Roy looks at the results for the last 5 years.
   Damien looks at the results for the 5 years before that.
   (i) What type of data are they using?
   (ii) Whose data is likely to be the more reliable and why?

3. A confectionery company want to produce a new type of chocolate bar.
   Should they collect primary data or use secondary data?
   Give a reason for your answer.

4. A design company is given an assignment to design and market a new magazine aimed at younger women.
   (i) Explain how and why they could use both secondary and primary data.
   (ii) State one method of collecting primary data.

**5.** A government agency carried out a survey to find out what percentage of letters posted arrived at their destination on the following day. It surveyed ten businesses in Dublin city centre.

    (i) Do you think the results of this survey would match the results of the same survey if carried out in County Kerry?

    (ii) Would the information gathered be primary or secondary data?

# SECTION 1.4 Questionnaires

A **questionnaire** is a set of questions designed to obtain data from individuals.

People who answer questionnaires are called **respondents**.

There are two ways in which the questions can be asked.
- An interviewer asks the questions and fills in the questionnaire
- People are given a questionnaire and asked to fill in the responses.

When you are writing questions for a questionnaire,
- be clear what you want to find out and what data you need
- ask short, simple questions
- start with simple questions to encourage the person who is giving the responses
- provide response boxes where possible:   Yes ☐     No ☐
- avoid leading questions such as
  
  'Don't you agree that there is too much sport on television?'
  
  or   'Do you think that professional footballers are overpaid?'
- avoid personal questions such as those which involve name, exact weight or age.

## Multiple-response questions

A choice of responses can be very useful in replying to the question, 'What age are you?'

Here is an example:      Tick your age in the box below:

           ☐        ☐       ☐       ☐

   Under 18 years   18–30   31–50   Over 50

Notice that there are no gaps in the ages and that only one response applies to each person.

## Opinion scales

If you use an opinion scale, responses tend to cluster around the middle of the scale as often people do not want to appear extreme.

An opinion scale generally looks like this:

☐    ☐    ☐    ☐    ☐

strongly   disagree   no opinion   agree   strongly
disagree                                    agree

> One way to avoid a middle cluster is to provide an even number of options so that there is no middle choice.

Sometimes respondents are asked to mark a point somewhere along a scale like that shown on the right.

disagree             agree

Again, there is a tendency to choose a point around the middle.

## Avoiding bias

When you are collecting data, you need to make sure that your survey or experiment is **fair** and avoids **bias**. If bias exists, the data collected might be unrepresentative.

The boxes given below contain questions that should be avoided because they are too **vague**, too **personal**, or may **influence** the answer.

How often do you play tennis?

Sometimes ☐    Occasionally ☐    Often ☐

The three words *sometimes*, *occasionally* and *often* mean different things to different people.

Normal people enjoy swimming.
Do you enjoy swimming?

Yes ☐      No ☐

This is a leading question and may cause the result to be biased.
The first sentence should not be there.

Have you ever stolen goods from a supermarket?

Yes ☐      No ☐

Few people are likely to answer this question honestly if they have already stolen.

Do you agree that the EU is now big enough?

Yes ☐      No ☐

This question suggests that the right answer is yes.
It is **biased?**.

Whenever you undertake a survey or experiment it is sensible to do a **pilot survey**. A pilot survey is one that is carried out on a very small scale to make sure the design and methods of the survey are likely to produce the information required. It should identify any problems with the wording of questions and likely responses.

Avoid **personal** questions like 'Are you well educated?' or 'Where do you live?'

## Exercise 1.4

1. Here is a list of questions and statements.
   For each one, write down the letter of the style of response you would use.

   (a) ☐ Yes    ☐ No    ☐ Don't know

   (b) ☐ Agree    ☐ Disagree    ☐ Don't know

   (c) ☐ 0    ☐ 1    ☐ 2    ☐ 3 or more

    (i)   How many children are there in your family?
    (ii)  Is Bulgaria is a member of the European Union?
    (iii) Smoking damages your health.
    (iv)  Everybody should exercise for at least one hour each day.

2.  Susan wants to find out what people think about the Green Party.
    She is trying to decide between these two questions for her questionnaire.
    (i)   Do you like the Green Party?
          Yes ☐         No ☐
    (ii)  Do you agree that the Green Party is the best party?
          Yes ☐         No ☐
    Which question should she use? Explain your answer.

3.  Jack wants to find out what students think about the library service at his college.
    Part of the questionnaire he has written is shown.

    Q1.  What is your full name? ...................................................................
    Q2.  How many times a week do you go to the library?
         ☐ Often       ☐ Sometimes       ☐ Never

    (i)   Why should Q1 not be asked?
    (ii)  What is wrong with the choices offered in Q2?

4.  Terry is writing a questionnaire about people's ages. In it she asks the question:

    How old are you?     Young ☐     Middle-aged ☐     Elderly ☐

    (i)   What is wrong with the question and answers?
    (ii)  Rewrite the question and answers in a better way.

5.  Carol wants to find out what people think of the HSE.
    Part of the questionnaire she has written is shown.

    Q1.  What is your date of birth? ...............................................................
    Q2.  Don't you agree that waiting times for operations are too long?
         Yes ☐   No ☐
    Q3.  How many times did you visit your doctor last year?
         ☐ less than 5     ☐ 5–10     ☐ 10 or more

    (i)   Why should Q1 not be asked?
    (ii)  Give a reason why Q2 is unsuitable.
    (iii) (a) Explain why the responses to Q3 are unsuitable in their present form.
          (b) Rewrite a more suitable question to be included in the questionnaire.

6. Which of the following questions do you think are biased?
   Write down their letters and explain what makes them biased.
   A: Did you go to a cinema in the last month?
   B: It is important to eat fruit. Do you eat fruit?
   C: How many hours of television do you watch each week?
   D: In view of the huge numbers of road accidents outside this school, do you think the speed limit should be reduced?

7. Decide if the given question is suitable for use in a questionnaire.
   If it is not, give a reason why and rewrite the question to improve it.

   How much pocket money do you get?
   a little ☐   some ☐
   a lot ☐

8. Angela is doing a questionnaire because she wants some information about the weights of people in her school. She asks them:
   How much do you weigh?
   (i)   Explain why that is not a good question to ask.
   (ii)  Write a better question and give a set of response boxes with it.

9. Give a reason why questions A and B below should be re-worded before being included in a questionnaire.
   Rewrite each one showing exactly how you would present it in a questionnaire.
   **Question A:**   Do you live in a working-class or middle-class area?
   **Question B:**   The new supermarket seems to be a great success. Do you agree?

10. Steve is doing a survey on football teams.
    He writes a question and response boxes:
    (i)   Give your reasons why Steve should not ask the question in such a way.
    (ii)  Write a better question for Steve to use.

    How often do you watch a football match?
    Never ☐   Once a week ☐
    When I can ☐

11. In preparing questions for a survey on the use of a library, the following questions were considered. Explain why each question in its present form is unsuitable and rewrite the question.
    (i)    Are you well educated or poorly educated?
    (ii)   How often do you use the library?
    (iii)  What type of books do you read?

12. A mobile phone company wants to carry out a survey.
    It wants to find out the distribution of the age and sex of customers and the frequency with which they use their phones.
    The company intends to use a questionnaire.
    Write three questions and corresponding responses that will enable the company to carry out the survey.

13. A market research company is conducting a survey to find out whether most people had a holiday in Ireland, elsewhere in Europe or in the rest of the world, last year. It also wants to know if they stayed in self-catering accommodation, hotels or went camping.

    Design **two** questions that could be used in a questionnaire to efficiently find out all this information.

14. Niamh has to carry out a survey into the part-time jobs of all the 16-year-olds in her school.

    She has to find out:
    - what proportion of these 16-year-olds have part-time jobs
    - whether more girls than boys have part-time jobs.

    Design **two** questions which she could include in her questionnaire.

15. Ian is writing a questionnaire.

    These are two of his questions:
    (a)  Do you spend a lot of time surfing the Internet?
    (b)  What do you weigh?
      (i)   What is wrong with each of these questions?
      (ii)  Rewrite each question, showing exactly how Ian should present it in a questionnaire.

16. Grace and Gemma were carrying out a survey on the food people eat in the school canteen.

    Grace wrote the question 'Which foods do you eat?'

    Gemma said that this question was too vague.

    Write down two ways in which this question could be improved.

17. Design a questionnaire consisting of six questions to find out about the kind of holidays people had last year.

18. A survey of reading habits is to be conducted.

    Suggest five questions which could be included.


# SECTION 1.5  Sampling

If you were asked to investigate the claim that

> '14 year-old boys are taller than 14-year old girls in Ireland',

do you measure the heights of all 14-year olds in Ireland and compare the results for boys and girls? This could be an enormous task as there are about 60 000 14-year olds in this country.

In this study, we use the word **population** to describe all the 14-year old boys and girls in Ireland. In statistics a **population** is everything or everybody that could possibly be involved in a particular investigation or study.

When a population is too large for a study, we collect data or information from some of the population only.

In statistics this group is called **a sample**. The purpose of a sample is to collect data from some of the population and use it to draw conclusions about the whole population.

The **size** of a sample is important. If the sample is too small, the results may not be very reliable. If the sample is too large, the data may take a long time to collect and analyse.

## Bias

The sample you select for your study is very important. If the sample is not properly selected, the results may be **biased**. If **bias** exists, the results will be distorted and so will not be representative of the population as a whole.

**Bias** in a sample may arise from any of the following:

- **Choosing a sample which is not representative**

    **Example**    Cara is doing a survey on people's attitude towards gambling. If she stands outside a casino and questions people as they enter or leave, the results will be biased as these people are already involved in gambling.

- **Not identifying the correct population**

    **Example**    The school principal wants to find out about students' attitudes to school uniforms. She questions 10 Leaving Certificate students only. This may lead to biased results as the opinions of the younger students (from 1st year to 5th year) are not included.

- **Failure to respond to a survey**
    Many people do not fill in responses to questionnaires sent through the post. Those who do respond may not be representative of the population being surveyed.

- **Dishonest answers to questions**

---

### Example 1

Conor carries out a survey to find out if people in his town enjoy watching sport.
He stands outside a football ground and surveys people's opinions as they go in to watch a match.
Write two reasons why this is not a good sample to use.

(i)   People who go to watch football matches usually enjoy sport; hence the sample may be biased.
(ii)  Generally more men than women go to watch football, so the survey could be gender-biased.

---

## Simple random sample

One of the ways to avoid bias in a survey is to take a **simple random sample** (or more commonly called a **random sample**).

In a random sample every member of the population being considered has an equal chance of being selected. Random samples need to be carefully chosen.

Methods for choosing a **simple random sample** could involve giving each member of the population a number and then selecting the numbers for the sample in one of these ways:
- putting the numbers into a hat and then selecting however many you need for the sample
- using a random number table
- using a random number generator on your calculator or computer

---

### Example 2

A football club with 80 members has 5 tickets for an international match. Describe two methods of choosing 5 members at random to receive these tickets.

**Method 1**    Each member is given a number and each number is written on a piece of paper.
The pieces of paper are put into a box and mixed up well and five pieces are chosen.
The members with the five numbers chosen receive the tickets.

**Method 2**    Below is an extract from a random number table:

526338    127642    463919    394821    563271
265389    276153    584326    427534    307263

We need to give each of the 80 members a two-digit number. Start at 11 and end at 90.
We now have to select five two-digit numbers from the random numbers above. These numbers have to be between 11 and 90 inclusive.
If we start at the beginning of the first row and select two digit numbers we get:

52, 63, 38, 12, 76.

(Ignore any number over 90 or any repeated number.)
The members with the five selected numbers receive the tickets.

---

Electronic calculators are very useful for generating random numbers.

If you want to generate 3-digit numbers, press $\boxed{\text{SHIFT}}$, and then press $\boxed{\text{Ran \#}}$ .

Now press $\boxed{=}$ and disregard the decimal point.

If the number displayed is 0.107, write 107.

Press $\boxed{=}$ repeatedly to get more random numbers.

## Exercise 1.5

1. Dara wants to find out how people get to work each day.
   Which of the following is the most appropriate group to question?
   A: Every fourth person at a bus stop.
   B: A group of people at lunch break.
   C: People arriving late for work.

2. Jennifer wants to investigate if people want longer prison sentences for criminals.
   Which of the following is the most appropriate group to question?
   A: Members of the gardaí.
   B: People at a football match.
   C: People who have been in prison.

3. Kate is doing a survey to find out how often people go to the cinema and how they
   travel to get there.
   She stands outside a cinema and questions people as they go in.
   Give a reason why this sample could be biased.

4. A county engineer is carrying out a traffic survey.
   He is trying to find out how busy a particular road is.
   Each day, he counts the numbers of cars passing a particular point between 2 p.m. and 3 p.m.
   He uses this information to write a report.
   State why his sample is likely to be biased.

5. Amy wants to find out how often people play sport.
   She went to a local sports shop and questioned the people she met.
   Explain why this sample is likely to be biased.

6. Trudy is investigating shopping habits.
   She interviews 50 women at her local supermarket on a Tuesday morning.
   Give three reasons why her sample may be biased.

7. Amanda wants to choose a sample of 500 adults from the town where she lives.
   She considers these methods of choosing her sample:
   Method 1:   Choose people shopping in the town centre on Saturday mornings.
   Method 2:   Choose names at random from the electoral register.
   Method 3:   Choose people living in the streets near her house.
   Which method is most likely to produce an unbiased sample?
   Give a reason for your answer.

8. Below is an extract from a table of random numbers.
   Use these numbers to select a simple random sample of 5 from a population of 50:

   | | | | | |
   |---|---|---|---|---|
   | 88715 | 59454 | 76218 | 59364 | 20641 |
   | 57169 | 94386 | 27856 | 10856 | 35728 |

9. The chart on the right gives the sex and heights in metres of 30 children.

   (i)  From this population of 30 children, choose a random sample of 5 children. Use the random number table below to do this.

   | 55 | 97 | 62 | 89 |
   |----|----|----|----|
   | 10 | 83 | 12 | 22 |
   | 55 | 23 | 52 | 11 |
   | 27 | 19 | 29 | 43 |
   | 93 | 86 | 46 | 14 |

   | Child | Height | Sex | Child | Height | Sex |
   |-------|--------|-----|-------|--------|-----|
   | 01 | 1.43 | M | 16 | 1.25 | F |
   | 02 | 0.98 | F | 17 | 0.89 | F |
   | 03 | 1.24 | M | 18 | 1.62 | M |
   | 04 | 0.87 | F | 19 | 1.20 | F |
   | 05 | 1.10 | F | 20 | 1.53 | M |
   | 06 | 1.15 | F | 21 | 1.60 | M |
   | 07 | 1.29 | M | 22 | 1.23 | F |
   | 08 | 0.94 | M | 23 | 1.44 | M |
   | 09 | 1.00 | M | 24 | 1.30 | F |
   | 10 | 1.21 | F | 25 | 1.00 | F |
   | 11 | 1.53 | F | 26 | 1.54 | F |
   | 12 | 1.43 | M | 27 | 1.12 | M |
   | 13 | 1.27 | M | 28 | 0.98 | F |
   | 14 | 1.24 | M | 29 | 1.06 | M |
   | 15 | 1.42 | F | 30 | 1.25 | F |

   Begin by using the first row. Write down the height and sex of each child in the chosen sample.

   (ii)  Choose a second sample of 5 children.
        Use the same random number table, but begin by using the second line.
        Write down the height and sex of each child in the chosen sample.

10. Use the ⌊Ran #⌋ key on your calculator to choose another random sample of 5 children from the chart in question 9 above.

11. Paul needs to choose a sample of 100 members from his sports club.
    He writes down three possible methods of choosing his sample.
    (i)   He chooses the names at random from the complete list of members on the club's database.
    (ii)  He chooses the members who play in the club football teams.
    (iii) He asks people using the club on a Monday morning.
          For each of Paul's methods, state whether the sample is likely to be biased, explaining your answer.

12. Describe three ways of selecting a simple random sample of 10 pupils from a school of 100 pupils.

13. There are 1000 pupils in Alan's school. Alan samples 50 pupils at random and asks them to complete his survey.
    He finds that 15 of the pupils in the sample read comics.
    Estimate the number of pupils in the school who read comics.

# TEST YOURSELF 1

1. State whether each of the following sets of data is numerical or categorical:
    (i)    The heights of trees in a wood.
    (ii)   The types of vegetables grown on a farm.
    (iii)  The favourite football team of the students in my school.
    (iv)   The distance between home and school.
    (v)    County of birth.
    (vi)   Time taken to complete a cross-country race.
    (vii)  The brands of toothpaste on sale in supermarkets.

2. Which of the following are discrete data and which are continuous data?
    (i)    The numbers of windows in houses.
    (ii)   The number of pupils who wear glasses.
    (iii)  The weights of eggs in a carton.
    (iv)   The time taken to complete a maths puzzle.
    (v)    The numbers of matches in a selection of match boxes.
    (vi)   The lengths of material used to make curtains.

3. State whether each of the following is primary data or secondary data:
    (i)    Counting the number of hatchback cars passing the school gate.
    (ii)   Looking at records to see how many people passed through Shannon Airport each day in June one year.
    (iii)  Phoning local supermarkets and stores to find the hourly pay rates for part-time work.
    (iv)   Checking the internet to see how many medals each  country won at the Vancouver Winter Olympics.
    (v)    Examining tourist brochures to find the average midday temperatures of selected cities for the month of June.

4. State whether each of the following is univariate data or bivariate data:
    (i)    the shirt size of men
    (ii)   hours of study and marks scored in a Science test
    (iii)  midday temperature and number of ice-creams sold
    (iv)   weekly pocket money of the students in your class
    (v)    the weight of a parcel and the cost of posting that parcel.

5. For each of these questions or statements, what would be the best way to collect the data? Choose from the box.
    (i)    What sport do people in your class watch most often?

    **A** questionnaire or data collection sheet
    **B** experiment        **C** other source

    (ii)   How often do people go to the cinema? On which days?
    (iii)  What percentage of motor vehicle accidents in Ireland occur between 6 p.m. and midnight?
    (iv)   Eoin wants to find out if a dice is biased.

(v) Sarah wants to find out how many people in her class can run 100 metres in less than 15 seconds.
(vi) How people intend to vote in the next election?
(vii) The number of times a person scores a double in a game of darts.
(viii) What people think of the local bus service?
(ix) Where people go for their summer holidays.
(x) What percentage of accidents are caused by drunk drivers?

**6.** Matthew decides to do a survey in his school about the benefits of physical exercise. This is part of Matthew's questionnaire

**Question** *Don't you agree that adults who were sportsmen when they were younger suffer more from injuries as they get older?*

**Response** *Tick one box*
☐ Yes     ☐ Usually     ☐ Sometimes     ☐ Occasionally

(i) Write down one criticism of Matthew's question.
(ii) Write down one criticism of Matthew's response section.

**7.** Pam writes a questionnaire to survey opinion on whether cars should be banned from the town centre.
(i) Which two of the following points are important when she is deciding which people to ask?
   A   Ask people who look friendly.
   B   Ask people at different times of the day.
   C   Ask some men and some women.
   D   Ask the first people she sees.
(ii) Which two of the following points are important when she is writing the questionnaire?
   A   Write polite questions.
   B   Write as many questions as she can think of.
   C   Write questions for car drivers only.
   D   Write questions that do not require long answers.

**8.** Katie is conducting a survey on television viewing habits.
She thinks of two questions for the questionnaire.

**Question 1.**   Do you consider yourself to be intelligent?
**Question 2.**   When do you watch television?

(i) Explain why each of these questions is unsuitable.
(ii) Rewrite each of these questions so that she could include them in her questionnaire.

**9.** Write two questions for a questionnaire to test the truth of these statements:
   A:  Most people choose to shop in a supermarket where it is easy to park a car.
   B:  Children of school-going age watch more television than their parents.

10. This statement is made on a television programme about health.

"Three in every eight pupils do not take any exercise out of school."

  (i)  A school has 584 pupils.
       According to the television programme, how many of these pupils do not take any exercise outside school?
  (ii) Claire says, 'I go to the gym twice a week after school.'
       She decides to do a survey to investigate what exercise other pupils do outside of school.
       Write down **two** questions that she could ask.

11. Describe how you would choose a simple random sample of 20 children from a year-group with 100 pupils.

12. A teacher, with responsibility for school meals, wants to hear students' opinions on the meals currently provided. She waits next to the dinner queue and questions the first 50 students as they pass.
    Do you think this sample might be biased in some way?
    Explain your answer.

13. A pollster working for RTE wants to know how many people are watching a new series which is being shown. She questions 200 people as they are leaving a supermarket between 10:00 and 12:00 one Thursday.
    (i)  Do you think that this sample might be biased? Explain your answer.
    (ii) Suggest a more suitable way of selecting a sample.

14. A survey is being conducted in a school containing roughly equal numbers of boys and girls. For each of the following methods, say whether the results would be a random sample or if they would be biased.
    If you think the results are biased, explain why.
    A:  Taking all surnames on a school list beginning with H.
    B:  Taking only 10 boys in each year group.
    C:  Putting all the names into a box and picking out 50 without looking.
    D:  Asking an equal number of boys and girls from each year group.
    E:  Taking every 20th name from the alphabetical school list.
    F:  Only asking 10 girls and 10 boys in both fifth and sixth year.

# Summary of Key Points

## Types of data

**Primary data** is information you collect yourself.

**Secondary data** is information that you get from existing records.

**Numerical data** is data that can be counted or measured.

**Discrete data** can only take particular values such as shoe sizes or goals scored in a match.

**Continuous data** can take any value in a particular range. Weight, temperature and length are all examples of continuous data.

**Categorical data** is described using words such as colour, favourite fruit or country of birth.

**Univariate data** consists of one item of information such as colour of hair.

**Bivariate data** contains two items of information such as the heights of children and their ages.

## Questionnaires

A **survey** collects primary data.

One way of collecting primary data is to design and complete a **data collection sheet** or **questionnaire**.

When designing questions for a questionnaire:
- Be clear about what you want to find out.
- Keep each question as simple as possible.
- Never ask a leading question designed to get a particular response.
- Provide response boxes where possible.

## Sampling

A **population** is everybody or everything that could be included in a particular survey or investigation.

A **sample** is part of the population selected in a way that makes it representative of the whole population.

In a **simple random sample** every member of the population has an equal chance of being chosen.

If data obtained from a sample does not properly represent the population as a whole, the results may well be **biased**.

# chapter 2

# Measures of Location and Spread

## Key Words

mode      median      mean      range      variability

consistent      quartile      inter-quartile range      frequency distributions

grouped frequency distributions      weighted mean      standard deviation

## SECTION 2.1 Mode – Median – Mean

**Average** is a word that is frequently used in everyday language. For example, we refer to the average weekly wage, the average daily temperature, the average score in a golf competition or the average mark in an examination.

In each of the above examples we are representing all the values in a set of data by a **single value** or **typical value** which we call the average.

The idea of an average is extremely useful because it enables us to compare one set of data with another by comparing just two values, namely their averages.

There are several ways of expressing an average, but the most commonly used averages are the **mode**, the **median** and the **mean**.

### 1. The Mode

The **mode** is the most common value in a set of data. The mode is very useful when one value appears much more often than any other. It is easy to find and can be used for non-numerical data such as the colours of cars sold by a garage.

---

**Example 1**

The ages of students on a school bus are:

$$12, \ 15, \ 12, \ 13, \ 14, \ 16, \ 15, \ 11, \ 12$$
$$16, \ 15, \ 16, \ 14, \ 10, \ 13, \ 17, \ 15, \ 17$$

Placing these in order we get:

$$10, \ 11, \ 12, \ 12, \ 12, \ 13, \ 13, \ 14, \ 14, \ 15, \ 15, \ 15, \ 15, \ 16, \ 16, \ 16, \ 17, \ 17$$

The number in this list with the greatest frequency is 15.

$\therefore$    the mode = 15

---

## 2. The Median

To find the median of a list of numbers, put the numbers in order of size, starting with the smallest. The **median** is the middle number.

If there are 11 numbers in the list, the middle value is $\frac{1}{2}(11 + 1)$, i.e. the 6th value.

If there are 10 numbers in the list, the middle number is $\frac{1}{2}(10 + 1)$, i.e., the $5\frac{1}{2}$th value.

This value is half the sum of the 5th and 6th values.

> If there are $n$ numbers in a list, the middle term is $\frac{1}{2}(n + 1)$.
> If $\frac{1}{2}(n + 1) = 4$, then the 4th number is the median.

---

### Example 2

Find the median of these numbers:  5, 8, 12, 4, 9, 3, 7, 2.

Writing the numbers in order of size we get:

$$2, \ 3, \ 4, \ \boxed{5, \ 7,} \ 8, \ 9, \ 12$$

> Write the numbers in order of size to find the median.

The median is $\frac{1}{2}(5 + 7) = \dfrac{5 + 7}{2} = \dfrac{12}{2} = 6$

∴    the median = 6

---

## 3. The Mean

To find the mean of a set of numbers,

1. Find the sum of all the numbers.
2. Divide this sum by the number of numbers.

The mean is the most frequently used 'average'.

It is important because it considers every piece of data. However, it can be affected by extreme values.

> The mean is $= \dfrac{\text{sum of the numbers}}{\text{number of numbers}}$

---

### Example 3

Find the mean of these numbers:

$$12, \ 14, \ 10, 17, 21, 22$$

$$\text{Mean} = \dfrac{12 + 14 + 10 + 17 + 21 + 22}{6} = \dfrac{96}{6} = 16$$

---

## Example 4

Five girls and three boys took part in a quiz.

The mean mark for the girls was 54.

The mean mark for the boys was 62.

Find the mean mark for the whole group.

To find the mean, add the total of the marks for the girls to the total of the marks for the boys and divide the result by 8.

Total of the marks for the girls $= 54 \times 5 = 270$

Total of the marks for the boys $= 62 \times 3 = 186$

Total for all 8 $= 270 + 186 = 456$

Mean for the whole group $= \dfrac{456}{8} = 57$

## Exercise 2.1

1. Find the mean of each of these arrays of numbers:
    (i)   2, 6, 10, 14, 18
    (iii)  3, 7, 8, 13, 4, 12, 9
    (ii)  0, 2, 8, 16, 6, 22
    (iv)  5, 12, 3, 4, 3, 6, 9

2. Rewrite each of the following arrays of numbers in order of size and then write down
    (i)   the mode
    (ii)  the median.
       (a)  8, 11, 2, 5, 8, 7, 8, 2, 5    (b)  3, 3, 7, 8, 7, 9, 8, 5, 7, 11, 12

3. The speeds, in kilometres per hour, of 11 cars travelling on a road are shown:
       41, 42, 31, 36, 42, 43, 42, 34, 41, 37, 45
    (i)   Find the median speed.
    (ii)  Find the mean speed.

4. A rugby team played 10 games.
    Here are the numbers of points the team scored.
       12, 22, 14, 11, 7, 18, 22, 14, 36, 14
    (i)    Write down the mode.
    (ii)   What is the median number of points scored?
    (iii)  Find the mean number of points scored.

5. Rearrange the following marks in order and then write down the median in each case.
    (i)   9, 5, 8, 3, 2, 7, 6
    (ii)  8, 12, 18, 9, 14, 7, 10, 6

6. Write down seven different numbers with a median of 12.

7. The mean of four numbers is 7 and three of these numbers are 5, 12 and 9.
    (i)   Find the sum of the four numbers.     (ii)  Find the fourth number.

8. The mean of four numbers is 19. Three of them are 21, 25 and 16.
   Find the fourth number.

9. The mean of four sums of money is €4.90. When a fifth sum is added, the mean of the
   five sums is €5.34. Find the fifth sum of money.

10. Write five numbers so that
    the  mode is 4
    the mean is 6
    the median is 5.

11. (i)   The mean of 3, 7, 8, 10 and $x$ is 6. Find $x$.
    (ii)  The mean of 1, $k$, 3, 6 and 8 is 7. Find $k$.

12. The mean of 5 numbers is 11.
    When a sixth number is included the mean of the six numbers is 12.
    Find the sixth number.

13. The mean weight of five dates was 50 g.
    Kate ate one and the mean weight of the
    four remaining dates was 40 g.
    What was the weight of the date that Kate ate?

14. Nicky's marks in four tests were:

    8,  4,  5,  3

    What mark did she get in her fifth and sixth tests if her modal mark was 4 and her
    mean mark was 5 after the six tests?

15. Matthew's marks in eight tests are shown below.
    What mark did he score in the ninth test if his median mark was 6?

    | 5 | 9 | 7 | 3 | 7 | 4 | 5 | 8 |
    |---|---|---|---|---|---|---|---|

16. In a survey a group of boys and girls wrote down how many hours of television they
    watched one week.

    | Boys | 17 | 22 | 21 | 23 | 16 | 12 | Girls | 9 | 13 | 15 | 19 | 10 | 12 |
    |------|----|----|----|----|----|----|-------|---|----|----|----|----|----|
    |      | 0  | 5  | 13 | 15 | 13 | 14 |       | 9 | 8  | 12 | 14 | 15 | 11 |

    (i)   Find the mean time for the boys.
    (ii)  Find the mean time for the girls.
    (iii) Find the median time for each group.
    (iv)  Do the boys spend more time watching television
          than the girls? Explain your answer.

**17.** The numbers 4, 8, 12, 17, $x$ are arranged in order of size.
If the mean of the numbers is equal to the median, find $x$.

**18.** The mean height of a group of eight students is 165 cm.
  (i)  What is the total height of all eight students?
A ninth student joins the group. He is 168 cm tall.
  (ii)  What is the mean height of all nine students?

**19.** The mean of five numbers is 39.
Two of the numbers are 103 and 35 and each of the other three numbers is equal to $x$.
Find    (i)   the total of the five numbers;
        (ii)  the value of $x$.

**20.** On four tests, each marked out of 100, my average was 85.
What is the lowest mark I could have scored on any one test?
A  0          B  40          C  60          D  81          E  85
Explain your answer.

**21.** Fred went fishing each week.
Each week he recorded the number of fish caught.
After several weeks he calculated the following averages.

| |
|---|
| The **mean** number of fish caught per week was 9.3. |
| The **modal** number of fish caught per week was 12. |
| The **median** number of fish caught per week was 10. |

The next week he did not catch any fish.
This had never happened before.
Fred recalculated his averages.
  (i)   Which of these averages could not have been affected?
        Give a reason for your answer.
  (ii)  Which of the averages was certainly affected?
        Explain your answer.

# SECTION 2.2  Range and variability ———————————

The **range** for a set of data is the highest value of the set minus the lowest value.

The range is not an average.

It shows the **spread** of the data.
It is very useful when comparing two sets of data.

> The range of a set of data is the largest value minus the smallest value.

The range is a crude measure of spread because it uses only the largest and the smallest values of the data.

## Example 1

Jane's marks, out of 20, in ten maths tests were as follows:

$$8, \ 8, \ 14, \ 12, \ 12, \ 10, \ 14, \ 12, \ 18, \ 12$$

Conor's marks in the same tests were

$$12, \ 14, \ 12, \ 16, \ 10, \ 12, \ 10, \ 12, \ 10, \ 12$$

Find   (i)  the mean          (ii)  the range

of Jane's marks and Conor's marks and comment on the results.

For Jane:    (i)   the mean $= \dfrac{8 + 8 + 14 + 12 + 12 + 10 + 14 + 12 + 18 + 12}{10}$

$$= \frac{120}{10} = 12$$

(ii)   the range $=$ highest mark $-$ lowest mark

$$= 18 - 8$$

$$= 10$$

For Conor:    (i)   the mean $= \dfrac{12 + 14 + 12 + 16 + 10 + 12 + 10 + 12 + 10 + 12}{10}$

$$= \frac{120}{10} = 12$$

(ii)   the range $= 16 - 10$

$$= 6$$

*Comment:*   Although the means are the same, Conor's marks have a smaller range. This shows that Conor's results are **more consistent** than Jane's.

The more spread-out nature of Jane's marks compared to Conor's, in Example 1 above, illustrates the **variability** of data and how important it can be.

The **range** is often used as a measure of variability because it is easy to calculate and easy to understand.

## Quartiles and Interquartile range

When data is arranged in order of size, we have already learned that the **median** is the value half-way into the data.

So we can say that the median divides the data into two halves.

The data can also be divided into four quarters.

When the data is arranged in ascending order of size:

- the **lower quartile** is the value one quarter of the way into the data
- the **upper quartile** is the value three quarters of the way into the data
- the upper quartile minus the lower quartile is called the **interquartile range**.

Consider the following data which is arranged in order of size. It contains 15 numbers.

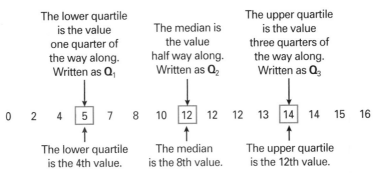

The lower quartile is the value one quarter of the way along. Written as $Q_1$

The median is the value half way along. Written as $Q_2$

The upper quartile is the value three quarters of the way along. Written as $Q_3$

0   2   4   [5]   7   8   10   [12]   12   12   13   [14]   14   15   16

The lower quartile is the 4th value.

The median is the 8th value.

The upper quartile is the 12th value.

The lower quartile $Q_1 = 5$.
The median $Q_2 = 12$.
The upper quartile $Q_3 = 14$.
The interquartile range $= Q_3 - Q_1$
$$= 14 - 5$$
$$= 9$$

The interquartile range is
upper quartile − lower quartile
$$= Q_3 - Q_1$$

## Example 2

These are the test marks of 11 students:

$$52, 78, 61, 49, 79, 47, 54, 58, 72, 62, 73$$

Find    (i)   the median                (ii)   the lower quartile
(iii)   the upper quartile        (iv)   the interquartile range.

We first rewrite the numbers in order, starting with the smallest:

$$47, 49, 52, 54, 58, 61, 62, 72, 73, 78, 79$$

(i)   The median is the middle value of the list.
Since there are 11 values, the middle value is
$\frac{1}{2}(11 + 1)$ i.e. the 6th value.
The 6th value is 61 $\Rightarrow$ the median = 61.

(ii)   The lower quartile is the value that is $\frac{1}{4}$ way through the distribution.
This value is found by getting $\frac{1}{4}(11 + 1) =$ the 3rd value.
The 3rd value is 52 $\Rightarrow$ the lower quartile $(Q_1) = 52$.

(iii)   The upper quartile is the value that is $\frac{3}{4}$ way through the distribution.
This value is found by getting $\frac{3}{4}(11 + 1) =$ 9th value.
This ninth value is 73 $\Rightarrow$ the upper quartile $(Q_3) = 73$.

(iv)   The interquartile range $= Q_3 - Q_1$
$$= 73 - 52$$
$$= 21$$

**Note:** If there is an even number of values in a distribution, e.g.,

$$2, \quad 5, \quad 6, \quad 8, \quad \boxed{9, \; 12,} \quad 15, \quad 17, \quad 20, \quad 25$$

The middle value is $\frac{1}{2}(10 + 1) = \frac{1}{2}(11) = 5\frac{1}{2}$ th value

This is the average of the 5th and 6th values.

The median is $\frac{1}{2}(9 + 12) = \frac{1}{2}(21) = 10\frac{1}{2}$.

## Exercise 2.2

1. Find the range for each of the following sets of data:
   (i)   6, 3, 8, 2, 9, 5, 10
   (ii)  21, 16, 72, 40, 67, 65, 55, 34, 17, 48, 32, 19, 44, 61, 73
   (iii) 8, 2, 9, 6, 7, 10, 12, 13, 5, 12, 10, 8, 10, 4

2. Miss Moore gave her class a maths test.
   Here are the marks for the girls:

   7, 5, 8, 5, 2, 8, 7, 4, 7, 10, 3, 7, 4, 3, 6

   What is   (i)   the median mark                    (ii)   the range of marks?
   The median mark for the boys in her class was 7 and the range of marks for the boys was 4.
   By comparing the results, explain whether the boys or girls did better in the test.

3. Nine students submitted their assignments which were marked out of 40.
   The marks obtained were:

   37, 34, 34, 29, 27, 27, 10, 4, 34

   (i)   Write down the range of marks.       (ii)  Write down the median mark.
   (iii)  Find   (a) the lower quartile
                 (b) the upper quartile
                 (c) the interquartile range.

4. Find   (i)   the lower quartile
          (ii)  the upper quartile
          (iii) the interquartile range
   for this set of data:

   4, 12, 7, 6, 10, 5, 11, 14, 2, 3, 9

5. Here are the times, in minutes, for a bus journey:

   15, 7, 9, 12, 9, 19, 6, 11, 9, 16, 8

   (i)   Find the range of these times.      (ii)  Find the lower quartile.
   (iii)  Find the upper quartile.            (iv)  Write down the interquartile range.

**6.** A group of boys and girls took a French test. These are the marks which the boys got:

      13, 14, 14, 15, 14, 14, 15, 17, 16, 14, 16, 12

  (i)   Find the range of the boys' marks.

  (ii)  Calculate the mean mark of the boys.

The mean mark for the girls in the class was 13.2 and the girls' marks had a range of 7.

  (iii)  Make two statements about the differences between the boys' and girls' marks in the French test.


**7.** Conor played nine rounds of crazy golf. Here are his scores:

      51, 53, 50, 41, 59, 64, 66, 65, 50

Find     (i)  the range       (ii)  the lower quartile

          (iii)  the upper quartile     (iv)  the interquartile range.


**8.** A greengrocer sold bags of apples from different countries.
A bag contained 9 French apples.
The weight of each apple is given below, in grams.

      101, 107, 98, 109, 115, 103, 96, 112, 104

  (i)  Calculate the mean weight of a French apple.

  (ii)  Find the range of the weights of the French apples.

Another bag contained 9 South African apples.
Their mean weight was 107 g and their range was 19 g.

  (iii)  Make two comments on the weights of the apples in the two bags.


**9.** A set of cards has these numbers on them

  (i)  Find five cards from this set with median 6 and range 4.

  (ii)  Find four cards with median 6 and range 3.


**10.** Solve these two problems:

In my family the ages of the three kids are 6, 10 and 16. The mean age of the whole family is 24. The range is 41. How old are my Mum and Dad?

(i)

There are 5 children in my family. The youngest is 8 and I am 15. The median child's age is 13. The range of childrens' ages is 17. The mean of our ages is 14. How old are we?

(ii)

**11.** The PE teacher in a school measures the time, in seconds, it takes the members of the football team and the hockey team to run 100 metres.

**Football team**

13   14   15   11   14   12   12   13   11   13   15

**Hockey team**

12   13   14   11   14   16   15   13   15   17   11

(i)   Calculate the mean, median and range for each team.

(ii)  Which group do you think is the faster?
      Give a reason for your answer.

# SECTION 2.3  Deciding which average to use

The three averages, the **mean**, the **mode** and the **median** are all useful but one may be more appropriate than the others in different situations.

The **mode** is useful when you want to know, for example, which shoe size is the most common.

The **mean** is useful for finding a 'typical' value when most of the data is closely grouped. The mean may not give a typical value if the data is very spread out or if it includes a few values that are very different from the rest. These values are known as **outliers**.

Take, for example, a small company where the chief executive earns €12 100 a month and the other eleven employees earn €2500 each a month.

Here the mean monthly salary is €3300 which is not typical of the monthly salaries.

In situations like this, the **median** or middle value may be more typical.

The table below, which compares the advantages and disadvantages of each type of average, should help you make the correct decision.

| Average | Advantages | Disadvantages |
|---------|-----------|---------------|
| **Mode** | • Easy to find<br>• Not influenced by extreme values | • May not exist<br>• Not very useful for further analysis |
| **Median** | • Unaffected by extremes<br>• Easy to calculate if data is ordered | • Not always a given data value<br>• Not very useful for further analysis |
| **Mean** | • Uses all the data<br>• Easy to calculate<br>• Very useful for further analysis | • Distorted by extreme results<br>• Mean is not always a given data value |

> ### Example 1
>
> There are 10 apartments in a block.
> On a particular day the number of letters delivered to each of the apartments is
>
> $$2, 0, 5, 3, 4, 0, 1, 0, 3, 15$$
>
> Calculate the mean, mode and median number of letters.
> Which of these averages is the most suitable to represent this data?
> Give a reason for your answer.
>
> Mean $= \dfrac{2 + 0 + 5 + 3 + 4 + 0 + 1 + 0 + 3 + 15}{10} = \dfrac{33}{10} = 3.3$
>
> Mode $= 0$
>
> Median: 0, 0, 0, 1, $\boxed{2, \ 3,}$ 3, 4, 5, 15
>
> $$\text{Median} = \frac{2 + 3}{2} = \frac{5}{2} = 2\tfrac{1}{2}$$
>
> Here the mean has been distorted by the large number of letters delivered to one apartment. It is, therefore, not a good measure of the 'typical' number of letters delivered.
> Neither is the mode a good measure of the 'typical' number of letters, since 7 out of 10 apartments do receive some letters.
> The median is the best measure of the 'typical' number of letters delivered since half of the apartments receive more than the median and half receive less than the median.

## Exercise 2.3

1. Decide which average you would use for each of the following.
   Give a reason for your answer.
   - (i) The average mark in an examination.
   - (ii) The average uniform size for all the pupils in a class.
   - (iii) The average height of the players in a football team.
   - (iv) The colours of the cars sold by a garage.
   - (v) The average salary of seven people who work for a small company.

2. The weights, in kilograms, of a boat crew are:

    96, 86, 94, 96, 91, 95, 90, 96, 43

   Calculate   (i)   their median weight.

                (ii)   their mean weight.

   Which of these two averages best describes the data above?
   Give a reason for your answer.

3. Find (i) the mean (ii) the median of these numbers:

9, 11, 11, 15, 17, 18, 100

Which of these two averages would you chose to best describe these numbers?

4. Shane recorded the midday temperatures for one week during his holiday in Spain.

| Day | 1 | 2 | 3 | 4 | 5 | 6 | 7 |
|---|---|---|---|---|---|---|---|
| Midday temperature (°C) | 32 | 30 | 30 | 28 | 33 | 31 | 30 |

   (i) Find the mean midday temperature.
   (ii) Give a reason why the mean is appropriate for this data.

5. (i) Find the mean of this set of numbers:

37, 26, 37, 18, 18, 20, 26, 18, 37, 37, 18.

   (ii) Why is the mode a bad choice of average in this case?

6. Find (i) the mean (ii) the median for the following set of data:

3, 5, 4, 7, 29, 9, 2, 4, 10, 8

Which of these two averages is the more suitable to represent the data?
Give a reason for your answer.

7. Katie is word processing her college assignment. She records the number of errors she makes on each page. These are the numbers of errors she recorded:

6, 19, 14, 17, 51, 16, 20, 13, 16

   (i) Write down the modal number of errors.
   (ii) Find the median number of errors.
   (iii) Calculate the mean number of errors, correct to one decimal place.
   (iv) Write down the average which best represents this data.
        Explain your answer.

8. The annual salaries of the employees in a small company are listed below:

€30,000, €25,000, €24,000, €22,000, €20,000, €105,000

   Find (i) the mean salary
        (ii) the median salary.
        (iii) Why can't you find the mode?

Which of the averages, mean or median, best represents the 'typical' salary?

9. A youth club leader gets a discount on cans of drinks if she buys one size only.
She took a vote on which size people wanted. The results were as follows:

| Size of can (ml) | 100 | 200 | 330 | 500 |
|---|---|---|---|---|
| Number of votes | 9 | 12 | 19 | 1 |

Mode = 330 ml
Median = 200 ml
Mean = 245.6 ml, correct to one decimal place.

Which size can should she buy?
Explain your answer.

# SECTION 2.4  Frequency distributions

The table below shows the numbers of emails received in a day by 31 people in an office.

| Number of emails | 0 | 1 | 2 | 3 | 4 | 5 | 6 | 7 |
|---|---|---|---|---|---|---|---|---|
| Frequency (number of people) | 4 | 11 | 8 | 6 | 1 | 0 | 0 | 1 |

This table is called a **frequency distribution table**.
From the table we can see that the number of people who received 3 emails is 6.

We will now show how to find the **mode, median** and **mean** of a frequency distribution.
The frequency table below shows the numbers of letters in the answers to a crossword.

| No. of letters in word | 3 | 4 | 5 | 6 | 7 |
|---|---|---|---|---|---|
| Frequency | 3 | 4 | 9 | 5 | 2 |

The **mode** is the number of letters (in the word) that occurs most frequently.
Thus the mode is 5 as it occurs more often than any other number.

The **median** is the middle number in the distribution.

The total frequency is $3 + 4 + 9 + 5 + 2$, i.e., 23.

The middle value of 23 values is $\frac{1}{2}(23 + 1)$, i.e., the 12th value.

The 23 values could be listed like this:

3   3   3   4   4   4   4   5   5   5   5   $\boxed{5}$   5   5   5   5   6   6   6   6   6   7   7

middle value

The middle number in this list is the 12th number.
This number is 5.
∴   the median = 5

**Note:**   The median can be read from the table without listing all the numbers.
We take the frequency row and find the column that contains the 12th number.
The sum of the first two frequencies is $3 + 4 = 7$.
The sum of the first three frequencies is $3 + 4 + 9 = 16$.
Thus the 12th value occurs in the third column, where the number of letters in the word is 5.
∴   the median = 5

## The mean of a frequency distribution

The table below shows the marks (from 1 to 10) scored by the 20 pupils in a class.

| Marks | 1 | 2 | 3 | 4 | 5 | 6 | 7 | 8 | 9 | 10 |
|---|---|---|---|---|---|---|---|---|---|---|
| No. of pupils | 1 | 1 | 1 | 3 | 5 | 3 | 2 | 2 | 1 | 1 |

The average or mean mark of this distribution is found by dividing the total number of marks by the total number of pupils.

To find the total number of marks we multiply each mark (or *variable*) by the number of pupils (*frequency*) who received that mark.

$$\therefore \quad \text{the mean} = \frac{1(1) + 2(1) + 3(1) + 4(3) + 5(5) + 6(3) + 7(2) + 8(2) + 9(1) + 10(1)}{1 + 1 + 1 + 3 + 5 + 3 + 2 + 2 + 1 + 1}$$

$$= \frac{110}{20} = 5.5 \text{ marks}$$

If $x$ stands for the variable and $f$ stands for the frequency, then

$$\text{mean} = \frac{\Sigma fx}{\Sigma f},$$

$$\boxed{\text{Mean} = \frac{\Sigma fx}{\Sigma f}}$$

where $\Sigma fx$ is the sum of all the variables multiplied by the corresponding frequencies and $\Sigma f$ is the sum of the frequencies.

---

**Example 1**

If the mean of the frequency distribution below is 3, find the value of $x$. Write down the mode of the distribution.

| Goals scored | 1 | 2 | 3 | 4 | 5 | 6 |
|---|---|---|---|---|---|---|
| Number of matches | 7 | 8 | 4 | 4 | 3 | x |

$$\text{Mean} = \frac{7(1) + 8(2) + 4(3) + 4(4) + 3(5) + x(6)}{7 + 8 + 4 + 4 + 3 + x}$$

$$= \frac{7 + 16 + 12 + 16 + 15 + 6x}{26 + x} = \frac{66 + 6x}{26 + x}$$

Since the mean = 3 $\Rightarrow$ $\dfrac{66 + 6x}{26 + x} = 3$

$$\Rightarrow \quad 66 + 6x = 3(26 + x)$$
$$\Rightarrow \quad 66 + 6x = 78 + 3x$$
$$\Rightarrow \quad 3x = 12$$
$$\Rightarrow \quad x = 4$$

The mode = 2, as 2 occurs with the greatest frequency.

---

## Exercise 2.4

1. The following table gives the numbers of goals scored in 60 matches on a particular week-end:

| Goals scored | 1 | 2 | 3 | 4 | 5 | 6 |
|---|---|---|---|---|---|---|
| No. of matches | 12 | 16 | 10 | 8 | 6 | 8 |

   (i) Write down the mode of the distribution.
   (ii) Find the median number of goals scored.

2. Calculate the mean of this frequency distribution:

| Variable (x) | 1 | 2 | 3 | 4 | 5 | 6 |
|---|---|---|---|---|---|---|
| Frequency (f) | 9 | 9 | 6 | 4 | 7 | 3 |

3. A test consisted of 10 questions, 1 mark per question, and 0 for an incorrect solution. The following table shows how a class of students scored in the test:

| Marks | 3 | 4 | 5 | 6 | 7 | 8 | 9 |
|---|---|---|---|---|---|---|---|
| No. of students | 3 | 2 | 6 | 10 | 0 | 3 | 1 |

   (i) How many students were in the class?
   (ii) Write down the mode of the data.
   (iii) Calculate the mean mark per student.
   (iv) How many students scored better than the mean mark?
   (v) Find the median mark.

4. Paula has 6 people in her family. She wonders how many people are in her friends' families. She asks each of her friends and records the information in a table.

| Number in family | 2 | 3 | 4 | 5 | 6 | 7 | 8 |
|---|---|---|---|---|---|---|---|
| Frequency | 2 | 4 | 6 | 5 | 2 | 0 | 1 |

   (i) Write down the modal number of people in the family.
   (ii) Find the median number of persons per family.
   (iii) Calculate the mean of the distribution.

5. Carol is trying to estimate how many words she has written in an essay. She records the number of words she wrote on each line of one page. Her results are given in the table below.

| Words per line | 10 | 11 | 12 | 13 | 14 | 15 |
|---|---|---|---|---|---|---|
| No. of lines | 1 | 3 | 6 | 9 | 7 | 4 |

   (i) How many lines in total were there on the page?
   (ii) How many lines contained 14 words?
   (iii) What was the modal number of words per line?
   (iv) Find the median number of words per line.
   (v) Calculate the mean of the distribution.

6. The table below shows the number of goals scored in 100 football matches on a particular Saturday.

| Goals scored | 0 | 1 | 2 | 3 | 4 | 5 |
|---|---|---|---|---|---|---|
| No. of matches | 10 | 25 | 30 | 25 | 10 | 0 |

   (i) Write down the modal number of goals scored.
   (ii) Calculate the mean of the distribution.
   (iii) Find the greatest number of matches that could have ended in a draw.
   (iv) How many matches could have ended in a two-all draw?

7. If the mean of the frequency distribution below is 2, find the value of $x$.

| Variable | 0 | 2 | 3 | 4 |
|---|---|---|---|---|
| Frequency | 4 | 3 | $x$ | 3 |

**8.** The mean mark from the following frequency distribution table was found to be 6. Calculate the value of $y$.

| Marks | 3 | 5 | 8 |
|---|---|---|---|
| No. of students | 3 | $y$ | 7 |

**9.** The frequency table below has two missing values.

| Variable ($x$) | 1 | 3 | 4 | 6 | |
|---|---|---|---|---|---|
| Frequency ($f$) | 2 | 4 | 6 | | 3 |

    (i)   The range of $x$ is 7 and the sum of the frequencies is 20. Use this information to complete the table.

    (ii)  What is the modal value of $x$?

    (iii)  Find the mean value of $x$.

# SECTION 2.5 Grouped Frequency Distributions ———

## 1. The Mean

When dealing with a large number of variables, such as the ages of people in a certain district, it is often convenient to arrange the data in **groups** or **classes**.

Thus, when recording the ages of people, the results could be grouped (0–9) years, (10–19) years ... etc.

The grouped frequency distribution table below shows the marks (out of 25) achieved by 50 students in a test.

| Marks achieved | 1–5 | 6–10 | 11–15 | 16–20 | 21–25 |
|---|---|---|---|---|---|
| No. of students | 11 | 12 | 15 | 9 | 3 |

While it is not possible to find the exact mean of a grouped frequency distribution, we can find an estimate of the mean by taking the **mid-interval value** of each class.

The mid-interval value in the (1–5) class is found by adding 1 and 5 and dividing by 2,

i.e., $\dfrac{1 + 5}{2} = 3$

Similarly, the mid-interval value of the (6–10) class is $\dfrac{6 + 10}{2} = 8$.

The table given above is reproduced again with the mid-interval values written in smaller size over each class interval.

| | 3 | 8 | 13 | 18 | 23 |
|---|---|---|---|---|---|
| Marks achieved | 1–5 | 6–10 | 11–15 | 16–20 | 21–25 |
| No. of students | 11 | 12 | 15 | 9 | 3 |

$$\text{Mean} = \frac{\Sigma fx}{\Sigma f} = \frac{11(3) + 12(8) + 15\,(13) + 9(18) + 3(23)}{11 + 12 + 15 + 9 + 3} = \frac{555}{50} = 11.1$$

## 2. The Mode and the Median

The table below gives the daily sales of mobile phones in a local shop.

| No. of phones | 0–4 | 5–9 | 10–14 | 15–19 | 20–24 |
|---|---|---|---|---|---|
| Frequency | 5 | 8 | 4 | 9 | 3 |

From this **grouped** table we cannot give the exact mode, but we can say that the **modal class** is the interval (15–19) because this interval contains the greatest frequency.

When you are dealing with grouped data, you will never be able to state what the median is, but you can identify the class interval in which the median lies.

In the table above the total frequency is $5 + 8 + 4 + 9 + 3$, i.e., 29.

The middle value of this distribution is $\frac{1}{2}(29 + 1)$, i.e., the 15th value.

The sum of the first two frequencies is $5 + 8 = 13$.

The sum of the first three frequencies is $5 + 8 + 4 = 17$.

Thus the 15th value lies in the class interval (10–14).

$\therefore$ the median lies in the (10–14) class interval.

## Exercise 2.5

1. People attending a course were asked to choose one of the whole numbers from 1 to 12. The results were recorded as follows:

| Number | 1–3 | 4–6 | 7–9 | 10–12 |
|---|---|---|---|---|
| No. of people | 3 | 17 | 2 | 8 |

   (i)   Write down the modal class of the distribution.
   (ii)  Use the mid-interval value of each class to estimate the mean of the distribution.
   (iii) In which interval does the median lie?

2. The ages of children in a youth-club are given in the following table:

| Ages (in years) | 10–12 | 12–14 | 14–16 | 16–18 | 18–20 |
|---|---|---|---|---|---|
| No. of children | 12 | 24 | 18 | 12 | 4 |

   (i)   What is the modal age group?
   (ii)  Use the mid-interval value of each class to estimate the mean of the distribution, giving your answer to the nearest half year.
   (iii) In which interval does the median lie?

3. Use the mid-interval values to estimate the mean of the following frequency distribution:

| Class | 14–16 | 16–18 | 18–20 | 20–22 | 22–24 |
|---|---|---|---|---|---|
| Frequency | 1 | 5 | 12 | 3 | 0 |

   Give your answer correct to one decimal place.

**4.** The time taken by 20 students to run a cross-country course were noted, to the nearest minute, and the results are given in the following table:

| Time (in minutes) | 12–14 | 15–17 | 18–20 | 21–23 |
|---|---|---|---|---|
| No. of students | 3 | 5 | 8 | 4 |

    (i)   Use the mid-interval value of each class to estimate the mean of the distribution, giving your answer correct to the nearest minute.

    (ii)  In which interval does the median lie?

**5.** The ages of some people watching a film are given in this frequency table:

| Age (in years) | 10–20 | 20–30 | 30–40 | 40–50 |
|---|---|---|---|---|
| No. of people | 4 | 15 | 11 | 10 |

    (i)   Use the mid-interval value of each class to estimate the mean of the distribution, giving your answer correct to the nearest year.

    (ii)  In which interval does the median lie?

**6.** One hundred people were asked to record the number of mobile phonecalls they received on a particular day. The results are shown in the table below.

| No. of calls | 0–4 | 5–9 | 10–14 | 15–19 | 20–24 |
|---|---|---|---|---|---|
| Frequency | 45 | 29 | 17 | 8 | 1 |

    (i)   In which interval does the median lie?

    (ii)  What is the modal group?

    (iii)  Use the mid-interval values to estimate the mean number of calls. Give your answer correct to the nearest whole number.

# SECTION 2.6 Weighted mean

The table below gives the percentage increase in 5 items over a 12-month period.

| Item | Food | Clothing | Fuel | Travel | Rent |
|---|---|---|---|---|---|
| Percentage increase | 5 | 3 | 6 | 4 | 7 |

The mean % increase $= \dfrac{5 + 3 + 6 + 4 + 7}{5} = \dfrac{25}{5} = 5\%$

As these five items represent the vast majority of household expenditure, do we conclude that the cost of living has increased by 5% over the 12-month period?

We could if every household spent the same amount of money on each of these areas of expenditure. We know, for example, that the average household spends far more money on food that it does on fuel.

In order to indicate the order of importance of these items in household expenditure, we attach a **weight** to each one of them. Sample weights are given in the table below.

| Item | Food | Clothing | Fuel | Travel | Rent |
|---|---|---|---|---|---|
| **Percentage increase** | 5 | 3 | 6 | 4 | 7 |
| **Weight** | 6 | 3 | 2 | 3 | 4 |

We now multiply each percentage increase by the corresponding weight and divide by the sum of the weights.
This gives us the **weighted mean**.

> Finding the weighted mean is very similar to finding the mean of a frequency distribution.

$$\text{Weighted Mean} = \frac{6(5) + 3(3) + 2(6) + 3(4) + 4(7)}{6 + 3 + 2 + 3 + 4}$$

$$= \frac{91}{18} = 5.06\%$$

---

### Example 1

The following table gives the results of an examination in four subjects and the weight assigned to each subject:

| Subject | Science | French | History | Maths |
|---|---|---|---|---|
| **Results (in %)** | 80 | 54 | 62 | 75 |
| **Weight** | 3 | 2 | 1 | 4 |

Find the weighted mean mark of the four subjects.

$$\text{Weighted Mean} = \frac{3(80) + 2(54) + 1(62) + 4(75)}{3 + 2 + 1 + 4}$$

$$= \frac{710}{10} = 71\%$$

---

## Exercise 2.6

1. Find the weighted mean of the following array of numbers and their attached weights:

| Variable | 2 | 5 | 7 | 10 | 12 |
|---|---|---|---|---|---|
| Weight | 3 | 2 | 5 | 3 | 5 |

2. The following table shows the percentage price increase for various drinks over a three-year period and the weights assigned to them:

| Drink | Wine | Spirits | Beer | Soft drinks |
|---|---|---|---|---|
| **% Price increase** | 8 | 15 | 20 | 10 |
| **Weight** | 3 | 7 | 9 | 6 |

Calculate the weighted mean of the increases, correct to one decimal place.

3. The following table gives Robert's % marks and their respective weights in his music exam.

|  | Performance | Theory | Composition |
|---|---|---|---|
| **% Mark** | 68 | 72 | 88 |
| **Weight** | 50 | 30 | 20 |

An overall mark of 75% would give Robert a distinction for the exam.
What percentage did Robert get? Did he gain a distinction?

4. The percentage price increase in 5 grocery items in a given year and the weight attached to each are given in the table below.

| Item | Meat | Bread | Milk | Vegetables | Butter |
|---|---|---|---|---|---|
| **% Price increase** | 2 | 7 | 5 | 10 | 12 |
| **Weight** | 3 | 4 | 2 | 1 | 2 |

Calculate the weighted mean percentage price increase.

5. Find the weighted mean of the numbers 25, 30, 35, 40 if their assigned weights are 3, 5, 6 and 7 respectively. Give your answer correct to the nearest whole number.

6. The percentage increase in the prices of 5 items $A$, $B$, $C$, $D$ and $E$ over a two-year period is given in the table below. The weight attached to each item is also given.
If the weighted mean percentage price increase is 18, find the value of $x$.

| Item | $A$ | $B$ | $C$ | $D$ | $E$ |
|---|---|---|---|---|---|
| **% Price increase** | 12 | 10 | 32 | 10 | 20 |
| **Weight** | 2 | 1 | 3 | $x$ | 1 |

7. The table opposite shows the three parts of a French examination and the weights attached to these parts. The table also shows the marks out of 100 achieved by two students, Aisling and Barry.

|  | Paper 1 | Paper 2 | Oral |
|---|---|---|---|
| **Aisling** | 73 | 58 | 67 |
| **Barry** | 64 | 70 | 53 |
| **Weight** | 4 | 6 | 3 |

Which student scored the higher weighted mean mark?

8. Simon interviewed Katie, Sarah and Emma for the post of personal assistant.
The criteria upon which he judged them, their relative importance and the scores they achieved are given in the table.

|  | Appearance | Personality | Telephone voice | ICT skills |
|---|---|---|---|---|
| **Weighting** | 5 | 4 | 3 | 8 |
| **Katie** | 4 | 8 | 9 | 6 |
| **Sarah** | 7 | 4 | 4 | 5 |
| **Emma** | 3 | 3 | 8 | 8 |

The person with the highest overall score was given the post. Who was it?

# SECTION 2.7  Standard deviation

Consider the marks scored in two tests shown below:

| | | | | | | | |
|---|---|---|---|---|---|---|---|
| **English** | 46 | 48 | 51 | 53 | 64 | 67 | 70 |
| **Mathematics** | 14 | 38 | 49 | 58 | 67 | 84 | 89 |

The mean in each test is 57, but the spread of marks in the tests is quite different.
While the mean gives an indication of the central or typical value, very often the spread or
**dispersion** of the marks about the mean is more important.

One of the most important and frequently-used measures of spread
is called **standard deviation**. It shows how much variation there
is from the average (mean). It may be thought of as the average
difference of the scores from the mean, that is, how far they are
away from the mean. A low standard deviation indicates that the
data points tend to be very close to the mean; a high standard
deviation indicates that the data is spread out over a large range of
values.

> The Greek letter $\sigma$ is used to denote standard deviation.

Take, for example, all adult men in Ireland. The average
height is about 177 cm with a standard deviation of about
8 cm.
For this large population, about 68% of the men have a
height within 8 cm of the mean

> If the mean is $\bar{x}$ and $\sigma$ is the standard deviation of this large sample, then 68% will lie between $\bar{x} + \sigma$ and $\bar{x} - \sigma$

## Procedure for finding the standard deviation

The steps used to find the standard deviation of a set of numbers are as follows:

1. Calculate the mean of the numbers. This is written $\bar{x}$.

2. Find the deviation (or difference) of each variable, $x$, from the mean.
   This is denoted by $(x - \bar{x})$.

3. Square each of these deviations, i.e., find $(x - \bar{x})^2$.

4. Find the sum ($\Sigma$) of these values, i.e., find $\Sigma(x - \bar{x})^2$.

5. Divide this result by $n$, the number of numbers.
   This gives $\dfrac{\Sigma(x - \bar{x})^2}{n}$.

6. Finally get the square root of the result in **5**.

   There is no need to use this formula if you can
   remember the steps listed above.
   Alternatively, you may use a calculator.

> Standard deviation
> $$\sigma = \sqrt{\frac{\Sigma(x - \bar{x})^2}{n}}$$

## Example 1

Find the standard deviation of the numbers 6, 9, 10, 12, 13.

The mean $= \dfrac{6 + 9 + 10 + 12 + 13}{5} = \dfrac{50}{5} = 10.$

$$\sigma = \sqrt{\dfrac{(6-10)^2 + (9-10)^2 + (10-10)^2 + (12-10)^2 + (13-10)^2}{5}}$$

$$= \sqrt{\dfrac{(-4)^2 + (-1)^2 + (0)^2 + (2)^2 + (3)^2}{5}}$$

$$= \sqrt{\dfrac{16 + 1 + 0 + 4 + 9}{5}} = \sqrt{\dfrac{30}{5}} = \sqrt{6} = 2.45$$

$\therefore$ the standard deviation is 2.45

## Finding the Standard Deviation of a Frequency Distribution

When finding the standard deviation from a frequency distribution, the deviation of each variable from the mean is squared and then multiplied by the frequency ($f$) of that variable. The result is then divided by the sum of the frequencies.
Finally, we get the square root of the result.

This procedure can be represented by the formula

$$\sqrt{\dfrac{\Sigma f(x - \bar{x})^2}{\Sigma f}}$$

where $\Sigma f(x - \bar{x})^2$ is the sum of the $f(x - \bar{x})^2$ column and $\Sigma f$ is the sum of the frequencies.

The worked example below will show how to lay out your work when finding the standard deviation of a frequency distribution.

## Example 2

Find the standard deviation of the following frequency distribution:

| Variable (x) | 1 | 2 | 3 | 4 | 5 | 6 |
|---|---|---|---|---|---|---|
| Frequency (f) | 9 | 9 | 6 | 4 | 7 | 3 |

First find the mean of the distribution.

The mean $= \dfrac{(9 \times 1) + (9 \times 2) + (6 \times 3) + (4 \times 4) + (7 \times 5) + (3 \times 6)}{9 + 9 + 6 + 4 + 7 + 3}$

$\Rightarrow \quad \bar{x} = \dfrac{114}{38} = 3$

Now set out a table like this.

| $x$ | $f$ | $x - \bar{x}$ | $(x - \bar{x})^2$ | $f(x - \bar{x})^2$ |
|---|---|---|---|---|
| 1 | 9 | $-2$ | 4 | 36 |
| 2 | 9 | $-1$ | 1 | 9 |
| 3 | 6 | 0 | 0 | 0 |
| 4 | 4 | 1 | 1 | 4 |
| 5 | 7 | 2 | 4 | 28 |
| 6 | 3 | 3 | 9 | 27 |

$$\downarrow \qquad\qquad\qquad\qquad\qquad\qquad\qquad\qquad \downarrow$$

$$\Sigma f = 38 \qquad\qquad\qquad\qquad\qquad\qquad \Sigma f(x - \bar{x})^2 = 104$$

$$\sigma = \sqrt{\frac{\Sigma f(x - \bar{x})^2}{\Sigma f}} = \sqrt{\frac{104}{38}} = 1.65$$

**Note:** To calculate the standard deviation of a grouped frequency distribution, take the mid-interval values of the variables and proceed as in Example 2, above.

## Use of calculator to find standard deviation

The tedious work involved in calculating the standard deviation of a large set of data can be substantially reduced by using a scientific calculator.

In the following examples we will use the **Casio fx-83ES** calculator to illustrate the keys and steps involved in finding standard deviation.

### Example 3

Find (a) the mean (b) the standard deviation of the following set of numbers
(i)  5, 3, 1, 8, 2 (ii)  10, 6, 2, 16, 4

(i)  Key in MODE and select 2 for statistics mode.

Then select 1 for 1 − VAR.

Now input the numbers

| | X | FREQ |
|---|---|---|
| 1 | 5 | 1 |
| 2 | 3 | 1 |
| 3 | 1 | 1 |
| 4 | 8 | 1 |
| 5 | 2 | 1 |

CASIO                     fx-83ES

To get your answers, key in $\boxed{AC}$ to clear, and $\boxed{SHIFT}$ $\boxed{1}$ to go to menu.

Now select $\boxed{5}$ to get statistics on variables.

Then select $\boxed{2}$ for $\bar{x}$ (the mean), then $\boxed{=}$

The mean $\bar{x}$ is 3.8.

To proceed to get the standard deviation, key in $\boxed{AC}$ to clear.

Now key in $\boxed{SHIFT}$ $\boxed{1}$ to go to menu and select $\boxed{5}$ to get statistics on variables.

Now key in $\boxed{3}$ for $x\,\sigma\,n$ (standard deviation) $\boxed{=}$.

The result is 2.4819... = 2.5

∴ standard deviation = 2.5

(ii)  10, 6, 2, 16, 4.

Here are the sequence of keys to find the mean and standard deviation.

$\boxed{MODE}$ $\boxed{2}$ $\boxed{1}$

$\boxed{10}$ $\boxed{=}$ $\boxed{6}$ $\boxed{=}$ $\boxed{2}$ $\boxed{=}$ $\boxed{16}$ $\boxed{=}$ $\boxed{4}$ $\boxed{=}$

$\boxed{AC}$ $\boxed{SHIFT}$ $\boxed{1}$ $\boxed{5}$ $\boxed{2}$ $\boxed{=}$   7.6 = mean

$\boxed{AC}$ $\boxed{SHIFT}$ $\boxed{1}$ $\boxed{5}$ $\boxed{3}$ $\boxed{=}$   4.963869... = 5.0 = standard deviation

## Example 4

The following frequency distribution table shows the number of goals scored per match.

| No. of goals | 0 | 1 | 2 | 3 | 4 | 5 | 6 |
|---|---|---|---|---|---|---|---|
| Frequency | 5 | 6 | 4 | 6 | 3 | 1 | 0 |

Find the mean and standard deviation, correct to one decimal place.

Key in $\boxed{MODE}$ and select $\boxed{2}$ for statistics mode.

The select $\boxed{1}$ for 1 − VAR and input variables.

For answers key in

AC SHIFT 1 5 2 =    1.96 = 2.0 = mean (goals per match)

AC SHIFT 1 5 3 =    1.4554... = 1.5 = standard deviation

∴ Mean = 2.0 and standard deviation = 1.5

## Exercise 2.7

1. Calculate the standard deviation of each of the following arrays of numbers, giving your answer correct to one decimal place:

    (i)  2, 5, 6, 7       (ii)  3, 6, 7, 9, 10       (iii)  2, 4, 6, 8, 10

    (iv)  1, 3, 7, 9, 10       (v)  8, 12, 15, 9       (vi)  1, 3, 4, 6, 10, 12

    Use your calculator to verify your answer in each case.

2. Show that the following sets of numbers have the same standard deviation:

    (a)  2, 3, 5, 7, 8               (b)  6, 7, 9, 11, 12

3. Find the standard deviation of the numbers

    2, 3, 4, 5, 6.

    Now find the standard deviation of these numbers

    12, 13, 14, 15, 16.

    (i)   What is the relationship between the two sets of numbers?

    (ii)  What is the relationship between their standard deviations?

    (iii) What conclusion can you draw from the results?

4. Verify that 2 is the mean of this distribution. Hence calculate the standard deviation, correct to 1 decimal place.

| Variable | 0 | 2 | 3 | 4 |
|---|---|---|---|---|
| Frequency | 4 | 3 | 2 | 3 |

5. Show that the mean of the given frequency distribution is 3 and hence find the standard deviation, correct to 2 decimal places.

| Variable | 1 | 2 | 3 | 4 |
|---|---|---|---|---|
| Frequency | 1 | 4 | 9 | 6 |

6. Calculate the standard deviation of the following frequency distribution, correct to 1 decimal place.

| Variable | 2 | 4 | 6 | 8 |
|---|---|---|---|---|
| Frequency | 4 | 3 | 0 | 2 |

7. Calculate the mean and hence the standard deviation of the following frequency distribution.

| Variable | 0 | 4 | 6 | 8 |
|---|---|---|---|---|
| Frequency | 4 | 3 | 2 | 3 |

8. Ms Byrne gave the 30 students in her class a quick spelling test.
The marks obtained are presented in the table below.

| Mark | 0 | 1 | 2 | 3 | 4 | 5 |
|---|---|---|---|---|---|---|
| Number of students | 3 | 3 | 3 | 6 | 12 | 3 |

Calculate the mean and standard deviation of the distribution, correct to one decimal place.

9. The number of letters delivered to a business premises on each day of the 5-day working week were as follows:

   18, 26, 22, 34, 25

   (i) Calculate the mean number of letters delivered.
   (ii) Calculate the standard deviation, correct to one decimal place.
   (iii) If $\bar{x}$ is the mean and $\sigma$ is the standard deviation, find the values of $\bar{x} + \sigma$ and $\bar{x} - \sigma$.
   (iv) On how many days is the number of letters delivered within one standard deviation of the mean?

10. The data below gives the number of books read in the last month by a class of 20 students.

| Number of books, x | 0 | 1 | 2 | 3 | 4 |
|---|---|---|---|---|---|
| Number of students, f | 2 | 5 | 6 | 5 | 2 |

Find the mean and standard deviation of the number of books.

11. Using the mid-interval values, find the standard deviation of the given grouped frequency distribution. Give your answer correct to 1 decimal place.

| Class interval | 1–3 | 3–5 | 5–7 | 7–9 |
|---|---|---|---|---|
| Frequency | 4 | 3 | 0 | 2 |

12. The following table shows the times taken by 15 pupils to solve a problem.

| Time (in minutes) | 2–4 | 4–6 | 6–10 |
|---|---|---|---|
| No. of students | 3 | 5 | 7 |

By taking mid-interval values, calculate
   (i) the mean
   (ii) the standard deviation.

13. There are two routes for a worker to get to his office. Both the routes involve delays due to traffic lights. He records the time it takes over a series of six journeys for each route. The results are shown in the table.

| Route 1 | 15 | 15 | 11 | 17 | 14 | 12 |
|---|---|---|---|---|---|---|
| Route 2 | 12 | 15 | 18 | 16 | 17 | 12 |

   (i) Work out the mean time taken for each route.
   (ii) Calculate the standard deviation of each of the two routes.
   (iii) Using your answers to (i) and (ii) suggest which route you would recommend. State your reason clearly.

# TEST YOURSELF 2

1. (i) The mean of 3, 7, 8, 10, $x$ is 6. Find $x$.
   (ii) The mean of 3, 3, $y$, 7, 8, 10, $y$ is 7. Find $y$.

2. The number of goals scored by the 11 members of a hockey team in 2009 were as follows:
   6    0    8    12    2    1    2    9    1    0    11
   (i) Find the median.
   (ii) Find the upper and lower quartiles.
   (iii) Find the interquartile range.

3. Jenny obtained these scores for the first eight modules of her course.
   63    49    51    52    70    67    52    76
   (i) Find her mean score.
   (ii) She needs a mean score of 62 over 9 modules to pass her course.
   What does she need to score in her ninth module?

4. The range for the eight numbers shown is 40.
   Find **two** possible values for the missing number.

5. These are the salaries of five employees in a small business.
   Mr A: €45 000      Mr B: €35 800      Mr C: €42 800
   Mr D: €45 000      Mr E: €170 600
   (i) Find the mean, median and mode of their salaries.
   (ii) Which does not give a fair average?
   Explain why in one sentence.

6. The mean of five numbers is 15.
   The numbers are in the ratio $1:2:3:4:5$.
   Find the smallest number.

7. Find (i) the median (ii) the upper quartile (iii) the lower quartile for these numbers
   12    6    4    9    8    4    9    8    5    9    10

8. Ten men travelled to watch a rugby match.
   The mean age of the men was 25 years and
   the range of their ages was 6.
   Write each statement below and then write
   next to it whether it is
       (i) true     (ii) could be true    or   (iii) false.
   (a) The youngest man was 18 years old.
   (b) All the men were at lest 20 years old.
   (c) The oldest person was 4 years older than
   the youngest.
   (d) Every man was between 20 and 26 years old.

**9.** Ian had 16 boxes of matches.
He counted the number of matches in each box.
The table below gives his results.

| No of matches per box | 41 | 42 | 43 | 44 |
|---|---|---|---|---|
| No. of boxes | 2 | 7 | 4 | 3 |

    (i)   Write down the modal number of matches per box.

   (ii)   What is the median number of matches per box?

  (iii)   Calculate the mean number of matches per box.

**10.** Alan has six different trees in his small garden. He is a keen gardener and wishes to know how many trees his neighbours have. He records the number of trees in each garden on his road.

| No. of trees | 3–7 | 8–12 | 13–17 | 18–22 |
|---|---|---|---|---|
| No. of gardens | 4 | 9 | 5 | 3 |

    (i)   What is the modal group?       (ii)   In which interval does the median lie?

  (iii)   Estimate the mean number of trees per garden, correct to one decimal place.

**11.** There are four parts in an English test.
Marks are awarded for speaking, reading, writing and spelling in the ratio $3:3:4:2$ respectively.
Jasmine sat the test and scored 57%, 63%, 78% and 42% respectively for each part of the test.
Find her weighted average percentage for the English test.

**12.** A television production company needs a new production assistant.
The first impression an interviewee gives is from their clothes style.
However it is four times more important that they are resourceful and three times more important that they have a good sense of humour.
Each person interviewed is given a score out of ten for each of these criteria.
Colin scored 9 for dress style, 7 for his resourcefulness and 5 for his sense of humour.
Find his weighted mean score.

**13.** Find (i) the mean (ii) the standard deviation for these numbers:

     7, 11, 6, 8, 13

Give your answer to (ii) correct to one decimal place.

**14.** The times taken by a group of 16 students to run 100 metres are shown below:

| Time (in seconds) | 11 | 12 | 13 | 14 |
|---|---|---|---|---|
| No. of students | 2 | 5 | 6 | 3 |

Work out the mean and standard deviation of this data, correct to one decimal place in each case.

**15.** Two supermarkets, $S_1$ and $S_2$, made reductions in the prices of the four items $A, B, C, D$ as shown in the table:

|  | A | B | C | D |
|---|---|---|---|---|
| $S_1$ | 10c | 3c | 5c | 20c |
| $S_2$ | 8c | 4c | 3c | 21c |

Which supermarket has the better mean reduction per item?
If the sales of the four items $A, B, C, D$ in each supermarket were in the ratio $2:4:1:3$ respectively, which, now, has the better mean reduction?

**16.** These are the scores of two players over six rounds of golf.

| Rory | 87 | 69 | 80 | 86 | 84 | 80 |
|---|---|---|---|---|---|---|
| **Darren** | 77 | 91 | 90 | 85 | 67 | 70 |

  (i)   Calculate the mean score for each player.
  (ii)  Use your calculator or otherwise to find the standard deviation of the scores for each player, correct to 1 decimal place.
        Use the data to state whom you think is the better player.
        Give a reason for your answer.

**17.** The marks obtained, in a spelling test, by two groups of people are given in the following table:

| Group 1 | 46 | 50 | 46 | 52 | 46 | 55 | 58 | 54 | 60 |
|---|---|---|---|---|---|---|---|---|---|
| **Group 2** | 39 | 72 | 39 | 68 | 48 | 74 | 39 | 52 | 75 |

  (a)  Find (i) the mode (ii) the median and (iii) the mean of both groups correct to one decimal place.
  (b)  Compare your findings and comment on which group was the better at spelling.

## Summary of Key Points

### Averages

The **mode** is the value that occurs most often.

The **median** is the middle number in a list of numbers after they have been put in order.

The **mean** is found by adding up all the numbers and dividing by the number of numbers.

The mean of a frequency distribution is:

$$\text{Mean} = \frac{\Sigma fx}{\Sigma f}$$

### Range and quartiles

| | |
|---|---|
| **Range** | Largest value minus smallest value |
| **Lower quartile, $Q_1$** | The lower quartile is the value one-quarter of the way through the data. |
| **Upper quartile, $Q_3$** | The upper quartile is the value three-quarters of the way through the data. |
| **Interquartile range** | The interquartile range = upper quartile − lower quartile, i.e., $Q_3 - Q_1$ |

If there are $n$ values in a data set,
$Q_1 = \frac{1}{4}(n + 1)$th value
$Q_3 = \frac{3}{4}(n + 1)$th value

### Weighted mean

The weighted mean $= \frac{\Sigma wx}{\Sigma w}$, where $w$ is the weight given to each value of $x$.

### Which average to use

The **mode** is useful when we need the most frequent value.
It is the only average for categorical data.

The **median** gives the middle value and is useful when the data is very spread out.

The **mean** is useful when we need a 'typical' value when most of the data is closely grouped. It may not be a good average if the data contains a few values very different from the rest.

### Standard deviation

The standard deviation, $\sigma$, of a set of data is given by the formula on the right.

$$\sigma = \sqrt{\frac{\Sigma(x - \bar{x})^2}{n}}$$

The bigger the standard deviation the more spread out the data is.

When using a **calculator** to find the standard deviation of 10, 6, 2, 16, 4 use the following sequence of keys:

MODE 2 1

10 = 6 = 2 = 16 = 4 =

AC SHIFT 1 5 2 =   7.6 = mean

AC SHIFT 1 5 3 =   4.963869... = 5.0 = standard deviation

# chapter 3

# Representing Data

## Key Words

bar chart    line plot    pie chart    histogram    shape
continuous data    symmetrical    positive skew    negative skew
stem and leaf diagram    back-to-back stem and leaf diagram
bivariate data    scatter graph    correlation    causal relationship

## SECTION 3.1  Bar charts and Pie charts

### 1. Bar charts

**Bar charts** are a simple but effective way of displaying data.

A bar chart consists of a series of bars of the same width, drawn either vertically or horizontally from an axis.

The heights (or lengths) of the bars always represent the frequencies.

The bars are generally separated by narrow gaps of equal width.

---

### Example 1

The frequency table below shows the numbers of text messages received by a group of students on a particular Sunday.

Illustrate the information by a bar chart.

| No. of messages | 0 | 1 | 2 | 3 | 4 | 5 | 6 | 7 | 8 | 9 |
|---|---|---|---|---|---|---|---|---|---|---|
| Frequency | 0 | 1 | 2 | 4 | 6 | 9 | 11 | 14 | 9 | 4 |

The bar chart is shown below.

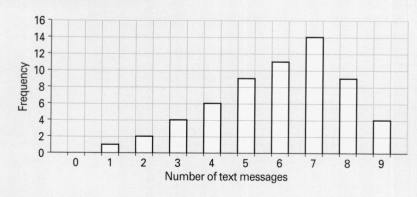

---

## 2. Line plots

A **line plot** is used to display small sets of discrete or categorical data. It is similar to a bar chart with dots (•) or crosses (×) used instead of a bar. Each dot represents one unit of the variable.

The line plot below shows the sales of the different-sized shoes by a shoe shop on a particular day.

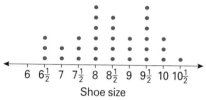

Shoe size

The number of pairs sold was $3 + 2 + 3 + 6 + 5 + 3 + 6 + 3 + 1 = 32$

## 3. Pie charts

A **pie chart** is a good way of displaying data when you want to show how something is shared or divided. It is particularly suitable for displaying categorical data.

The pie chart below shows how Shane spent the last 24 hours.

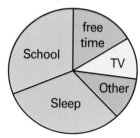

The pie chart is divided up into sectors.

The whole circle represents the 24 hours.

We can see that Shane spent roughly the same time sleeping as he did at school.

The angle of each sector is proportional to the frequency of the category that it represents.

Pie charts are particularly suitable for displaying categorical data.

---

### Example 2

In a survey on holidays, 120 people were asked to state which type of transport they used on their last holiday. This table shows the results of the survey. Draw a pie chart to illustrate the data.

| Type of transport | Train | Coach | Car | Ship | Plane |
|---|---|---|---|---|---|
| Frequency | 24 | 12 | 59 | 11 | 14 |

We need to find the fraction of 360° which represents each type of transport. This is usually done in a table, as shown below.

| Type of transport | Frequency | Calculation |
|---|---|---|
| Train | 24 | $\frac{24}{120} \times 360 = 72°$ |
| Coach | 12 | $\frac{12}{120} \times 360 = 36°$ |
| Car | 59 | $\frac{59}{120} \times 360 = 177°$ |
| Ship | 11 | $\frac{11}{120} \times 360 = 33°$ |
| Plane | 14 | $\frac{14}{120} \times 360 = 42°$ |
| Totals | 120 | 360° |

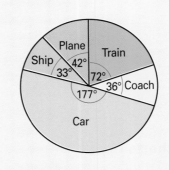

The pie chart is shown on the right.
A protractor was used to measure the angles.

This pie chart gives information about the medals won by an Athletics Club at a sports meeting.

If a total of 24 medals were won, we find the number of each type as follows:

(i)   Gold medals:   $\dfrac{75°}{360°} \times \dfrac{24}{1} = 5$

(ii)  Silver medals:   $\dfrac{150°}{360°} \times \dfrac{24}{1} = 10$

(iii) The angle in the bronze sector is $360° - 150° - 75° = 135°$.

Bronze medals:   $\dfrac{135°}{360°} \times \dfrac{24}{1} = 9$

## Exercise 3.1

1.  The hair colours of all the students in a class are recorded.
    The bar chart on the right shows the results.
    (i)   How many students have black hair?
    (ii)  Which hair colour is the mode?
    (iii) How many students are there in the class?

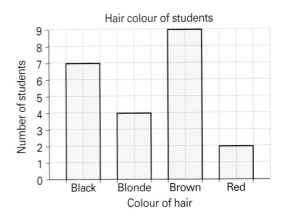

2. This bar chart shows the number of pictures remembered by each student in a memory experiment.

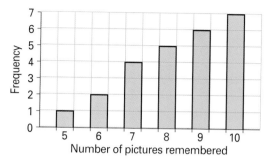

(i) How many students took part in the experiment?
(ii) What is the modal number of pictures remembered?
(iii) How many students remembered less than 7 pictures?
(iv) What is the range of the number of pictures remembered?
(v) What is the median number of pictures remembered?

3. Paul's class got these marks for a project.

| 19 | 16 | 45 | 43 | 40 | 39 | 36 | 30 | 28 | 42 | 35 | 40 |
| 32 | 38 | 41 | 48 | 27 | 18 | 29 | 38 | 42 | 26 | 41 | 35 |

(i) Use a copy of this table. Fill it in.

| Mark | 11–20 | 21–30 | 31–40 | 41–50 |
|---|---|---|---|---|
| Tally | | | | |
| Frequency | | | | |

(ii) Draw a bar chart for this data.

4.

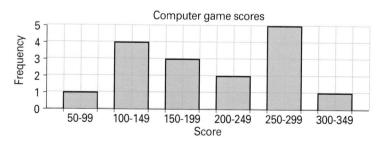

This graph shows scores in a computer game.
(i) Scores of 250 or more won a prize. How many people won a prize?
(ii) How many people played altogether?
(iii) A paper said that 'Five people scored between 270 and 299 points.'
Is this correct?
Choose one of these answers.
(a) Yes          (b) No          (c) Can't tell

**5.** This bar chart shows the numbers who attended five first-aid training sessions and the months during which these sessions took place.

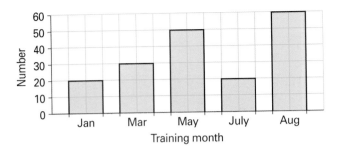

(i) Find the total number who attended the five sessions.

(ii) Which two months accounted for half the total that attended?

(iii) What was the mean number of people who attended each session?

**6.** This bar chart shows the average monthly temperature at noon for each of four months.
Brenda says 'the dotted line shows the mean for the four months'
Use the bar chart to explain why Brenda cannot be correct.

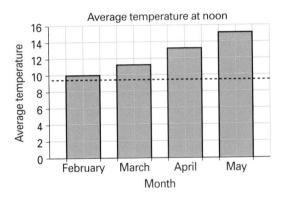

**7.** The line plot below illustrates the number of goals scored per match by a hockey team.

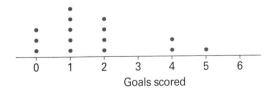

(i) How many matches have the team played?

(ii) Which number of goals scored is the mode?

(iii) What is the range of the number of goals scored?

(iv) What percentage of their matches were scoreless?

**8.** These bar charts show the number of hours of TV watched by four boys in one week.

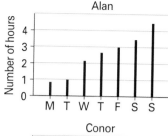

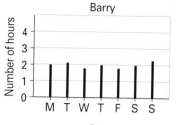

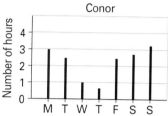

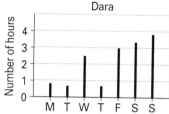

Whose graph matches these comments?
  (i)   I watched most TV at the beginning and end of the week.
  (ii)  I watched about the same amount of TV each day.
  (iii) I watched quite a lot of TV on four days and not much on the other three days.
  (iv)  Each day I watched more TV that the day before.

**9.** The bar chart below is called a dual bar chart.
It compares two sets of data.
It gives the number of patients attending surgeries in the mornings and evenings for six days.

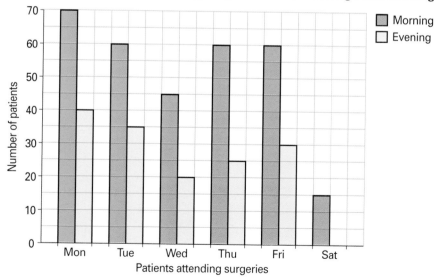

  (i)   On which day did most patients attend?
  (ii)  On which day did fewest patients attend?
  (iii) On which day was there no evening surgery?
  (iv)  On which day did 90 patients attend?
  (v)   How many more patients attended on Tuesday morning than on Tuesday evening?

10. The sizes of dresses sold in a shop during one week are given in the table on the right: Draw a pie chart to illustrate this data.

| Size | 8 | 10 | 12 | 14 | 16 | 18 |
|------|---|----|----|----|----|----|
| Frequency | 3 | 7 | 10 | 12 | 6 | 2 |

11. The pie chart on the right illustrates the grades achieved by a group of 264 students.
Find the number of students that achieved grade E.

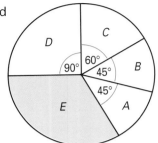

12. The given pie chart illustrates the favourite lessons of 120 Junior Cert students in a Cork school.
How many pupils named each of these as their favourite lessons?
   (i)   maths            (ii)   PE

What percentage of pupils chose science as their favourite lesson?

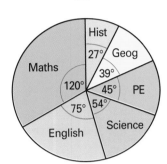

13. An ice cream stall sells vanilla, strawberry and chocolate ice creams. The pie chart illustrates the sales of ice cream for last Saturday. The number of vanilla and the number of chocolate ice creams sold were the same. The stall sold 60 strawberry ice creams. How many chocolate ice creams were sold?

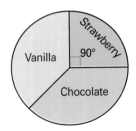

14. In a survey, 320 people on an aircraft and 800 people on a ferry were asked to state their nationality.

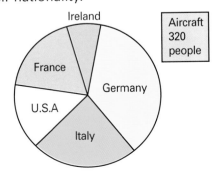

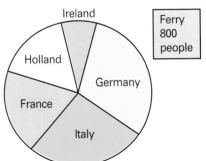

Jane looked at the charts and said 'There were about the same number of people from Italy on the aircraft and on the ferry'.
Explain why Jane is wrong.

# SECTION 3.2 Histograms

One of the most common ways of representing a frequency distribution is by means of a **histogram**.

Histograms are very similar to bar charts but there are some important differences:
- there are no gaps between the bars in a histogram
- histograms are used to show **continuous data**
- the data is always **grouped**; the groups are called classes
- the **area** of each bar or rectangle represents the frequency.

Histograms may have equal or unequal class intervals.

For our course we will confine our study to histograms with **equal class intervals**.

When the class intervals are equal, drawing a histogram is very similar to drawing a bar chart.

## Example 1

The frequency table below shows the times taken by 32 students to solve a problem.

| Time (in secs) | 0–10 | 10–20 | 20–30 | 30–40 | 40–50 | 50–60 |
|---|---|---|---|---|---|---|
| No. of students | 1 | 2 | 8 | 12 | 6 | 3 |

   (i)   Draw a histogram to represent this data.
   (ii)   Write down the modal class.
   (iii)   In which interval does the median lie?

We first draw two axes at right angles to each other.

We plot the variables (time in this case) on the horizontal axis and plot the frequencies (number of students) on the vertical axis.

   (i)   The histogram is shown below.

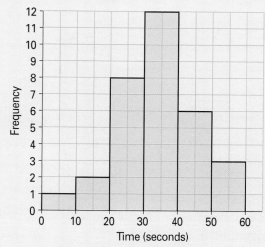

[**NOTE**: It is important to label each axis.]

(ii) The modal class is the class with the highest frequency.
This is the (30–40) second class.

∴   the modal class is (30–40) seconds.

(iii) The median is the value halfway through the distribution.

There are 32 students altogether; so the middle students are the 16th and 17th students.

The sum of the numbers of students in the first three intervals is
    1 + 2 + 8 i.e. 11

The 16th and 17th students will lie in the next interval, (30–40) seconds.

Thus, the median lies in the (30–40) second interval.

## Exercise 3.2

1. At the end of their journeys, 30 motorists were asked how many kilometres they had travelled. Their responses are shown in the table below:

| Distance (in km) | 0–20 | 20–40 | 40–60 | 60–80 | 80–100 |
|---|---|---|---|---|---|
| Frequency | 6 | 12 | 7 | 4 | 1 |

[0–20 means ⩾0 and <20]

(i)   Draw a histogram to illustrate this data.
(ii)  How many motorists had travelled 40 km or more?
(iii) What is the modal class?
(iv)  What percentage of the motorists travelled between 20 km and 40 km?

2. The histogram below shows the ages of people living in a village.

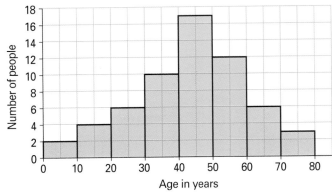

(i)   How many people were aged between 30 years and 40 years?
(ii)  Which is the modal class?
(iii) How many people were aged under 30 years?
(iv)  How many people lived in the village?
(v)   Which interval contains 20% of the people surveyed?
(vi)  In which interval does the median age lie?

3. The frequency table below gives the waiting times of a group of patients at a doctor's surgery.

| Waiting time (in mins) | 0–4 | 4–8 | 8–12 | 12–16 | 16–20 |
|---|---|---|---|---|---|
| No. of patients | 2 | 6 | 10 | 12 | 8 |

    (i)   Draw a histogram to illustrate this data.
   (ii)  How many patients were included in the survey?
  (iii)  Which is the modal class?
  (iv)  In which interval does the median lie?
   (v)  What is the greatest number of patients who could have waited longer than 10 minutes?

4. The histogram below shows the times taken, in seconds, for a group of pupils to solve a puzzle.

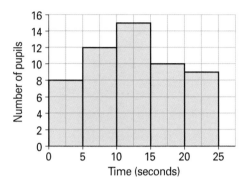

    (i)   How many pupils took 15 seconds or longer to solve the puzzle?
   (ii)  How many pupils took part in the test?
  (iii)  Which is the modal class?
  (iv)  In which interval does the median lie?
   (v)  What is the greatest number of pupils who could have solved the puzzle in less than 8 seconds?
  (vi)  What is the least number of pupils who could have solved the puzzle in less than 12 seconds?

5. The grouped frequency table opposite shows the minutes spent in a shopping complex by a number of people:

| Minutes | Number of people |
|---|---|
| 5–15 | 8 |
| 15–25 | 14 |
| 25–35 | 28 |
| 35–45 | 20 |

    (i)   Draw a histogram to illustrate the data.
   (ii)  Write down the modal class.
  (iii)  In which interval does the median lie?
  (iv)  Which interval contains exactly 20% of the people?
   (v)  What is the greatest number of people who could have spent more than 30 minutes in the shopping complex?
  (vi)  Use the mid-interval values to calculate the mean time spent in the shopping complex, correct to the nearest minute.

# SECTION 3.3 The shape of a distribution

In the previous section we encountered histograms of various shapes.
The diagrams below show four histograms, all with different shapes.

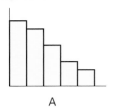 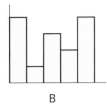 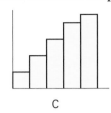 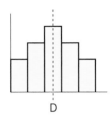

| A | B | C | D |

Only histogram D appears balanced or symmetrical as it has an axis of symmetry.
The other three histograms are less balanced or **skewed** in some way.

Histograms are very useful when you want to see where the data lies and so get a clear
picture of the shape of the distribution. For example, in histogram A above, we can see that
most of the data is concentrated at the lower values. In histogram C the data is concentrated
at the higher values.

There are some shapes that occur frequently in distributions and you should be able to
recognize and name them. The most common and frequently occurring shapes follow.

## 1. Symmetrical distributions

- This distribution has an axis of symmetry down the middle.
  It is called a **symmetrical distribution**.

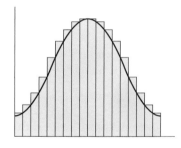 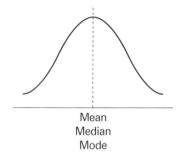

Mean
Median
Mode

Mean = Median = Mode

- It is one of the most common and most important distributions in statistics.
  It is generally referred to as the **normal distribution**.
- Real-life examples of a symmetrical (or normal) distribution are
  (i) the heights of a random sample of people
  (ii) the intelligence quotient (IQ) of a population

## 2. Positive skew

- When a distribution has most of the data at the lower values,
  we say it has a **positive skew**. The following histogram
  shows a positive skew as most of the data, represented by the
  higher bars, are mainly to the left.

  > If there is a positive
  > skew, most of the
  > data is to the left.

Notice that there is a long tail to the right of the distribution.

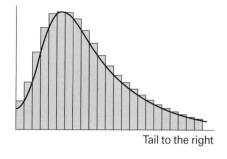

Tail to the right

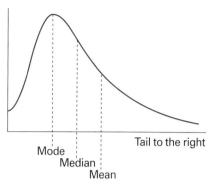

Tail to the right

Mode
Median
Mean

Mean > Median > Mode

- Real-life examples of a distribution with a positive skew are
   (i)   the number of children in a family
   (ii)  the age at which people first learn to ride a bicycle
   (iii) the age at which people marry.

## 3. Negative skew

- When a distribution has most of the data at the higher values, we say that the distribution has a **negative skew**.
  When a distribution has a negative skew the tail will be to the left.

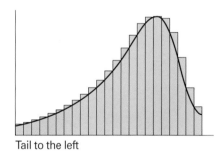

Tail to the left

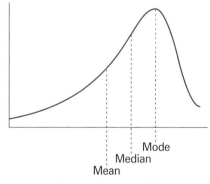

Mode
Median
Mean

Mean < Median < Mode

In a distribution with a **positive** skew, the tail is to the **right**; with a **negative** skew, the tail is to the **left**.

- Real-life examples of a distribution with a negative skew are
   (i)   the ages at which people have to get their first pair of reading glasses
   (ii)  the heights of players playing in a basketball league.

# Exercise 3.3

1. Describe the distribution shown below.

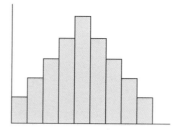

   (i)  What is this distribution commonly known as?
   (ii) Give one real-life example of this distribution.

2. Describe the distribution shown on the right.
   Give one real-life example of this distribution.

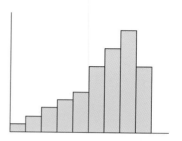

3. Is this distribution positively or negatively skewed?
   You will notice that most of the values are
   at the lower end of the distribution.
   Give one real-life situation that is an example
   of this type of distribution.

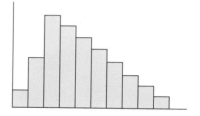

4. Here are three distributions:

   (a) 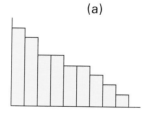   (b) 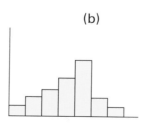   (c)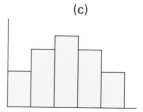

   (i)   Which of these distributions is symmetrical?
   (ii)  Which distribution is positively skewed?
   (iii) Which distribution is negatively skewed?
   (iv)  Which distribution is the most likely to represent this data?
         'The weights of international rugby players'
   (v)   Which distribution best describes this data?
         'The intelligence quotients (IQ) of a large number of second-level students.'

**5.** Describe the distribution shown.

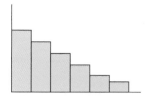

Which of the three averages, the mode, the mean or the median is the most suitable average to describe this data?

**6.** Two distributions (A) and (B) are shown below:

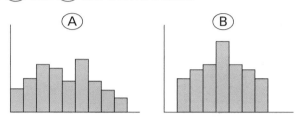

Name the distribution that is likely to represent each of these situations.
- (i) 'The marks achieved in maths by all the leaving certificate students last year'.
- (ii) 'The marks achieved in biology by a class of 30 students'.
- (iii) What is distribution (B) generally known as?

**7.** The histogram below shows the distribution of the times taken to solve a puzzle.

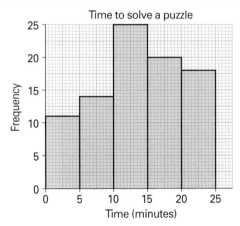

- (i) Is the distribution positively or negatively skewed?
- (ii) Explain why the mode is higher than the mean in this distribution.

**8.** Describe the distribution illustrated on the right.
For the mode, mean and median of this distribution,
- (i) state which of the three is the smallest
- (ii) state which of the three is the largest.

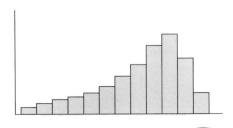

**9.** A safety officer records the speeds of cars passing a school. The table shows the speeds that he recorded.

| Speed (km/hr) | 25–30 | 30–35 | 35–40 | 40–45 | 45–50 |
|---|---|---|---|---|---|
| Frequency | 25 | 20 | 10 | 5 | 3 |

  (i) Draw a histogram to show this data.

  (ii) Is the distribution positively skewed or negatively skewed?
       Explain your answer.

  (iii) Copy the statement below and place the symbols $>$ or $<$ in the boxes in relation
        to the data given in the table above

   Mode ☐   Median ☐   Mean ☐

# SECTION 3.4  Stem and leaf diagrams

A **stem and leaf diagram** is a very useful way of presenting data. It is useful because it shows all the original data and also gives you the overall picture or shape of the distribution.

It is similar to a horizontal bar chart, with the numbers themselves forming the bars.

Stem and leaf diagrams are suitable only for small amounts of data.

Often the stem shows the tens digit of the values and the leaves show the units digit.
If you put them together you get the original value.

For example $4|2$ represents 42.

A typical stem and leaf diagram is shown below.

```
0 | 6  9
1 | 2  5  (7) ◄─────────── This represents 17.
2 | 3  3  6  8
3 | 0  2  7
4 | 1  2  6
5 | 3                    Key: 3|2 = 32
```

> You must always add a key to show
> how the stem and leaf combine.

The data represented above is:

  6, 9, 12, 15, 17, 23, 23, 26, 28, 30, 32, 37, 41, 42, 46, 53

---

**Example 1**

Here are the marks gained by a class of students in a science test.

  58  65  40  59  68  63  81  76  63  57  44  47  53  70  80
  68  81  61  57  49  70  54  75  69  65  59  52  63  63  74

  (i) Construct a stem and leaf diagram to represent this data.
  (ii) What is the mode of the data?
  (iii) What is the median?
  (iv) What is the range of the data?

---

(i) First draw the stem of the diagram.

```
4
5       The smallest value in the list is 40 and
6       the largest is 81.
7       The stem of the diagram will be the
8       tens digits from 4 to 8.
```

Now work through the data values and put the second digit on the appropriate row.

```
4 | 0  4  7  9
5 | 8  9  7  3  7  4  9  2
6 | 5  8  3  3  8  1  9  5  3  3
7 | 6  0  0  5  4
8 | 1  0  1
```

For the first value, 58, the 8 will go on the 5 row.

The numbers on the right of the diagram are the leaves

Finally rewrite the diagram with all the leaves in order, with the smallest nearest to the stem.
Remember to include a key.

```
4 | 0  4  7  9
5 | 2  3  4  7  7  8  9  9
6 | 1  3  3  3  3  5  5  8  8  9
7 | 0  0  4  5  6
8 | 0  1  1
```
Key: $6|3 = 63$

(ii) The mode is 63 as this is the value that occurs most often.

(iii) As there are 30 values, the median will be the mean of the 15th and 16th values.
Count the values in the stem and leaf diagram to find the 15th and 16th values.
Since these are both 63, the median is 63.

> If there are 30 values, the middle value is $\frac{1}{2}(30 + 1)$ i.e. $15\frac{1}{2}$
> This will be half the sum of the 15th and 16th values.

(iv) The range is the highest value minus the lowest value
$$= 81 - 40$$
$$= 41$$

## Different values for the stems

Here are the times, in seconds, for the contestants in a 60-metre race.

    6.6    4.9    5.7    7.6    8.2    6.3    6.5    7.4    5.1    5.3    6.2    7.8

This time we will use the units as the stems.

**Step 1** Draw the first diagram.
The units are the stems.
The tenths are the leaves.

**Step 2** Put the leaves in numerical order.

```
4 | 9                                   4 | 9
5 | 7  1  3                             5 | 1  3  7
6 | 6  3  5  2                          6 | 2  3  5  6
7 | 6  4  8                             7 | 4  6  8
8 | 2        Key: 6|3 = 6.3 seconds    8 | 2
```

## Back-to-back stem and leaf diagrams

Two stem and leaf diagrams can be drawn using the same stem.

These are known as back-to-back stem and leaf diagrams.

The leaves of one set of data are put to the right of the stem.

The leaves of the other set of data are put on the left.

A back-to-back stem and leaf diagram is very useful to compare two sets of data.

Jack and Ciara compared the length of time they spent each evening on their homework.

Their times are shown in the back-to-back stem and leaf diagram.

```
               Jack    |    Ciara
    6   5   5   3   2  | 2 |
            8   6   5  | 3 | 6  7
                3   2  | 4 | 4  6  6
                    1  | 5 | 2  3  4  5
                       | 6 | 4  8
```

Key: 5|3 = 35 minutes                         Key: 4|6 = 46 minutes

We read Jack's times from the stem to the left.

Thus Jack's times are:

    22, 23, 25, 25, 26, 35, 36, ...

Ciara's times are:

    36, 37, 44, 46, 46, 52, ...

> Sometimes the key is given as 5|3|6.
> This means 36 for Ciara and 35 for Jack.

The following example shows how a back-to-back stem and leaf diagram can be used to compare two sets of data.

## Example 2

Robert and Jane compared the lengths of time they spent each evening watching television.

Their times are shown in the following back-to-back stem and leaf diagram.

| | | | | Robert | | | Jane | | | |
|---|---|---|---|---|---|---|---|---|---|---|
| 7 | 4 | 4 | 2 | 3 | 2 | | | | | |
| | | 9 | 6 | (4) | 3 | 4 | 6 | | | |
| | | | 5 | 3 | 4 | 5 | 7 | 7 | | |
| | | | | 2 | 5 | (3) | 3 | 4 | 6 | |
| | | | | | 6 | 5 | 7 | | | |

Key: 3|4 = 43 minutes          Key: 4|5 = 45 minutes

(i) What does the diagram show about the lengths of time Robert and Jane spent watching television?

(ii) What was Jane's median time spent watching television?

(iii) What was Robert's median time?

(iv) Do these median times support your conclusion in (i) above?

(i) By looking at the diagram we can see that most of Robert's times are between 23 and 39 minutes.
Most of Jane's times are between 45 and 67 minutes.
This shows that Jane spends more time watching television than Robert does.

(ii) For Jane, the value that is half way through the distribution is 53.
Thus her median time spent watching television is 53 minutes.

(iii) Robert's median time is 34 minutes.

(iv) Because Jane's median time is greater than Robert's, it supports the view expressed in (i) above that she spends more time than Robert watching television.

## Finding the interquartile range from a stem and leaf diagram

In Chapter 2 we found that the lower quartile is the value in the data that is one quarter way through the distribution. The upper quartile is the value that is three quarters way through the distribution. The difference between the upper quartile and the lower quartile is the **interquartile range**.

We will now show how to find the two quartiles and the interquartile range of a distribution presented as a stem and leaf diagram.

Example 3

The stem and leaf diagram on the right shows
the marks, out of 50, obtained in a maths test.

Find (i) the median mark
    (ii) the lower quartile
    (iii) the upper quartile
    (iv) the interquartile range.

Marks obtained

| 1 | 2 | 8 |   |   |   |
|---|---|---|---|---|---|
| 2 | 1 | 4 | 7 | 7 | 8 |
| 3 | 1 | 4 | 5 | 7 |   |
| 4 | 1 | 2 | 8 |   |   |
| 5 | 0 |   |   |   |   |

Key: $2|1 = 21$

(i) The median mark is the mark that is halfway through the distribution.
There are 15 data values.
The halfway value is $\frac{1}{2}(15 + 1)$ i.e. the 8th value.
Starting at the lowest value, the 8th value is 31
$\therefore$ the median $= 31$

(ii) The lower quartile is the value that is one quarter way through the
distribution.
This value is $\frac{1}{4}(15 + 1)$ i.e. 4th value
This value is 24.
$\therefore$ the lower quartile $= 24$

(iii) The upper quartile is the value that is three quarters of the way
through the distribution.
This value is $\frac{3}{4}(15 + 1)$ i.e. the 12th value.
This value is 41.
$\therefore$ the upper quartile $= 41$

(iv) The interquartile range $=$ upper quartile minus lower quartile
$$= 41 - 24$$
$$= 17$$

## Exercise 3.4

1. The stem and leaf diagram on the right
shows the marks obtained by a group
of students in a maths test.
    (i) How many students took this test?
    (ii) How many students got between
        70 and 79 marks?
    (iii) What was the highest mark achieved?
    (iv) What was the lowest mark?
    (v) How many students got 80 marks or more?

| stem | leaf |   |   |   |   |   |
|------|------|---|---|---|---|---|
| 5 | 1 | 4 | 6 |   |   |   |
| 6 | 2 | 3 | 3 | 6 |   |   |
| 7 | 2 | 3 | 5 | 7 | 8 |   |
| 8 | 0 | 0 | 2 | 4 | 6 | 6 |
| 9 | 3 | 4 |   |   |   |   |

Key: 7|3 means 73

2. The stem and leaf diagram below show the ages, in years, of 25 people who wished to enter a 10 km walking competition.

```
1 | 4  4  6  9
2 | 1  3  7  7  7  8
3 | 3  6  6  7  9
4 | 0  2  3  3  8  8
5 | 1  3  4  7        Key: 1|6 means 16 years old
```

(i) How many people were less than 20 years old?
(ii) Write down the modal age.
(iii) How many people were between 35 and 45 years old?
(iv) What was the median age?

3. The amount of petrol, in litres, bought by 20 motorists is shown

| 16 | 23 | 27 | 10 | 35 | 42 | 26 | 25 | 24 | 17 |
|----|----|----|----|----|----|----|----|----|----|
| 23 | 41 | 33 | 35 | 25 | 19 | 16 | 31 | 12 | 29 |

Construct a stem and leaf diagram to represent this information.

4. Twenty four pupils were asked how many CDs they had in their collection.
The results are shown below:

| 23 | 2 | 18 | 14 | 7 | 4 | 25 | 21 | 32 | 26 | 31 | 6 |
|----|----|----|----|----|----|----|----|----|----|----|----|
| 17 | 6 | 18 | 19 | 31 | 21 | 12 | 1 | 0 | 8 | 14 | 15 |

(i) Draw a stem and leaf diagram to represent this information.
(ii) How many pupils had more than 20 CDs?
(iii) What is the median number of CDs per pupil?

5. The times, in seconds, taken to answer 24 telephone calls are shown.

| 3.2 | 5.6 | 2.4 | 3.5 | 4.3 | 3.6 | 2.8 | 5.8 | 3.3 | 2.6 | 3.5 | 2.8 |
|-----|-----|-----|-----|-----|-----|-----|-----|-----|-----|-----|-----|
| 5.6 | 3.5 | 4.2 | 1.5 | 2.7 | 2.5 | 3.7 | 3.1 | 2.9 | 4.2 | 2.4 | 3.0 |

Copy and complete the stem and leaf diagram to represent this information.

```
1 |
2 |
3 | 2
4 |
5 |      Key: 3|2 means 3.2 seconds
```

(i) How many of the calls took longer than 4 seconds to answer?
(ii) What is the difference, in seconds, between the shortest and the longest times to answer the calls?
(iii) What is the median length of time taken to answer the calls?
(iv) What is the modal length of time?

**6.** The stem and leaf diagram below shows the marks achieved by 19 students in a test.

| stem | leaf |
|------|------|
| 2 | 2 |
| 3 | 4  6 |
| 4 | 2  7  9 |
| 5 | 3  4  5  8  9 |
| 6 | 0  2  6  7 |
| 7 | 2  6 |
| 8 | 1  4 |

Key: $4|2 = 42$ marks

(i) Write down the range of the marks.

(ii) Find the value of the lower quartile.

(iii) What is the upper quartile?

(iv) What is the interquartile range?

**7.** These are the ages, in years, of the members of a table tennis club.

| 15 | 17 | 12 | 16 | 24 | 29 | 36 | 25 | 38 | 42 | 17 |
|----|----|----|----|----|----|----|----|----|----|----|
| 53 | 44 | 49 | 53 | 29 | 21 | 11 | 38 | 14 | 29 | |

(i) Draw a stem and leaf diagram to show these ages.

(ii) What is the lower quartile?

(iii) Find the upper quartile.

(iv) What is the interquartile range?

**8.** The results for examinations in Science and French for a class of students are shown in the back-to-back stem and leaf diagram below:

| Science | | French |
|---------|---|--------|
| 7  5 | 2 | |
| 8  0 | 3 | 6 |
| 5  5 | 4 | 0  5  7  8 |
| 9  5  4  3  2 | 5 | 1  5  8 |
| 9  7  5 | 6 | 2  4  4  5  7 |
| 3  1 | 7 | 2  4  5  6 |
| 6  3 | 8 | 3  5 |
| 1 | 9 | |

Key: $1|7 = 71$ marks                    Key: $3|6 = 36$ marks

(i) How many students took the examinations?

(ii) What is the range of marks in

(a) Science     (b) French?

(iii) What is the median mark in Science?

(iv) What is the interquartile range of the French marks?

9. Brian and Martin played ten rounds on a 9-hole golf course.
The stem and leaf diagram shows the number of strokes they took for each round.

| | Brian | | Martin |
|---|---|---|---|
| | 9 7 | 3 | |
| 9 5 5 3 1 0 | 4 | 5 9 |
| | 3 2 | 5 | 0 2 3 5 7 |
| | | 6 | 2 4 |
| | | 7 | 1 |

Key: 2|5 = 52 strokes

Key: 4|5 = 45 stroke

Write down (i) Brian's lowest score
 (ii) Brian's median score
 (iii) Martin's median score
 (iv) the range of Brian's scores
 (v) the range of Martin's scores.
Which of the two players is the better golfer?
Explain your answer.

10. The back-to-back stem and leaf diagram below shows the pulse rates of a group of college students in Galway. They are split into those who smoked and those who didn't.

| | Smoke | | Do not smoke |
|---|---|---|---|
| | | 5 | 0 8 9 |
| | 9 8 5 | 6 | 0 4 4 5 6 6 6 8 8 |
| 6 6 5 0 0 | 7 | 0 1 1 8 9 |
| 8 8 6 3 0 | 8 | 0 1 6 8 8 |
| | 2 0 | 9 | |

Key: 5|6 = 65

Key: 5|8 = 58

(i) Find the median and range of the pulse rates of the group who smoked.
(ii) Find the median and range of the pulse rates of the group who did not smoke.
(iii) If a lower pulse rate indicates a higher level of fitness, which of the two groups is the fitter? Explain your answer.

11. Ten men and ten women were asked how much television they watched the previous weekend. Their times, in minutes, were as follows:

| Men | 40 | 41 | 42 | 52 | 52 | 52 | 64 | 65 | 65 | 71 |
|---|---|---|---|---|---|---|---|---|---|---|
| Women | 40 | 41 | 51 | 62 | 63 | 75 | 87 | 88 | 93 | 95 |

Copy and complete the back-to-back stem and leaf diagram opposite.
 (i) What is the modal time for men?
 (ii) What is the median time for
  (a) men  (b) women?
 (iii) What is the range of times for
  (a) men  (b) women?
 (iv) Use the results in (ii) and (iii) to show that women spend more time watching television than men do.

| Men | | Women |
|---|---|---|
| | 4 | 0 |
| | 5 | |
| 4 | 6 | |
| | 7 | |
| | 8 | |
| | 9 | |

Key: 4|6 = 64

Key: 4|0 = 40

**12.** Ann and Conor played nine rounds of crazy golf on their summer holidays. Their scores are shown in the back-to-back stem and leaf diagram below.

|        |   |   | Ann |   |   |     | Conor |   |   |   |
|-------:|---|---|-----|---|---|:---:|-------|---|---|---|
|        |   |   |     |   | 3 | 0   | 0     | 2 |   |   |
|        |   |   |     | 1 | 4 | 1   | 1     | 1 | 2 |   |
| 9      | 3 | 1 | 0   | 0 | 5 | 2   |       |   |   |   |
|        |   | 6 | 5   | 4 | 6 | 8   |       |   |   |   |

Key: 1|4 = 41                                                        Key: 4|1 = 41

   (i)   Conor's lowest score was 30. What was Ann's lowest score?
   (ii)  What was Conor's modal score?
   (iii) What was Ann's median score?

In crazy golf the player with the lowest score wins. Conor actually shot the highest score that summer but was still chosen as the better player.
   (iv)  Give a reason for this choice.

**13.** The table below gives the examination marks in French and English for a class of 20 pupils.

| French  | 75 | 69 | 58 | 58 | 46 | 44 | 32 | 50 | 53 | 78 |
|---------|----|----|----|----|----|----|----|----|----|----|
|         | 81 | 61 | 61 | 45 | 31 | 44 | 53 | 66 | 47 | 57 |
| English | 52 | 58 | 68 | 77 | 38 | 85 | 43 | 44 | 56 | 65 |
|         | 65 | 79 | 44 | 71 | 84 | 72 | 63 | 69 | 72 | 79 |

   (i)   Construct a back-to-back stem and leaf diagram to represent these results.
   (ii)  What is the median mark in French?
   (iii) What is the median mark in English?
   (iv)  In which subject did the pupils perform better? Explain your answer.

# SECTION 3.5  Scatter graphs

Statements such as 'Drink driving causes accidents' or 'Obesity can cause heart-attacks' are often made in the media. The Road Safety Authority, for example, might produce data to show that there is a relationship between drink driving and having a car accident.

This section shows you how to compare two sets of data to find out if a relationship exists between them. For example, you could expect that a relationship exists between the number of ice-creams sold in a seaside shop and the average daytime temperatures.

Jane and her friend collected the following data to find out.

| Average temperature (°C) | 10 | 12 | 16 | 20 | 13 | 16 | 14 | 17 | 19 | 20 | 21 | 16 |
|--------------------------|----|----|----|----|----|----|----|----|----|----|----|----|
| No. of ice-creams sold   | 1  | 5  | 20 | 50 | 15 | 25 | 14 | 30 | 32 | 42 | 50 | 30 |

They plotted each pair of values, (10, 1), (12, 5), (13, 15) and so on, on graph paper.

They used the horizontal axis for the temperature and the vertical axis for the numbers of ice-creams sold.

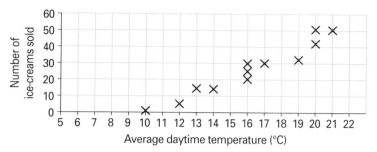

Data such as (10, 1) and (12, 5) which comes in pairs is called **bivariate data**.

The points plotted above are called a **scatter diagram** or **scatter graph**. The diagram shows that the number of ice-creams sold increases as the temperature increases. This indicates that there is an association or relationship between the temperature and the number of ice-creams sold.

If the points on a scatter graph lie approximately on a straight line, we say that there is a linear relationship between the two sets of data. The closer the points are to a straight line, the stronger the relationship will be.

## Example 1

On a journey between two towns, Andrew wrote down the number of kilometres that were left on the journey. He did this every ten minutes. The table below shows the data he recorded

| Time (mins) | 10 | 20 | 30 | 40 | 50 | 60 | 70 | 80 | 90 | 100 |
|---|---|---|---|---|---|---|---|---|---|---|
| Kilometres to go | 72 | 60 | 50 | 42 | 40 | 32 | 25 | 18 | 10 | 0 |

Draw a scatter graph to illustrate this data.

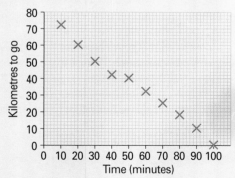

The scatter graph shows that there is a linear relationship between the two sets of data. The greater the time spent travelling, the fewer kilometres there are to go.

Sometimes there is no relationship between two sets of data.

The table below shows the relationship between temperature and rainfall every Sunday over an 11-week period.

| Temperature (in °C) | 20 | 21 | 24 | 26 | 30 | 33 | 34 | 35 | 38 | 40 | 44 |
|---|---|---|---|---|---|---|---|---|---|---|---|
| Rainfall (mm) | 12 | 4 | 22 | 8 | 16 | 4 | 2 | 10 | 14 | 0 | 2 |

This is the scatter graph of the data.

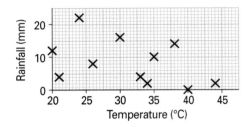

There does not appear to be any relationship between the two sets of data as the points are well scattered and there is no indication of a linear pattern.

## Correlation

The strength of the relationship between two sets of data is known as **correlation**. If the points on a scatter graph lie on or close to a straight line, a **strong correlation** is said to exist.

The three scatter graphs below show some different types of relationships between two sets of data.

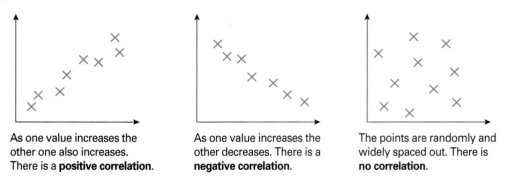

As one value increases the other one also increases. There is a **positive correlation**.

As one value increases the other decreases. There is a **negative correlation**.

The points are randomly and widely spaced out. There is **no correlation**.

We could have strong or weak positive correlation, and strong or weak negative correlation.

The scatter diagrams below illustrate different types of correlation.

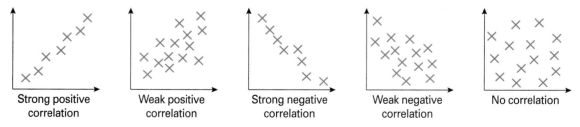

Strong positive correlation

Weak positive correlation

Strong negative correlation

Weak negative correlation

No correlation

**Example 2**

The table shows the weights and heights of 12 people.

| Height (cm) | 150 | 152 | 155 | 158 | 158 | 160 | 163 | 165 | 170 | 175 | 178 | 180 |
|---|---|---|---|---|---|---|---|---|---|---|---|---|
| Weight (kg) | 57 | 62 | 63 | 64 | 58 | 62 | 65 | 66 | 65 | 70 | 66 | 67 |

(i) Draw a scatter graph to show this data.

(ii) Describe the strength and type of correlation between these heights and weights.

(i) We draw two axes at right angles.
We put the heights on the horizontal axis.
We start with 140 cm and go up to 180 cm.
We put the weights on the vertical axis, starting at 55 kg and going up to 70 kg.
We then plot the points (150, 57), (152, 62), ... etc.
The scatter graph is shown below.

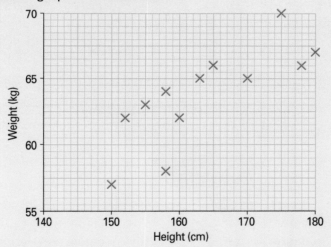

(ii) The correlation is weak positive as the points do not lie very close to a straight line. The correlation is positive because the weight generally increases as the height increases.

# Exercise 3.5

**1.** Four scatter graphs are shown below.

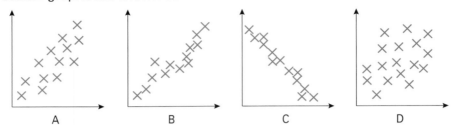

(i) Which of these graphs shows the strongest positive correlation?

(ii) Which of these graphs shows negative correlation?

(iii) Which of these graphs shows the weakest correlation?

**2.** Here are sketches of six scatter graphs:

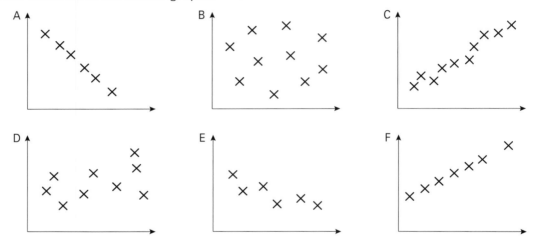

Which diagram(s) show
(i) positive correlation
(iii) no correlation
Describe the correlation in graph F.

(ii) negative correlation
(iv) strong negative correlation?

**3.** This scatter graph shows the number of books read by some children and the reading ages of these children.

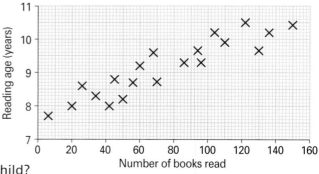

(i) How many children have read more than 100 books?

(ii) One of these children has read 50 books. What is the reading age of this child?

(iii) Describe the relationship shown by the scatter graph.

**4.** The examination marks of a sample number of students in both their mock and final examinations are shown in the given scatter graph.

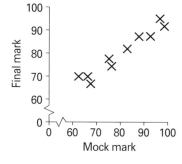

   (i) Describe the correlation shown in the graph.
   (ii) What can you say about the relationship between the mock and final marks of the students?

**5.** This scatter diagram shows the weights, in kg, and the heights, in cm, of 20 male members of a basketball club.

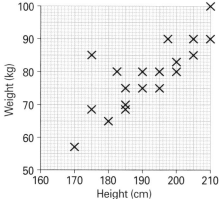

   (i) Write down the weight of the heaviest member.
   (ii) Write down the height of the shortest member.
   (iii) One member is particularly heavy for his height.
       Write down the height and weight of this member.
   (iv) Describe the correlation shown in this graph.

**6.** Ten children are given two tests to complete. One test involves some number puzzles. The other test involves spotting mistakes in pictures.
The table shows the scores in the tests for these children.

| Child | A | B | C | D | E | F | G | H | I | J |
|---|---|---|---|---|---|---|---|---|---|---|
| **Number puzzle score** | 12 | 7 | 10 | 3 | 7 | 10 | 5 | 5 | 12 | 14 |
| **Picture puzzle score** | 3 | 12 | 7 | 16 | 10 | 5 | 14 | 12 | 5 | 1 |

   (i) Draw a scatter graph to show this data.
       (Put the number score on the horizontal axis.)
   (ii) Describe the strength and type of correlation between these scores.
       Does the type of correlation surprise you? Explain.

**7.** Ben wants to buy a secondhand bike.
He records the age and price of the type he wants from a website.

| Age (years) | 6 | 3 | 2 | 4 | 6 | 1 | 4 | 8 | 2 | 7 |
|---|---|---|---|---|---|---|---|---|---|---|
| **Price (€)** | 60 | 180 | 240 | 120 | 100 | 280 | 160 | 40 | 200 | 50 |

   (i) Draw a scatter graph of this information on graph paper, putting age on the horizontal axis.
   (ii) What does the scatter graph tell you about the connection between the ages of these bikes and their prices?
   (iii) Describe, in two words, the correlation that exists.

8. The table shows the marks of 15 students taking Paper 1 and Paper 2 of a maths exam. Both papers were marked out of 40.

| Paper 1 | 36 | 34 | 23 | 24 | 30 | 40 | 25 | 35 | 20 | 15 | 35 | 34 | 23 | 35 | 27 |
|---------|----|----|----|----|----|----|----|----|----|----|----|----|----|----|----|
| Paper 2 | 39 | 36 | 27 | 20 | 33 | 35 | 27 | 32 | 28 | 20 | 37 | 35 | 25 | 33 | 30 |

    (i)   Draw a scatter diagram to show this information.

    (ii)  Describe the correlation shown in the scatter diagram.

9.

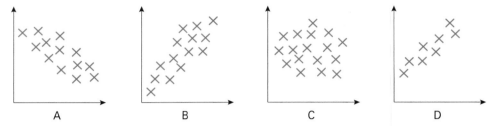

         A                   B                   C                   D

Four scatter graphs are shown above. For each of the following situations, choose the most appropriate of the scatter graphs. Explain your choice in each case.

    (i)    Boys' heights and their shoe sizes.

    (ii)   Men's weights and the times taken by them to complete a crossword puzzle.

   (iii)   Ages of cars and their selling prices.

   (iv)   Marks achieved in Maths Paper 1 and Maths Paper 2.

10. Describe the type of correlation you would expect between:

    (i)    the age of a boat and its secondhand selling price,

    (ii)   the heights of children and their ages,

   (iii)   the shoe sizes of children and the distances they travel to school,

   (iv)   time spent watching television and time spent studying,

    (v)   the number of cars on the road and the number of accidents.

# SECTION 3.6 Measuring correlation

The points on the scatter graph on the right are in a straight line.

In this case we say that there is **perfect positive correlation** between the two variables.

If we use the letter $r$ to represent the correlation and if perfect positive correlation exists, we say that $r = 1$.

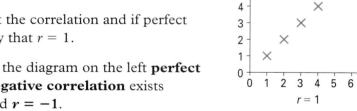

$r = 1$

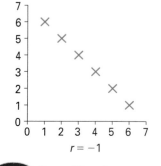

$r = -1$

In the diagram on the left **perfect negative correlation** exists and $r = -1$.

All other correlations will have values between 1 and $-1$.

If there is no correlation, $r = 0$.

The value of $r$ is called the **correlation coefficient**.

The scatter diagrams below give examples of some values of *r*.

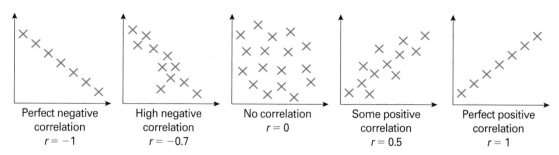

| Perfect negative correlation $r = -1$ | High negative correlation $r = -0.7$ | No correlation $r = 0$ | Some positive correlation $r = 0.5$ | Perfect positive correlation $r = 1$ |

## Example 1

Shown below are four scatter graphs A, B, C and D.

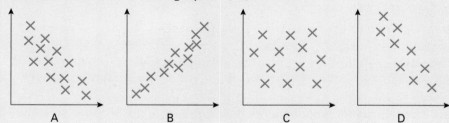

Here are six correlation coefficients (i.e. values for *r*)

$$0.2, \quad -0.8, \quad -0.2, \quad 0, \quad 0.9, \quad -0.6$$

Choose the most likely correlation coefficient from these to match the scatter graphs A, B, C and D above.

A: $-0.6$        B: $0.9$        C: $0$        D: $-0.8$

## Exercise 3.6

**1.** Describe in two words the correlation shown below.

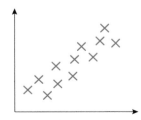

Which of these numbers is the most likely to represent this correlation?

$$-0.8, \quad 0.9, \quad 0, \quad 0.1, \quad 0.7$$

2. Four scatter graphs A, B, C and D are shown below.

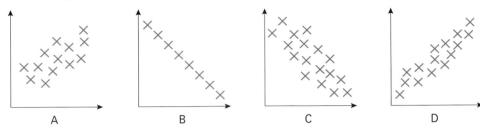

Match one of the following numbers with each of the graphs above so that it best represents the correlation:

0.1,    −0.4,    1,    −1,    0.6    −0.8,    0.8

3. Draw a separate scatter graph that might represent each of the following correlation coefficients:

   (i)   1               (ii)  −0.9               (iii)  0.5               (iv)  0

4. Which one of these numbers represents 'strong negative correlation'?

   (i)   0.3          (ii)  −0.1          (iii)  1          (iv)  −0.9          (v)  −0.5

5. Which of these correlation coefficients best represents the correlation shown in the given diagram?

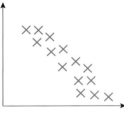

   (i)   0.8                    (ii)  −0.8                    (iii)  −1                    (iv)  0.5

6. Which of these correlation coefficients shows the strongest correlation?

   (i)   0.7               (ii)  −0.2               (iii)  −1               (iv)  0.9

7. Which of these correlation coefficients shows the weakest correlation?

   (i)   −0.8               (ii)  0.1               (iii)  −1               (iv)  0.9

8. Match one of these correlation coefficients to each of the descriptions below:

       0.9,    −0.1,    −1,    −0.8    0,    0.2

   (i)    Strong positive correlation
   (ii)   Strong negative correlation
   (iii)  No correlation
   (iv)   Perfect negative correlation
   (v)    Very weak negative correlation
   (vi)   Very weak positive correlation

# SECTION 3.7 Causal relationships and correlation

The price of a used car depends, among other things, on the age of the car. The age of the car **causes** the price of the car to decrease. We say that there is a **causal relationship** between the price of the car and the age of the car.

Definition | When a change in one variable causes a change in another variable, we say that there is a causal relationship between them.

The scatter graph below shows the relationship between the sales of iced drinks and temperature. The correlation is strong and positive. You would expect this as the rise in temperature would tend to result in an increase in the sales of iced drinks.

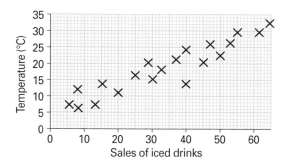

So it would be reasonable to conclude that there is a causal relationship between the sales of iced drinks and an increase in temperature.

The scatter diagram below shows the number of laptops and the number of fridges sold by an electrical shop over a ten-month period.

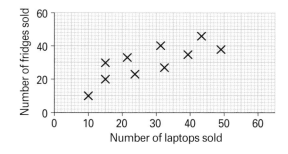

The graph shows that there is a reasonably strong positive correlation between the number of laptops sold and the number of fridges sold. However, this does not mean that there is a causal relationship between them; buying a laptop does not cause you to buy a fridge.

Correlation does not necessarily mean that there is a causal relationship.

## Exercise 3.7

1. Which of the following pairs of variables are likely to have a causal relationship?
   - (i) Sales of television sets and sales of DVD recorders.
   - (ii) A car's engine-size and its petrol consumption.
   - (iii) Marks in your maths test and the distance you live from your school in kilometres.
   - (iv) Sales of vegetables and sales of chocolate.
   - (v) Sales of computers and sales of software.
   - (vi) Outside temperature and the amount of gas used for central heating.

2. The scatter graph shows the age of cars and the number of kilometres travelled.

   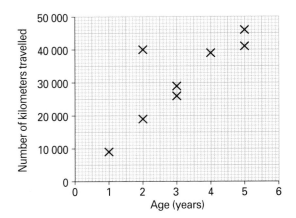

   - (i) One of these cars is 4 years old. How many kilometres has this car travelled?
   - (ii) Describe the relationship shown by this scatter graph.
   - (iii) Is there a causal relationship between these variables?
     Explain your answer.
   - (iv) The age and number of kilometres travelled by one of these cars looks out of place.
     - (a) What is the age of this car and how many kilometres has it travelled?
     - (b) Give a possible reason why the results for this car are different from the rest of the cars.

3. The scatter graph below shows the relationship between the ages and prices of used motorcycles.

   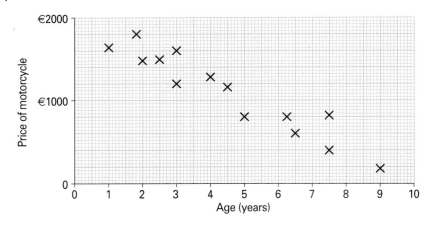

   - (i) Describe the correlation shown in this scatter graph.
   - (ii) Is there a causal relationship between the variables?
     Explain your answer.

4. The number of hours of sunshine and the maximum temperature at a seaside resort were measured on seven days in June.

| Hours of sunshine | 5 | 9 | 8 | 6 | 5 | 2 | 4 |
|---|---|---|---|---|---|---|---|
| Temperature (°C) | 26 | 30 | 29 | 26 | 24 | 19 | 23 |

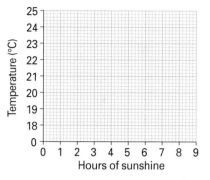

(i) Plot this data on a scatter graph.
Use the scales shown on the right.

(ii) Describe the relationship shown by your scatter graph.

(iii) Is there a causal relationship between the hours of sunshine and the maximum temperature at the resort? Explain your answer.

5. A small electrical shop recorded the yearly sales of radio sets and television sets over a period of 10 years.
The results are shown in the table below.

| Year | 1 | 2 | 3 | 4 | 5 | 6 | 7 | 8 | 9 | 10 |
|---|---|---|---|---|---|---|---|---|---|---|
| No. of televisions sold | 60 | 68 | 73 | 80 | 85 | 88 | 90 | 96 | 105 | 110 |
| No. of radios sold | 80 | 60 | 72 | 65 | 60 | 55 | 52 | 44 | 42 | 36 |

(i) Using scales going from 50 to 120 for the sales of televisions and 30 to 90 for the sales of radios, draw a scatter graph.

(ii) What sort of correlation does the scatter graph suggest?

(iii) Is there a causal relationship between the television sales and radio sales? Explain your answer.

# TEST YOURSELF 3

1. The number of laptops sold by a store was recorded each month for a period of 23 months. The results are shown in the stem and leaf diagram below.

| stem | leaf |
|---|---|
| 1 | 8  9 |
| 2 | 3  6  7  9 |
| 3 | 2  6  6  6  7  8 |
| 4 | 4  5  5  7  7  7  7 |
| 5 | 2  7  8  9 |

Key: 1|8 means 18 laptops

(i) Write down the modal number of laptops sold.
(ii) Write down the median.
(iii) Find the lower quartile.
(iv) Find the upper quartile.
(v) Work out the interquartile range.

**2.** Here are the marks scored by 19 girls in a science test.

| 54 | 42 | 61 | 47 | 24 | 43 | 55 | 62 | 30 | 27 |
|----|----|----|----|----|----|----|----|----|----|
| 28 | 43 | 54 | 46 | 25 | 32 | 49 | 73 | 50 |    |

  (i) Construct a stem and leaf diagram to show these results.
  (ii) Write down the range of the marks.
  (iii) What is the lower quartile?
  (iv) What is the upper quartile?
  (v) Write down the interquartile range.

**3.** The following stem and leaf diagram shows the amounts of money spent on a Friday night by a group of college students.

```
              Males     |    Females
                  8   0 | 6
          7   6   5   1 | 0   5   5   5   8   8
  9   9   9   8   6   6 2 | 5   5   8   8   9
          8   8   5   5   5 3 | 5   5
                  8   5   4 | 0
```
Key: 5|4 = €45                                      Key: 3|5 = €35

  (i) How many students were in the group?
  (ii) Write down the largest amount of money spent by the males.
  (iii) What is the median amount of money spent by the females.
  (iv) What is the median amount of money spent by the males.
  (v) Comment on whether males or females spent the most money.

**4.** The total cost of a holiday was €1800.
The pie chart shows how this cost was made up.

  (i) How much was spent on food?
  (ii) How much was spent on travel?
  (iii) How much was spent on the hotel?
  (iv) How much was spent on other items?

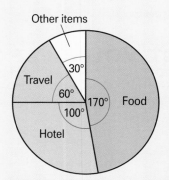

**5.** The table shows the temperature of water as it cools in a freezer.

| Time (minutes) | 5 | 10 | 15 | 20 | 25 | 30 |
|----------------|----|----|----|----|----|----|
| Temperature (°C) | 36 | 29 | 25 | 20 | 15 | 8 |

  (i) Draw a scatter diagram to illustrate this information.
      Keep temperature on the horizontal axis.
  (ii) What type of correlation is shown?

**6.** Four scatter diagrams A, B, C and D are shown below.

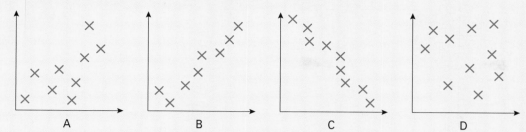

    A                         B                         C                         D

    (i)    Which diagram shows no correlation?

    (ii)   Which diagram shows negative correlation?

    (iii)  Which diagram shows weak positive correlation?

    (iv)  Associate one of these correlation coefficients with each of the diagrams above:

       (a)  0.8          (b)  0          (c)  $-0.7$        (d)  0.3

**7.** What type of correlation could you expect if you took readings of these variables and drew a scatter diagram?

Describe each correlation as

(a)  positive          (b)  negative         (c)  no correlation

    (i)   cars on roads; accident rate

    (ii)  sales of perfume; amount spent on advertising perfume

    (iii) birth rate; rate of inflation

    (iv) outside temperature; sales of sun cream

    (v)  height of adults; age of same adults.

**8.** Suggest the type of diagram that would be suitable to represent each of the following types of data:

    (i)   colours of sweaters in a store

    (ii)  the distance from school and the time taken to travel to school

    (iii) comparing the results of a maths test for the boys and girls in a class of 30

    (iv) the country of origin of a group of immigrants to Ireland

    (v)  the percentage share of the grocery market in Ireland of six leading supermarket chains

    (vi) speed of cars and the number of traffic accidents.

**9.** A distribution is represented by the histogram shown on the right.

    (i)   Describe this distribution.

    (ii)  Give two real-life examples of distributions of this type.

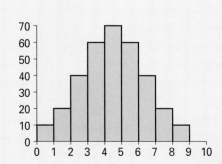

**10.** The histogram below represents a distribution.

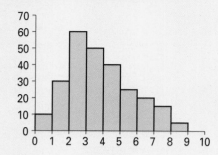

    (i)   Explain why the distribution is skewed.

    (ii)  Is it positively or negatively skewed?

    (iii) Give one example from everyday life of this type of distribution.

**11.**    (i)   Describe the distribution shown below.

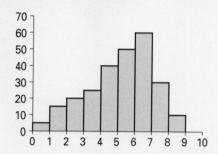

    (ii)  Give an example of a distribution from real-life that is skewed in this way.

**12.** Here is a back-to-back stem and leaf diagram showing the pulse rates of a group of men and women.

|        | Men   |   |   | Women |   |   |   |   |   |
|-------:|------:|--:|:-:|:------|---|---|---|---|---|
|        |     5 | 1 | 4 |       |   |   |   |   |   |
|      7 |     4 | 2 | 5 | 3     |   |   |   |   |   |
|      8 |     2 | 0 | 6 | 1     | 2 |   |   |   |   |
|        |     5 | 2 | 7 | 4     | 4 | 5 | 8 | 9 |   |
|        |     6 | 2 | 8 | 2     | 5 | 7 |   |   |   |
|        |       | 4 | 9 | 2     | 8 |   |   |   |   |

Key: 1|4 = 41                                  Key: 5|3 = 53

    (i)   How many men were tested?

    (ii)  What was the median pulse rate for
         (a) men    (b) women?

    (iii) What was the range of pulse rates for men?

    (iv) Which group do you think had overall, the higher pulse rate?
         Justify your answer.

# Summary of Key Points

## Bar charts and pie charts

1. Bar charts can be used to show patterns or trends in the data.
   The bars are of equal width and there are gaps between the bars.

2. Pie charts show how a quantity is shared or divided.
   All the sector angles in a pie chart add to 360°.

## Stem and leaf diagrams

1. A stem and leaf diagram keeps all the data values and shows the shape of a distribution.

2. A back-to-back stem and leaf diagram allows us to compare two sets of data by using the spread of the data and some other measure such as the median.

## Shape of a distribution

Histograms show the spread of the data and the shape of a distribution.
Three of the more common shapes are shown below.

Symmetrical distribution    Negatively-skewed distribution    Positively-skewed distribution

## Scatter graphs and correlation

1. Scatter graphs are used to show whether two sets of data are related.

2. Correlation is a measure of the strength of the relationship between two variables.

3. The closer the points on a scatter graph are to a straight line, the stronger the relationship.

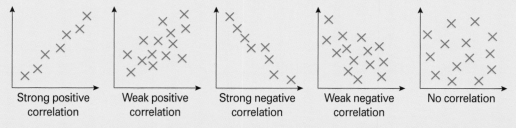

Strong positive correlation    Weak positive correlation    Strong negative correlation    Weak negative correlation    No correlation

4. When a change in one variable directly causes a change in another variable, there is said to be a causal relationship between them.

5. Correlation does not necessarily mean there is a causal relationship.

## Key Words

| likelihood | impossible | certain | outcome | equally likely |

likelihood    impossible    certain    outcome    equally likely

sample space    experiment    relative frequency    mutually exclusive

Venn diagrams    Bernoulli trials    permutation    combination

# SECTION 4.1  Probability and chance

If you listen to weather forecasts you could hear expressions like these:

'There is a strong **likelihood** of rain tomorrow'.

'In the afternoon there is a **possibility** of thunder'.

'The rain will **probably** clear towards evening'.

Weather forecasts are made by studying charts and weather data to tell us how likely it is, for example, that it will rain tomorrow.

**Probability** uses numbers to tell us how likely something is to happen.

The **probability** or **chance** of something happening can be described by using words such as

**Impossible**    **Unlikely**    **Even Chance**    **Likely**    **Certain**

An event which is **certain to happen** has a **probability of 1**.

An event which **cannot happen** has a **probability of 0**.

All other probabilities will be a number greater than 0 and less than 1.

The more likely an event is to happen, the closer the probability is to 1.

The line shown below is called a **probability scale**.

There is an **even chance** that the next person you meet on the street will be a male.

It is **certain** that the sun will rise tomorrow.

It is **impossible** to get 7 when a normal dice is rolled.

## Exercise 4.1

1. Describe each of the following events as Impossible, Evens or Certain:
   (i) The sun will not rise next week.
   (ii) The next baby born will be a boy.
   (iii) Christmas day will fall on 25th December this year.
   (iv) You draw a red card from a normal pack of cards.
   (v) A banana will grow on a pear tree.

2. There are seven labels on the probability scale below:

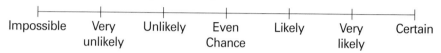

Which of these labels best describes the likelihood of each of these events occurring?
   (i) You will score 10 in a single throw of a normal dice.
   (ii) It will rain in Ireland sometime in the next week.
   (iii) You will win a prize in the club lottery with a single ticket.
   (iv) You will live to be 100 years old.
   (v) If I toss a coin it will show tails.
   (vi) A day of the week ending with the letter Y.
   (vii) You will draw an even number from these cards

3. David has these cards:
   He mixes the cards up
   and turns them face down.
   He turns one over. It has a 5 on it.
   He turns another card over.

   (i) Is it more likely he will get a number smaller than 5 or a number bigger than 5? Explain.
   (ii) Is it more likely that the card will show a circle rather than a triangle? Explain.

4. Make a copy of this probability scale.
   Put an arrow on the scale to show the probability of the events listed below:

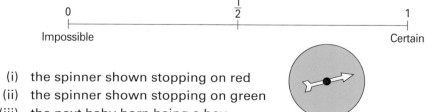

   (i) the spinner shown stopping on red
   (ii) the spinner shown stopping on green
   (iii) the next baby born being a boy
   (iv) a black bead being taken, without looking, from this bag
   (v) a red bead being taken, without looking, from this bag

**5.** Here are four spinners with different colours:

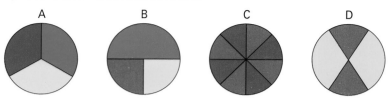

If the spinners are spun,
- (i) Which spinner has an even chance of showing blue?
- (ii) Which spinner has an even chance of showing red?
- (iii) Which spinner has the least chance of showing yellow?
- (iv) Which spinner has one chance in three of showing yellow?
- (v) Which spinner has one chance in four of showing red?
- (vi) Which spinner has the greatest chance of showing red?

**6.** Yoghurt is sold in packs of 12.
Robbie is going to take one without looking.

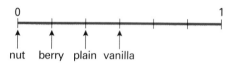

Use the probability scale to work out how many of these flavours are in a pack:
- (i) vanilla
- (ii) plain
- (iii) nut
- (iv) berry.

**7.**

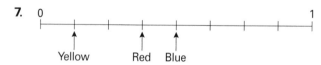

In a game Todd spins an arrow. The arrow stops on one of
sixteen equal sectors of a circle. Each sector of the circle is
coloured. The probability scale shows how likely it is for the
arrow to stop on any one colour. How many sectors are
- (i) coloured red
- (ii) coloured blue
- (iii) coloured yellow?

**8.**

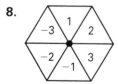

Maria uses a regular hexagon as a spinner for a game.
On a probability scale like this one below, draw an arrow to
show how likely Maria is to get these when she spins the spinner:
- (i) 2
- (ii) a number less than zero
- (iii) a number greater than 1.

A hexagon is a six-sided figure.

0                    $\frac{1}{2}$                    1

# SECTION 4.2 Events and Outcomes

Before you can start a certain game, you must throw a dice and get a six.

The act of throwing a dice is called a **trial**.

The numbers 1, 2, 3, 4, 5 and 6 are all the possible **outcomes** of the trial.

The required result is called an **event**.

If you require an even number when throwing a dice, then the
**event** or **successful outcomes** are the numbers 2, 4 and 6.

> The result we want
> is called an **event**.

## Equally likely outcomes

Two events are **equally likely** if they have the same chance of happening.

The chance of getting a red with this spinner is the same as the chance
of getting a blue. Getting a red and getting a blue are **equally likely**.

The chance of getting a red with this spinner is not the
same as the chance of getting a yellow. Getting a red
and getting a yellow are not equally likely.

In general, if $E$ represents an event, the probability
of $E$ occurring, denoted by $P(E)$ is given below:

$$P(E) = \frac{\text{number of successful outcomes in } E}{\text{number of possible outcomes}}$$

**Note**  **1.** The probability of any event E cannot be less than 0 or greater than 1,
i.e., $0 \leqslant P(E) \leqslant 1$.

**2.** The probability of a certainty is 1.

**3.** The probability of an impossibility is 0.

For the spinner on the right,

$P(\text{green}) = \frac{1}{5}$, because 1 of the 5 sections is green

$P(\text{yellow}) = \frac{2}{5}$, because 2 of the 5 sections are yellow.

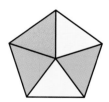

---

### Example 1

Tickets numbered 1 to 12 are placed in a box.
If one ticket is drawn at random, find the probability of getting
   (i)   the number 4
   (ii)  an even number
  (iii)  a two-digit number
  (iv)  a number divisible by 4

(i) There is one 4 in 12 equally likely numbers.

$\Rightarrow$ $P(4) = \frac{1}{12}$

(ii) The even numbers are 2, 4, 6, 8, 10, 12, i.e. 6 even numbers.

$\Rightarrow$ $P(\text{even number}) = \frac{6}{12} = \frac{1}{2}$

(iii) There are 3 two-digit numbers, i.e., 10, 11, 12.

$\Rightarrow$ $P(\text{two-digit number}) = \frac{3}{12} = \frac{1}{4}$

(iv) The numbers divisible by 4 are 4, 8, 12.

$\Rightarrow$ $P(\text{number divisible by 4}) = \frac{3}{12} = \frac{1}{4}$

## Example 2

If a card is drawn from a pack of 52, find the probability that it is

(i) a king
(ii) a spade
(iii) a red card.

(i) There are 4 kings in the pack

$\Rightarrow$ $P(\text{king}) = \frac{4}{52} = \frac{1}{13}$.

(ii) There are 13 spades in the pack

$\Rightarrow$ $P(\text{spade}) = \frac{13}{52} = \frac{1}{4}$.

(iii) There are 26 red cards in the pack $\Rightarrow$ $P(\text{red card}) = \frac{26}{52} = \frac{1}{2}$.

## Example 3

A letter is selected at random from the letters of the word *COMPANION*. Find the probability that the letter is

(i) P      (ii) N      (iii) a vowel      (iv) *M or N*.

(i) There is one *P* in nine letters $\Rightarrow$ $P(P) = \frac{1}{9}$.

(ii) There are 2 *N*s in the word $\Rightarrow$ $P(N) = \frac{2}{9}$.

(iii) There are 4 vowels in the word ... [O, A, I, O] $\Rightarrow$ $P(\text{vowel}) = \frac{4}{9}$

(iv) There is one *M* and 2 *N*s in the word, i.e., 3 in total.

$\Rightarrow$ $P(M \text{ or } N) = \frac{3}{9} = \frac{1}{3}$

## Probability words

In many probability questions words such as **random** and **fair** are used.

These are ways of saying that all outcomes are equally likely.

If $A$ is an event, it will either happen or not happen.
$P(A \text{ happening}) = 1 - P(A \text{ not happening})$.

For example:

A card is taken at **random** from a pack of cards.
This means that each card has an equal chance of being taken.
A **fair** dice is rolled.
This means that the outcomes 1, 2, 3, 4, 5 and 6 are equally likely.

## Exercise 4.2

1. A fair dice is rolled.
   What is the probability of getting
       (i)   a 5                    (ii)  a 1 or a 2        (iii)  4 or more
       (iv)  an odd number          (v)   less than 3       (vi)   a prime number?

2. The fair spinner shown is spun. Work out the
   probability of the arrow pointing to:
       (i)    yellow (Y),
       (ii)   green (G),
       (iii)  red (R),
       (iv)   blue (B),
       (v)    red or blue (R or B).

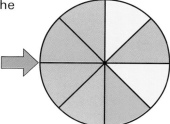

3. A letter is chosen at random from the word *GEOMETRY*.
   What is the probability that it is
       (i)   the letter *R*          (ii)  the letter *E*          (iii)  a vowel?

4. What is the probability of getting a 4 on each of these spinners?
   (i)                            (ii)                            (iii)

   What is the probability of getting a 2 or a 4 on spinner (iii)?

**5.** A card is drawn from a pack of 52 playing cards.
What is the probability that the card is
  (i)   a red card
  (ii)  a spade
  (iii) a king
  (iv)  a red king?

> There are four suits in a pack of cards: hearts and diamonds which are red; clubs and spades which are black.
> Each suit contains 2, 3, 4, 5, 6, 7, 8, 9, 10, jack, queen, king and ace.
> The picture cards are jack, queen and king.

**6.** A bag contains 5 red beads, 4 black beads and 3 green beads.
If a bead is drawn at random from the bag, find the probability that the bead is
  (i)   red          (ii)  green          (iii) red or black          (iv) not black.

**7.** In a casino a pointer is spun and you win the amount shown in the sector where it comes to rest. Assuming that the pointer is equally likely to come to rest in any sector, what is the probability that you win
  (i)   €5          (ii)  no money
  (iii) some money          (iv) more than €5?

**8.** A letter is chosen at random from the letters of the word *DEDICATION*.
What is the probability that the letter is
  (i)   *D*          (ii)  *I*          (iii) *D* or *I*          (iv) a vowel?

**9.** Megan has her birthday this week.
What is the probability that her birthday falls on
  (i)   Monday
  (ii)  a day beginning with *T*
  (iii) a Saturday or a Sunday?

**10.** A dice has its faces numbered 2, 3, 3, 3, 4, 7.
Find the probability of rolling
  (i)   a '7'          (ii)  an even number.

**11.** The 26 letters of the alphabet are written on discs.
The five discs with vowels are put in bag A and the other discs are put in bag B.
Find the probability of selecting
  (i)   an 'o' from bag A
  (ii)  a 'z' from bag B
  (iii) a 'w' from bag A.

Vowels          Consonants

12. In an examination, each candidate is awarded one of the grades *A, B, C, D, E, F*. Grade *A* is the highest and grade *F* is the lowest. The distribution of grades obtained by the 30 pupils in a class is shown in the table below.

| Grade | A | B | C | D | E | F |
|---|---|---|---|---|---|---|
| Number of pupils | 4 | 9 | 7 | 5 | 3 | 2 |

If a candidate is chosen at random, what is the probability that he/she obtained
  (i)  Grade *A*         (ii)  Grade *C* or *D*         (iii)  Grade *C* or higher?

13. A box contains 12 discs: 3 red, 2 yellow, 4 green and 3 white.
  (i)  Find the probability of selecting
    (a)  a red disc         (b)  a yellow disc
  (ii)  The 3 white discs are replaced by 3 yellow discs. Find the probability of selecting
    (a)  a red disc         (b)  a yellow disc.

14. At the end of a Summer Camp 50 boys and girls were asked to name their favourite game at the camp. The results are given in the table below:

|  | Tennis | Basketball | Volleyball |
|---|---|---|---|
| **Girls** | 15 | 10 | 5 |
| **Boys** | 6 | 12 | 2 |

If a person was selected at random from the group of 50, find the probability that the person
  (i)  was a boy
  (ii)  was a girl who named tennis as her favourite game
  (iii)  named basketball as her/his favourite game.
If a girl was selected, find the probability that she had named volleyball as her favourite game.

15. There are 6 counters in a box.
The probability of taking a green counter out of the box is $\frac{1}{2}$.
A green counter is taken out of the box and put to one side.
Gerry now takes a counter from the box at random.
What is the probability it is green?

16. This two-way table shows the numbers of males and females in a group of 50 who wear or do not wear glasses.

|  | Male | Female | Total |
|---|---|---|---|
| **Wearing glasses** | 16 | 18 | 34 |
| **Not wearing glasses** | 9 | 7 | 16 |
| **Total** | 25 | 25 | 50 |

Work out the probability that a person chosen at random is:
  (i)  female,         (ii)  not wearing glasses,         (iii)  a male who wears glasses.

17. This table shows the way that fifty red and blue
counters are numbered either 1 or 2.
One of the counters is chosen at random.
What is the probability that the counter is:

| | Red | Blue |
|---|---|---|
| **1** | 12 | 8 |
| **2** | 8 | 22 |

 (i)   a 1                              (ii)   blue                    (iii)   blue and a 1?
A blue counter is chosen at random.
 (iv)   What is the probability that the counter is a 1?
A counter numbered 1 is chosen at random.
 (v)   What is the probability that it is blue?

18. Mick put these numbered discs in a bag.
    (i)   He shakes the bag and takes one disc
          without looking.
          What  is the probability of getting a 2?

    (ii)   Mick wants to put more discs in the bag so that the chance of getting
          a 4 is twice the chance of getting a 3.
          What discs should he put in the bag?

19. Mark played a card game with Paul. The cards were dealt so that both players received
two cards. Mark's cards were a five and a four. Paul's first card was a six.

Mark                    Paul

Find the probability that Paul's second card was
    (i)   a five                    (ii)   a picture card [a King, Queen or Jack].

20. The circle on the right is divided into eight equal sectors.
Copy this diagram and in the sectors mark the letters R(red),
G(green) or B(blue) so that when a spinner is spun, the
probability of getting blue is $\frac{1}{4}$ and the probability of
getting red will be twice the probability of getting green.

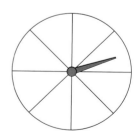

# SECTION 4.3

## Two events – Use of Sample Spaces

When two coins are tossed, the set of possible outcomes is

   $\{HH, HT, TH, TT\}$, where $H$ = head and $T$ = tail.

This set of possible outcomes is called a **sample space**.

By using this sample space, we can write down the probability of getting 2 heads, for example.

$P(HH) = \frac{1}{4}$

$P(\text{one head and one tail}) = \frac{2}{4} = \frac{1}{2}$

An experiment such as throwing two dice has a large number of possible outcomes, so we need to set out the sample space in an organised way, as shown in the following example.

---

### Example 1

If two dice are thrown and the scores are added, set out a sample space giving all the possible outcomes. Find the probability that
- (i) the total is exactly 7
- (ii) the total is 4 or less
- (iii) the total is 11 or more
- (iv) the total is a multiple of 5.

The sample space is set out on the right. There are 36 outcomes.

| | 1 | 2 | 3 | 4 | 5 | 6 |
|---|---|---|---|---|---|---|
| **1** | 2 | 3 | 4 | 5 | 6 | 7 |
| **2** | 3 | 4 | 5 | 6 | 7 | 8 |
| **3** | 4 | 5 | 6 | 7 | 8 | 9 |
| **4** | 5 | 6 | 7 | 8 | 9 | 10 |
| **5** | 6 | 7 | 8 | 9 | 10 | 11 |
| **6** | 7 | 8 | 9 | 10 | 11 | 12 |

(i) There are 6 totals of 7.

$\Rightarrow P(7) = \frac{6}{36} = \frac{1}{6}$

(ii) There are 6 totals of 4 or less.

$\Rightarrow P(4 \text{ or less}) = \frac{6}{36} = \frac{1}{6}$

(iii) There are 3 totals of 11 or more.

$\Rightarrow P(11 \text{ or more}) = \frac{3}{36} = \frac{1}{12}$

(iv) The multiples of 5 are 5 and 10. There are 7 totals of 5 or 10.

$\Rightarrow P(\text{multiple of 5}) = \frac{7}{36}$

---

## Exercise 4.3

**1.** A fair coin is tossed and a fair dice is thrown.
The table below shows all the possible outcomes.

| | | Dice | | | | | |
|---|---|---|---|---|---|---|---|
| | | 1 | 2 | 3 | 4 | 5 | 6 |
| **Coin** | **Head (H)** | H, 1 | H, 2 | H, 3 | H, 4 | H, 5 | H, 6 |
| | **Tail (T)** | T, 1 | T, 2 | T, 3 | T, 4 | T, 5 | T, 6 |

Write down the probability of getting each of these outcomes:
- (i) a head and a 5
- (ii) a tail and an even number
- (iii) a tail and 3 or greater
- (iv) a head and a multiple of 3.

**2.** The sample space on the right shows the outcomes when two dice are thrown and their scores are added.
Find the probability that the sum of the two numbers is

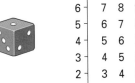

  (i)  9                     (ii)  10

  (iii)  3 or less         (iv)  10 or 11

```
6 -   7  8  9  10 11 12
5 -   6  7  8  9  10 11
4 -   5  6  7  8  9  10
3 -   4  5  6  7  8  9
2 -   3  4  5  6  7  8
1 -   2  3  4  5  6  7

      1  2  3  4  5  6
```

**3.** Three coins are tossed, each toss resulting in a head (H) or a tail(T).
Make out a sample space for the possible results and write down the probability that the coins show

  (i)   *HHH*

  (ii)  *HTH* in that order

  (iii)  2 heads and 1 tail in any order.

**4.** You play a game with two spinners, as shown.
They are spun at the same time and the scores are added.
Make out a sample space for the possible results and write down the probability of getting a total of

  (i)  6                   (ii)  10            (iii)  an even number

Which score do you get most often?

Hence write down the probability of getting this score.

**5.** Of three cards, two are blue and one is red. The three cards are placed side by side, in random order, on a table. One of these ways is B R B .

List all the other ways that the cards could be placed and write down the probability that the two blue cards are next to each other.

**6.** The arrows on both these spinners are spun.

  (i)   Make a list to show all the outcomes, e.g., (1, 5), (1, 6), ...

  (ii)  How many outcomes are there altogether?

  (iii)  What is the probability that

      (a)  both arrows point to an odd number

      (b)  both point to an even number

      (c)  the two numbers add up to 8?

**7.** *A*, *B* and *C* are horses equally likely to win a 3-horse race. List all the ways in which the horses can finish, assuming that all the horses finish the race and that there is no dead-heat.

   (i)  What is the probability that the horses finish in the order *A*, *B* and *C*?

   (ii) What is the probability that *A* wins?

**8.** A blue spinner and a green spinner are spun together and the scores are multiplied.

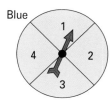 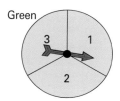

Copy and complete the table of possible outcomes shown below.

|  |  | **Blue** | | | |
|---|---|---|---|---|---|
| | | 1 | 2 | 3 | 4 |
| **Green** | 1 | | | | |
| | 2 | 2 | 4 | 6 | 8 |
| | 3 | | | 9 | |

Find the probability of getting

   (i)  a score of 4   (ii)  an even number   (iii)  a score of 8 or more.

**9.** Three fair coins are tossed. Make out a sample space for all the possible outcomes. Now write down the probability that the outcome will be

   (i)  three heads        (ii)  two heads and one tail
   (iii) no heads          (iv)  at least one head.

# SECTION 4.4

## Estimating probabilities from experiments

So far we have calculated probabilities on the basis that all outcomes are equally likely to happen. However, in real-life situations, events are not always equally likely and some other way must be found to make an estimate of the probability.

In such cases we carry out an experiment or survey to estimate the probability of an event happening.

## Experiment

John suspects that a coin is biased.

In an experiment he tossed the coin 200 times and records the number of heads after 10, 50, 100, 150 and 200 tosses.

The results are shown in the table on the right:

As the number of tosses increase, the number of heads divided by the number of tosses gets closer to 0.5, i.e., $\frac{1}{2}$.

This value is called **relative frequency** and it gives an **estimate of the probability** that the event will happen.

| Number of tosses | Number of heads | Heads ÷ tosses |
|---|---|---|
| 10 | 7 | 0.7 |
| 50 | 28 | 0.56 |
| 100 | 53 | 0.53 |
| 150 | 78 | 0.52 |
| 200 | 103 | 0.515 |

Thus an estimate of the probability that an event will occur by carrying out a survey or experiment is given by

$$\text{Relative frequency} = \frac{\text{Number of successful trials}}{\text{Total number of trials}}$$

In general, as the number of trials or experiments increases, the value of the relative frequency gets closer to the true or theoretical probability.

---

### Example 1

Derek collects data on the colours of cars passing the school gate. His results are shown in the table.

| Colour | Tally | Frequency |
|---|---|---|
| White | ЖНТ ЖНТ ЖНТ ЖНТ IIII | 24 |
| Red | ЖНТ ЖНТ ЖНТ ЖНТ ЖНТ ЖНТ II | 32 |
| Black | ЖНТ ЖНТ IIII | 14 |
| Blue | ЖНТ ЖНТ ЖНТ I | 16 |
| Green | ЖНТ ЖНТ | 10 |
| Other | IIII | 4 |

(i)   How many cars did Derek survey?
(ii)  What was the relative frequency of blue cars?
(iii) What was the relative frequency of red cars? Give your answer as a decimal.
(iv)  Write down an estimate of the probability that the next car passing the school gate will be green.
(v)   How can the estimate for the probability of green cars be made more reliable?

(i) The number of cars in the survey is the sum of the frequencies. This is 100 cars.

(ii) Relative frequency of blue cars $= \frac{16}{100} = \frac{4}{25}$.

(iii) Relative frequency of red cars $= \frac{32}{100} = 0.32$.

(iv) Probability of next car green = relative frequency of green cars
$$= \frac{10}{100} = \frac{1}{10}$$

(v) The estimate for the probability of green cars can be made more reliable by increasing the number of cars observed. Five hundred cars would give a very accurate estimate of the true probability.

## Expected frequency

A bag contains 3 red discs and 2 blue discs.

A disc is chosen at random from the bag and replaced.

The probability of getting a blue disc is $\frac{2}{5}$.

This means that, on average, you expect 2 blue discs in every 5 chosen or 20 blue discs in every 50 chosen.

To find the expected number of blue discs when you choose a disc 100 times,
   (i) Work out the probability that the event happens once.
   (ii) Multiply this probability by the number of times the experiment is carried out.
   Thus the expected number of blue discs is
$$\frac{2}{5} \times \frac{100}{1} = 40.$$

> Expected frequency is probability × number of trials.

---

### Example 2

The probability that a biased dice will land on each of the numbers 1 to 6 is given in the table on the right:

| Number | 1 | 2 | 3 | 4 | 5 | 6 |
|---|---|---|---|---|---|---|
| Probability | 0.1 | 0.1 | 0.2 | $a$ | 0.2 | 0.3 |

   (i) Write down the value of $a$.
   (ii) If the dice is thrown 300 times, how many sixes would you expect?

   (i) Since the dice must land on one of the numbers from 1 to 6, the sum of all the probabilities is 1.

> The sum of probabilities add up to 1.

$\therefore$ $\quad$ $0.1 + 0.1 + 0.2 + 0.2 + 0.3 + a = 1$

$\Rightarrow$ $\quad$ $0.9 + a = 1$

$\Rightarrow$ $\quad$ $a = 1 - 0.9 \Rightarrow a = 0.1$

   (ii) Expected number of sixes = P(6) × number of trials
$$= 0.3 \times 300 = 90$$

## Exercise 4.4

1. A fair coin is tossed 100 times.
   How many heads would you expect to get?

2. A fair six-sided dice is thrown 60 times.
   - (i) How many sixes would you expect to get?
   - (ii) How many twos would you expect to get?
   - (iii) How many twos or sixes would you expect to get?

3. One ball is selected at random from the bag
   shown and then replaced. This procedure
   is repeated 400 times.
   How many times would you expect to select:
   - (i) a blue ball,
   - (ii) a white ball?

4. Joe thinks his coin is biased.
   He tosses it 200 times and gets 130 heads and 70 tails.
   - (i) What is the experimental probability of getting a head with this coin?
   - (ii) In 200 tosses, how many heads would you expect to get if the coin was fair?
   - (iii) Do you think the coin is biased?
     Explain your answer.

5. A spinner, with 12 equal sectors, is spun 420 times.
   How often would you expect to spin:
   - (i) an E
   - (ii) an even number
   - (iii) a vowel?

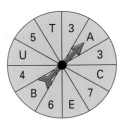

6. Helen wanted to find out if a dice was biased. She threw the dice 300 times.
   Her results are given in the table below.

| Number on dice | 1 | 2 | 3 | 4 | 5 | 6 |
|---|---|---|---|---|---|---|
| Frequency | 30 | 40 | 55 | 65 | 50 | 60 |

   - (i) For this dice, calculate the experimental probability of obtaining
     - (a) a 6
     - (b) a 2.
   - (ii) For a fair dice, calculate the probability of scoring
     - (a) a 6
     - (b) a 2.
   - (iii) Do your answers suggest that the dice is fair?
     Give your reasons.

7. A spinner is labelled as shown.
   The results of the first 30 spins are given below.

   | 1 | 2 | 3 | 3 | 5 | 1 | 3 | 2 | 2 | 4 | 5 | 3 | 2 | 1 | 2 |
   | 5 | 2 | 4 | 1 | 5 | 1 | 5 | 2 | 2 | 4 | 2 | 5 | 4 | 2 | 3 |

   Construct a table showing the number of ones, twos, etc. scored.
   If the spinner was fair, how many times would you expect each number to appear?
   Do you think this spinner is fair?  Give a reason for your answer.

8. Gemma keeps a record of her chess games with Helen.
   Out of the first 10 games, Gemma wins 6.
   Out of the first 30 games Gemma wins 21.
   Based on these results, estimate the probability that Gemma will win her next game of chess with Helen.

9. This spinner is biased.
   The probability that the spinner will land on each of the numbers 1 to 4 is given in the table below.

   | Number | 1 | 2 | 3 | 4 | 5 |
   |---|---|---|---|---|---|
   | Probability | 0.35 | 0.1 | 0.25 | 0.15 | |

   The spinner is spun once.
   (i)   Work out the probability that the spinner will land on 5.
   (ii)  Write down the number on which the spinner is most likely to land.
   (iii) If the spinner is spun 200 times, how many times would you expect it to land on 3?

10. Olivia, Ben and Joe each rolled a different dice 360 times.
    Only one of the dice was fair.
    Whose was it?
    Explain your answer.
    Whose dice is the most biased?
    Explain your answer.

    | Number | Olivia | Ben | Joe |
    |---|---|---|---|
    | 1 | 27 | 58 | 141 |
    | 2 | 69 | 62 | 52 |
    | 3 | 78 | 63 | 56 |
    | 4 | 43 | 57 | 53 |
    | 5 | 76 | 56 | 53 |
    | 6 | 67 | 64 | 5 |

11. The probability that a biased dice will land on each of the numbers 1 to 6 is given in the table below:

    | Number | 1 | 2 | 3 | 4 | 5 | 6 |
    |---|---|---|---|---|---|---|
    | Probability | $x$ | 0.2 | 0.1 | 0.3 | 0.1 | 0.2 |

    (i)   Calculate the value of $x$.
    (ii)  If the dice is thrown once, find the probability that the dice will show a number higher than 3.
    (iii) If the dice is thrown 1000 times, estimate the number of times it will show a 6.

**12.** A four-sided dice has faces numbered 1, 2, 3 and 4.
The 'score' is the number on which it lands. Five pupils throw
the dice to see if it is biased. They each throw it a different
number of times. Their results are shown in the table.

| Pupil | Total number of throws | Score | | | |
|---|---|---|---|---|---|
| | | 1 | 2 | 3 | 4 |
| Andy | 20 | 7 | 6 | 3 | 4 |
| Brian | 50 | 19 | 16 | 8 | 7 |
| Ciara | 250 | 102 | 76 | 42 | 30 |
| Dara | 80 | 25 | 25 | 12 | 18 |
| Emma | 150 | 61 | 46 | 26 | 17 |

(i)   Which pupil will have the most reliable set of results? Why?

(ii)  Add up all the score columns and work out the relative frequency of each score.
Give your answers to one decimal place.

(iii)  Is the dice biased? Explain your answer.

**13.** A red and blue dice were each tossed 100 times.
This bar chart shows the results.

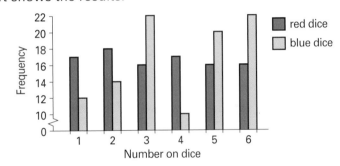

One of the dice is fair and the other unfair. Which do you think is the fair dice? Why?

**14.** Four friends are using a spinner for a game and they wonder if it is perfectly fair.
They each spin the spinner several times and record the results.

| Name | Number of spins | Results | | |
|---|---|---|---|---|
| | | 0 | 1 | 2 |
| Alan | 30 | 12 | 12 | 6 |
| Keith | 100 | 31 | 49 | 20 |
| Bill | 300 | 99 | 133 | 68 |
| Ann | 150 | 45 | 73 | 32 |

(i)   Whose results are most likely to give the best estimate of the probability of
getting each number?

(ii)  Make a table by adding together all the results.
Use the table to decide whether you think the spinner is biased or unbiased.

(iii)  Use the results to work out the probability of the spinner getting a '2'.

**15.** There are 100 sweets in a box.
Eric takes a sweet without looking.
He writes down what sort it is and then **puts it back**.
He does this 100 times. This chart shows Eric's results.

| toffee | 20 |
| --- | --- |
| mint | 38 |
| jelly | 14 |
| choco | 25 |
| caramel | 3 |

(i) Eric thought there must be exactly 20 toffees in the box.
Explain why he is wrong.

(ii) What is the smallest number of caramels that could be in the box?

(iii) Is it possible there is any other sort of sweet in the box? Explain.

(iv) Eric starts again and does the same thing another 100 times.
Will his chart have exactly the same numbers on it?

(v) Eric's friend takes a sweet. What sort is he most likely to get?

# SECTION 4.5

## Mutually exclusive events – The addition rule

Seven cards with different numbers and colours are shown:

Consider these two events:

(i) drawing a red card          (ii) drawing an even number.

These two outcomes cannot happen together as there is no red card with an even number on it.

These outcomes are said to be **mutually exclusive**.

If the events A and B cannot happen together, then

> $P(A \text{ or } B) = P(A) + P(B)$

This is called the **addition law** for mutually exclusive events.

Using the cards above,

> $P(\text{red card or even number}) = P(\text{red card}) + P(\text{even number})$
> $= \frac{3}{7} + \frac{2}{7} = \frac{5}{7}$

> Outcomes are mutually exclusive if they cannot happen at the same time.

> The addition law is sometimes called the **OR** Rule.

### When events are not mutually exclusive

Now consider these cards:

What is the probability of a red card or an even number?
There are 3 red cards and 3 even numbers.

The probability is not $P(\text{red card}) + P(\text{even number})$
i.e. not $\frac{3}{8} + \frac{3}{8}$ as the number 4 is counted twice.

There are only 5 red cards or even numbers.

> $\therefore \quad P(\text{red card or even number}) = \frac{5}{8}$

For the cards on the previous page,

$P$(red or even number) = $P$(red) + $P$(even number) − $P$(red and even number)

$$= \tfrac{3}{8} + \tfrac{3}{8} - \tfrac{1}{8}$$

$$= \tfrac{6}{8} - \tfrac{1}{8} = \tfrac{5}{8}$$

In general when two events A and B can occur at the same time,

**$P$(A or B) = $P$(A) + $P$(B) − $P$(A and B)**

---

### Example 1

A number is to be selected at random from the integers 1 to 30 inclusive. Find the probability that the number is

   (i)   a multiple of 3
  (ii)  a multiple of 5
 (iii)  a multiple of 3 or a multiple of 5.

   (i)   The multiples of 3 are:  3, 6, 9, 12, 15, 18, 21, 24, 27, 30.

     ⇒   $P$(multiple of 3) $= \tfrac{10}{30} = \tfrac{1}{3}$

  (ii)  The multiples of 5 are:  5, 10, 15, 20, 25, 30.

     ⇒   $P$(multiple of 5) $= \tfrac{6}{30} = \tfrac{1}{5}$

 (iii)  The numbers 15 and 30 are both multiples of 3 and 5.

     ⇒   $P$(multiple of 3 or 5) = $P$(multiple of 3) + $P$(multiple of 5)

                                 − $P$(multiple of 3 and 5)

$$= \tfrac{10}{30} + \tfrac{6}{30} - \tfrac{2}{30} = \tfrac{14}{30} = \tfrac{7}{15}$$

---

## Exercise 4.5

**1.** An unbiased dice is thrown.
   Find the probability that the number showing is
    (i)   3                   (ii)  an even number         (iii)  a 3 or an even number.

**2.** A box contains discs numbered 1 to 16.
   If a disc is selected at random, what is the probability that it is
    (i)   an odd number       (ii)  a multiple of 4
  (iii)  an odd  number or a multiple of 4?

**3.** A bag contains 4 red, 3 blue and 2 green marbles.
   If a marble is selected at random, what is the probability that it is
    (i)   a red marble         (ii)  a green marble      (iii)  a red or a green marble?

4. A card is selected at random from a pack of 52 playing cards.
   What is the probability that it is
   (i) a spade
   (ii) a red picture card
   (iii) a spade or a red picture card?

5. A number is selected at random from the integers 1 to 12 inclusive.
   Find the probability that the number is
   (i) even
   (ii) a multiple of 3
   (iii) even or a multiple of 3.

6. A card is drawn at random from a pack of 52.
   What is the probability that the card is
   (i) a club
   (ii) a king
   (iii) a club or a king
   (iv) a red card
   (v) a queen
   (vi) a red card or a queen?

7. A pair of dice are thrown. What is the probability of getting
   (i) a total of 12
   (ii) the same number on both dice
   (iii) a total of 12 or the same number on both dice?

8. Martin picks a card at random from this set.
   Martin says

   > The probability of picking a yellow card is $\frac{2}{5}$.
   >
   > The probability of picking a 3 is $\frac{2}{5}$.
   >
   > So the probability of picking a yellow card or a 3
   > is $\frac{2}{5} + \frac{2}{5} = \frac{4}{5}$.

   (i) Explain why Martin is wrong.
   (ii) What is the correct probability of picking a yellow card or a 3?

9. An ordinary dice is rolled.
   Explain whether or not these pairs of outcomes are mutually exclusive.
   The first one is done for you.

|  | First outcome | Second outcome |
|---|---|---|
| (i) | The score is 5. | The score is 3 |
| | These outcomes are mutually exclusive. A dice cannot show a score of 3 and a score of 5 at the same time. | |
| (ii) | The score is 3. | The score is an even number. |
| (iii) | The score is an even number. | The score is greater than 4. |
| (iv) | The score is a prime number. | The score is an even number. |
| (v) | The score is a multiple of 5. | The score is a multiple of 3. |

# SECTION 4.6 Use of Venn diagrams

The Venn diagram on the right shows two sets, A and B, in the universal set U.

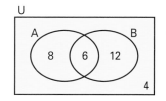

The number of elements in each region is also shown.
  8 is the number of elements in A but not in B.
12 is the number of elements in B but not in A.
  6 is the number of elements in both A and B.
  4 is the number of elements that are in neither A nor B.

If information is presented in the form of a Venn diagram, it is easy to write down the probability of different events occurring.

In the diagram above, the total number of elements is

$$8 + 6 + 12 + 4 = 30.$$

Probability of both A and B is written is $P$(A and B).

From the Venn diagram, $P(\text{A and B}) = \dfrac{6}{30} = \dfrac{1}{5}$

$P(\text{B only}) = \dfrac{12}{30} = \dfrac{2}{5}$

$P(\text{neither A nor B}) = \dfrac{4}{30} = \dfrac{2}{15}$

$P(\text{A or B}) = \dfrac{8 + 6 + 12}{30} = \dfrac{26}{30} = \dfrac{13}{15}.$

In the diagram below, the sets A and B do not intersect.

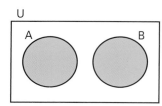

Thus A and B are **mutually exclusive** events as they cannot happen at the same time.

In this case, $P(\textbf{A or B}) = P(\textbf{A}) + P(\textbf{B})$.

---

### Example 1

The Venn diagram shows the sports played by members of a club.
How many members played
   (i)   both football and tennis
   (ii)  tennis but not football
   (iii)  neither of these two games
   (iv)  football or tennis?
Now write down the probability of each of the above.

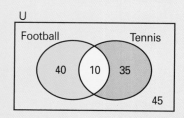

(i)  Both football and tennis = 10
(ii)  Tennis but not football = 35
(iii)  Neither of these two games = 45
(iv)  Football or tennis = 40 + 10 + 35 = 85

$$P(i) = \frac{10}{\text{total membership}} = \frac{10}{130} = \frac{1}{13}$$

$$P(ii) = \frac{35}{130} = \frac{7}{26}$$

$$P(iii) = \frac{45}{130} = \frac{9}{26}$$

$$P(iv) = \frac{85}{130} = \frac{17}{26}$$

## Exercise 4.6

**1.** The given Venn diagram shows the numbers of students who took History and Geography in a class of 40.

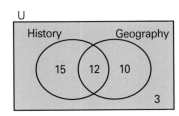

If a student is selected at random, find the probability that the student
  (i)  took Geography
  (ii)  took both History and Geography
  (iii)  took neither of these subjects
  (iv)  took History but not Geography.

**2.** In the given Venn diagram,

      $U$ = the students in class 2K

      $F$ = the students in 2K who play football

      $B$ = the students in 2K who play basketball.

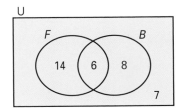

  (i)  How many students are there in the class?

If a student is selected at random, find the probability
that the student
  (ii)  plays football
  (iii)  plays basketball but not football
  (iv)  plays neither of these two games
  (v)  plays both football and basketball
  (vi)  plays football or basketball.

**3.** In the given Venn diagram,

> $U$ represents the houses in a given street,
>
> $C$ represents those which have a cat and
>
> $D$ those which have a dog.

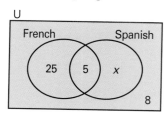

If a household is selected at random,
what is the probability that it has

(i) a cat

(ii) a cat and a dog

(iii) a dog but not a cat

(iv) a cat or a dog

(v) neither a cat nor a dog

**4.** The given Venn diagram shows the languages taken by a group of 50 students.

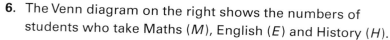

(i) Find the value of $x$.

If a student is selected at random, find the probability that the student takes

(ii) French

(iii) both French and Spanish

(iv) French or Spanish

(v) one of these languages only.

**5.** In a class of 30 students, 8 study music (M),
14 study art (A) while 6 study both music and art.

(i) Represent this information on a copy of the given Venn diagram.

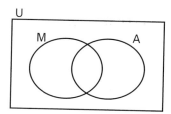

If a student is selected at random, what is the
probability that the student studies

(ii) both music and art

(iii) art but not music

(iv) neither music nor art

(v) music or art?

**6.** The Venn diagram on the right shows the numbers of
students who take Maths ($M$), English ($E$) and History ($H$).

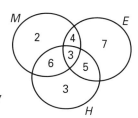

If a student is selected at random, find the probability
that the student takes

(i) English

(ii) both Maths and History

(iii) Maths or English

(iv) Maths only

(v) all three subjects

(vi) English or History.

**7.** In a class of 40 children, a survey was carried out to find out how many children liked chocolate and how many liked ice-cream. The Venn diagram shows the results but the region marked A is not filled in.

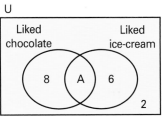

   (i)   What is the number in region A?
   (ii)  What can you say about the children in region A?
   (iii) If one child is chosen at random, what is the probability that the child liked ice-cream but not chocolate?
   (iv)  One of the children who liked chocolate is chosen at random. What is the probability that the child also liked ice-cream?

# SECTION 4.7

## The Multiplication Rule – Bernoulli trials

We show below, the sample space for tossing a coin and throwing a dice.

**Dice**

|      | 1   | 2   | 3   | 4   | 5   | 6   |
|------|-----|-----|-----|-----|-----|-----|
| **H** | H1  | H2  | H3  | H4  | H5  | H6  |
| **T** | T1  | T2  | T3  | T4  | T5  | T6  |

(Coin)

From the sample space, we can see that

$$P(\text{H}, 6) = \tfrac{1}{12}.$$

Whether or not the coin lands on 'heads' has no effect on whether the dice shows a 6 or any other score. The two events, 'getting a head' and 'scoring a 6' are independent.

Now the probability of getting a head when tossing a coin is $\frac{1}{2}$.

The probability of getting a 2 on the dice is $\frac{1}{6}$.

If we multiply the two probabilities $\frac{1}{2}$ and $\frac{1}{6}$ we get $\frac{1}{12}$, as found above.

This illustrates the **multiplication rule** of probability which is given below.

> **Multiplication Rule**: $P(\text{A and B}) = P(\text{A}) \times P(\text{B})$

The multiplication rule is particularly useful when dealing with two or more events where each event is independent of the other. It provides an alternative approach to problems such as throwing two dice, already dealt with in Section 4.3.

> The multiplication rule is generally referred to as the **AND** rule.

## Example 1

Amanda throws an ordinary dice and spins the spinner shown. Each colour is equally likely. Find the probability that she gets a red and an even number.

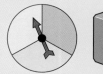 

$P(\text{red}) = \frac{1}{3}$    $P(\text{even number}) = \frac{3}{6} = \frac{1}{2}$

$\therefore$    $P(\text{red and even number}) = \frac{1}{3} \times \frac{1}{2} = \frac{1}{6}$

**Note:** You can also get this result by using a sample space.

## Example 2

Mary and John have their birthdays in the same week. Find the probability that
   (i)   Mary's birthday falls on Monday
  (ii)  both have their birthdays on Monday
 (iii)  both have their birthdays on either Saturday or Sunday.

(i)   $P(\text{Mary's birthday on Monday}) = \frac{1}{7}$

(ii)  $P(\text{both birthdays on Monday}) = P(M, \text{Mon}) \times P(J, \text{Mon})$
$$= \frac{1}{7} \times \frac{1}{7} = \frac{1}{49}$$

(iii)  $P(\text{both birthdays on Sat. or Sun.}) = \frac{2}{7} \times \frac{2}{7}$
$$= \frac{4}{49}$$

## Bernoulli trials

Consider the experiment of throwing a dice and requiring a 6 to start a game.

If a 6 is thrown it can be regarded as a 'success'. Any other number thrown is a 'failure'.

If each throw of the dice is regarded as a **trial**, then

- for each trial there are two possible outcomes, 'success' and 'failure'
- the probability of success (getting a 6) is the same for each trial
- each trial is independent of the outcomes of other trials.

When an experiment consists of repeated trials and the conditions listed above exist, such trials are known as **Bernoulli trials**, named after James Bernoulli.

James Bernoulli (1654–1705) was a Swiss mathematician who did pioneering work in probability and calculus.

In the experiment above, if a 6 is thrown for the first time on the third trial, we say that 'the first success occurs on the third trial'.

For our course, we will deal with problems that involve up to three Bernoulli trials only.

## Example 3

A fair coin is tossed until a head occurs.
Find the probability that the first head occurs on the third toss.

If the first head occurs on the 3rd toss, then the first two tosses result in tails,
i.e., TTH

T = tails
H = heads

$$P(H) = \frac{1}{2} \quad \text{and} \quad P(T) = \frac{1}{2}$$

$$P(TTH) = \frac{1}{2} \times \frac{1}{2} \times \frac{1}{2} = \frac{1}{8}$$

∴ the probability that a head occurs on the 3rd toss is $\frac{1}{8}$.

## Example 4

A fair dice is rolled repeatedly.
Find the probability that a 5 or a 6 first appears on the third throw.

Let a 5 or a 6 represent 'success' (S) and 1, 2, 3, 4 represent 'failure' (F).

$$P(\text{success}) = \frac{2}{6} = \frac{1}{3} \quad \text{and} \quad P(\text{failure}) = \frac{4}{6} = \frac{2}{3}$$

If the first 'success' is on the 3rd throw, the sequence is FFS.

$$P(FFS) = \frac{2}{3} \times \frac{2}{3} \times \frac{1}{3} = \frac{4}{27}$$

∴ probability that 5 or 6 first appears on 3rd throw is $\frac{4}{27}$.

## Example 5

A candidate takes a 3-question multiple choice test.
There are four choices in each question.
If she guesses on each question, what is the probability that
    (i)   she gets all three answers correct
    (ii)   she gets the first two answers wrong but the third correct?

    (i)   There are 4 choices;
       so    $P(\text{correct answer}) = \frac{1}{4}$ and $P(\text{wrong answer}) = \frac{3}{4}$.

         $P(\text{all three correct}) = \frac{1}{4} \times \frac{1}{4} \times \frac{1}{4} = \frac{1}{64}$

    (ii)   $P(\text{first 2 wrong and 3rd correct}) = P(\text{wrong}) \times P(\text{wrong}) \times P(\text{correct})$

$$= \frac{3}{4} \times \frac{3}{4} \times \frac{1}{4} = \frac{9}{64}$$

**Note:** If S stands for 'success' and F stands for 'failure' in Bernoulli trials, then the
probability of only one 'success' in three trials is the sum of these three probabilities:

$$P(FFS) + P(FSF) + P(SFF)$$

# Exercise 4.7

1. A coin is tossed twice. What is the probability of getting
   (i)  2 heads
   (ii)  a head on the first toss and a tail on the second?

2. A coin is tossed and a dice is thrown.
   What is the probability of getting
   (i)   a head and a 6
   (ii)  a tail and an even number
   (iii) a head and a multiple of 3?

3. Two dice are thrown. Find the probability of getting
   (i)   2 fives
   (ii)  2 even numbers
   (iii) both dice showing a number less than 3.

4. A bag contains 5 red discs and 4 blue discs. A disc is selected
   at random and then replaced. A second disc is then selected.
   Find the probability that
   (i)   both discs are red
   (ii)  the first is red and the second is blue
   (ii)  the first is blue and the second is red.

5. In an experiment, a card is drawn from a pack of 52 and a dice is thrown.
   Find the probability of obtaining
   (i)   a diamond and a 6 on the dice
   (ii)  a black card and an even number on the dice
   (iii) a heart and a multiple of 3 on the dice.

   > There are 13 diamonds,
   > 26 black cards and 13 hearts
   > in a pack of playing cards.

6. The letters of the word ALGEBRA are written on individual
   cards and the cards are then put into a box. A card is selected at
   random and then replaced. A second card is then selected.
   Find the probability of obtaining
   (i)   the letter A twice
   (ii)  the letters G and E in that order
   (iii) the letter R twice
   (iv)  two vowels.

7. When a tennis ball is dropped into the device shown, it is equally
   likely to come out any of the holes marked A, B, C and D.
   If a tennis ball is dropped in, find the probability that it
   will come out of the hole marked
   (i)   A
   (ii)  A or C.
   If two other balls are dropped in one after the other find the
       probability that
   (iii) both will come out the hole marked A
   (iv)  both will come out the hole marked A or both will come out the hole marked C.

   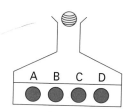

8. There are three tame mice, Sam, Pam and Ham in an enclosure.
   They can choose to eat at five containers (A, B, C, D and E).
   The choice is totally random.

   (i)   What is the probability that Sam will eat from
         container A?
   (ii)  What is the probability that Sam and Pam will both eat
         (a) from container A      (b) from the same container?

9. This spinner is spun twice. Each sector is equally likely.
   Find the probability that

   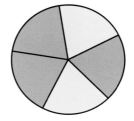

   (i)    the first colour is yellow
   (ii)   the first two colours are red and green in that order
   (iii)  the first two colours are red
   (iv)   the first two colours are both red or both yellow.

10. Ann and Barry celebrate their birthdays in a particular week.
    Assuming that the birthdays are equally likely to fall on any day of the week, what is
    the probability that
    (i)    Ann's birthday is on Wednesday
    (ii)   both birthdays are on Monday
    (iii)  both birthdays are on a day beginning with T?

11. James tosses a fair coin several times.
    Find the probability for each of these events:
    (i)   the first head occurs on the second toss
    (ii)  the first head occurs on the third toss.

12. Katie throws a fair dice until she gets a 6.
    Calculate the probability that she gets
    (i)   6 on the first throw
    (ii)  the first 6 on the third throw.

13. The probability of getting a head with a biased coin is $\frac{2}{3}$.
    Jack tosses the coin three times.
    (i)   Calculate the probability that he gets heads on all three throws.
    (ii)  Calculate the probability that he gets the first head on
          (a) the second throw      (b) the third throw.

14. 25% of pupils in a school travel to school by bus.
    Three pupils in the school are selected at random.
    Find the probability that
    (i)    all three travel by bus
    (ii)   the first two pupils selected do not travel by bus
    (iii)  the first two pupils do not travel by bus but the third does.

15. A bag contains 3 red beads and 2 green beads. A bead is selected from the bag and then replaced. This process is repeated.
    Find the probability that
    (i)   the first bead selected is green
    (ii)  the first green bead selected is at the third attempt.

16. Andy plays a series of tennis matches against the same opponent.
    The probability that he wins any match is $\frac{4}{5}$.
    Calculate the probability that
    (i)   Andy has his first win in his second match
    (ii)  Andy has his first win in his third match
    (iii) Andy loses all three matches.

17. The probability that it will rain on any given day in May is 0.3.
    If three days in May are selected at random, find the probability that
    (i)   the first day has no rain
    (ii)  the first two days will have rain
    (iii) the third day is the first day to have rain.

18. A cube has the letter 'A' on four faces and the letter 'B' on the remaining two faces.
    It is thrown three times.
    Calculate the probability of obtaining
    (i)   B on the first throw
    (ii)  the first B on the second throw
    (iii) the first A on the third throw.

19. Shane draws a card from a normal pack of playing cards and then replaces it.
    He does this three times.
    Calculate the probability that he selects
    (i)   a diamond on the first draw
    (ii)  the first diamond on the third draw
    (iii) only one diamond in the three draws.

20. A fair coin is tossed at the start of each match in a 3-match series.
    One captain tosses and the other calls 'Heads' or 'Tails'.
    Find the probability that the toss is called correctly
    (i)   three times          (ii)   exactly once          (iii)   exactly twice.

21. Andy is playing football and tennis.
    He has one match in each sport to play.
    The probability that he wins the football match is 0.3.
    The probability that he will draw is 0.5.

He has a 0.6 chance of winning the tennis match, otherwise he will lose.
Find the probability that
   (i)   Andy loses the football match
   (ii)  Andy wins both matches
   (iii) Andy loses both matches
   (iv)  Andy wins the football match and loses the tennis match.

22. In a board game, a counter is moved along the squares
    by an amount equal to the number thrown on a fair dice.
    If you land on a square at the bottom of a ladder you
    move the counter to the square at the top of that ladder.
       (i)   What is the probability that a player reaches
             square 4 with one throw of the dice?
       (ii)  What is the probability that a player can
             reach square 7 with one throw of the dice?
       (iii) What is the probability of taking two throws
             to get to square 2?
       (iv)  List the three possible ways to land on square
             18 with exactly three throws of the dice.
       (v)   Calculate the probability of landing on square 18 with exactly three throws of
             the dice.

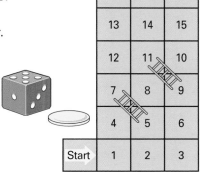

# SECTION 4.8

## The Fundamental Principle of Counting

A make of car comes in four different models as shown below:

Standard (S)          Classic (C)          Elegant (E)          Diamond (D)

Each model comes in three different colours: silver($s$), red($r$), and black($b$).
Here are the choices a customer has:

   $(S, s)$, $(S, r)$, $(S, b)$, $(C, s)$, $(C, r)$, $(C, b)$, $(E, s)$, $(E, r)$, $(E, b)$, $(D, s)$, $(D, r)$, $(D, b)$.

There are 12 choices listed.
For each of the **4** models, there are **3** colours.

The number of choices is found by multiplying the number of models by the number of
colours,

   i.e. $4 \times 3 = 12$.

This example illustrates the **Fundamental Principle of Counting** which is given on the right.

If an operation consists of choosing $x$ **and** $y$ we **multiply** the numbers $x$ and $y$.

> If one task can be done in $x$ ways, **and** following this, a second task can be done in $y$ ways, then the first task followed by the second task can be done in $xy$ ways.

---

**Example 1**

A team consists of 11 players.
In how many ways can a captain and vice-captain be chosen?

| Captain | **and** | Vice-captain | |
|---------|---------|--------------|------|
| 11 | × | 10 | = 110 |

> **and** indicates **multiplication**

∴   there are 110 ways of selecting a captain and vice-captain.

---

When dealing with two or more operations, it can be convenient to use 'boxes' for the selection, as shown on the right.

1st × 2nd × 3rd

---

**Example 2**

A code consists of a letter of the alphabet followed by two different digits from 1 to 9 inclusive. How many codes are possible?

There are 26 letters and 9 digits.
We use three 'boxes' as each code consists of 1 letter and 2 digits

| 26 | 9 | 8 |

The first box can be filled in 26 ways......
The second box can be filled in 9 ways......     9 digits
The third box can be filled in 8 ways......     1 digit used

> There are 26 letters in the alphabet.

∴   Number of Codes = 26 × 9 × 8
                    = 1872

---

## Exercise 4.8

1. A dice is thrown and a coin is tossed.
   How many different outcomes are possible?
   List these outcomes.

2. A lunch menu has 3 starters and 4 main courses.
   How many different two-course meals are possible?

**3.** A code consists of three different digits from 1 to 9.
How many codes are possible?

**4.** There are four roads from *A* to *B* and
five roads from *B* to *C*.
In how many different ways can
a person travel from *A* to *C*?

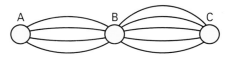

**5.** A pupil must choose one subject out of each of the following subject groups:
Group A has 3 modern language subjects.
Group B has 2 science subjects.
Group C has 2 business subjects.
How many different subject selections are possible?

**6.** A code consists of one of the letters *A*, *B*, *C*, *D*, *E* and *F* and one digit from 1 to 9.
How many different codes are possible?

**7.** A coin is tossed and a digit from 0 to 9 is selected. How many different outcomes are possible?

**8.** A car manufacturer produces different types of cars as follows:
• the model can be Saloon, Estate or Hatchback
• the colours can be silver, black or red
• the style can be Standard, Deluxe or Premium
How many different choices of car does a buyer have?

**9.** A committee consists of 10 people.
In how many ways can a chairperson and secretary be chosen?

**10.** How many different 3-digit numbers can be formed from the digits 4, 5, 6, 7, 8, 9 if each digit is used once only in a number?

**11.** There are eight horses in a race.
In how many ways can the first three places be filled?

# SECTION 4.9 Arrangements (Permutations)

The letters A, B and C can be arranged in a line in the following ways:

ABC    ACD    BAC    BCA    CAB    CBA

There are six different arrangements.

Using boxes for the number of choices for each letter, we have

| 3 | | 2 | | 1 |

> The first box can be filled in 3 ways; the 2nd box in 2 ways; the third box in 1 way.

$3 \times 2 \times 1 = 6$, as found above.

We use the notation **3!** , pronounced '3 factorial', to represent $3 \times 2 \times 1$.

Similarly,  $4! = 4 \times 3 \times 2 \times 1 = 24$

and  $5! = 5 \times 4 \times 3 \times 2 \times 1 = 120$

In general  $n! = n(n-1)(n-2) \dots 3.2.1$

**Permutation** is another word for an 'arrangement'.

> The number of arrangements (or permutations) of $n$ different objects is $n!$, where
> $$n! = n(n-1)(n-2) \dots 3.2.1.$$

### Example 1

How many different six-digit numbers can be formed from the digits 1, 2, 3, 4, 5, 6 using all the digits in each number?

The six digits can be arranged in 6! ways.
$$6! = 6 \times 5 \times 4 \times 3 \times 2 \times 1$$
$$= 720 \text{ numbers}$$

## Permutations with Restrictions

The letters of the word *LEAVING* can be arranged in 7! ways.
How many of these arrangements begin with the letter *L*?

In this type of problem we use 'boxes' into which we write the number of choices. The first box we fill is the one containing the restriction.

In this example, the first box can be filled in one way only, i.e., *L*.

*L*

| 1 | 6 | 5 | 4 | 3 | 2 | 1 |

The remaining boxes can be filled in

6, 5, 4, 3, 2 and 1 ways.

Therefore the number of arrangements beginning with *L* is

$$1 \times 6 \times 5 \times 4 \times 3 \times 2 \times 1 = 720$$

If there are two restrictions, fill in the boxes that relate to these restrictions first.

### Example 2

The letters of the word *TUESDAY* are arranged in a line.
  (i)   How many different arrangements are possible?
  (ii)  How many of these arrangements begin with *T* and end with a vowel?

(i) There are 7 letters in the word *TUESDAY*.
∴ the number of arrangements is 7!

$$7! = 7 \times 6 \times 5 \times 4 \times 3 \times 2 \times 1$$
$$= 5040$$

(ii) Using 'boxes' for arrangements beginning with *T* and ending in a vowel, we have:

| *T* | | | | | | Vowels |
|---|---|---|---|---|---|---|
| 1 | 5 | 4 | 3 | 2 | 1 | 3 |

The first box can be filled in 1 way only, i.e., with *T*.
The last box can be filled in 3 ways as there are 3 vowels, *U, E, A*.
There are 5 letters remaining; so the remaining boxes can be filled in 5, 4, 3, 2, 1 ways.
Therefore the number of arrangements is

$$1 \times 5 \times 4 \times 3 \times 2 \times 1 \times 3$$
$$= 360$$

---

## Example 3

(i) In how many ways can the letters of the word *NUMBERS* be arranged?

(ii) In how many of these arrangements are the letters *M* and *B* always together?

(i) There are seven letters in the word *NUMBERS*.
Therefore the number of arrangements is 7!

$$7! = 7 \times 6 \times 5 \times 4 \times 3 \times 2 \times 1$$
$$= 5040$$

(ii) If *M* and *B* come together we treat them as one unit or box.

| | | | MB | | |
|---|---|---|---|---|---|

There are now six boxes to be arranged.
This is done in 6! ways.
For each of these arrangements, | *MB* | can be arranged in 2! ways.
∴ the number of arrangements is 6! × 2!

$$6! \times 2! = 720 \times 2$$
$$= 1440$$

## Exercise 4.9

1. In how many ways can the letters of the word *EIGHT* be arranged if all the letters are taken each time?

2. How many different arrangements can be made using all of the letters of the word *RESORT?*
   (i) How many of these arrangements begin with *R?*
   (ii) How many of the arrangements begin with *R* and end with *T?*

3. How many different four-digit numbers can be formed using the digits 3, 4, 5, 6 if no digit can be repeated in a number?

4. How many three-digit numbers can be formed with the digits 1, 2, 3, 4, 5?
   (i) How many of these numbers begin with 5?
   (ii) How many of these numbers are greater than 400?

5. How many different arrangements can be made using all of the letters of the word *POLAND?*
   (i) How many of these arrangements begin with a vowel?
   (ii) How many of the arrangements begin with *P* and end with *D?*
   (iii) How many of the arrangements begin with *P* and end with a vowel?

6. How many arrangements of three letters can be made using the letters *A, B, C, D, E, F* if no letter can be repeated in an arrangement?

7. Six horses run in a race. Assuming that all the horses finish and that there is no dead-heat,
   (i) in how many ways can the horses finish the race?
   (ii) in how many ways can the first three places be filled?

8. How many arrangements can be made using the letters of the word *ORANGE?*
   (i) How many of these arrangements begin with *O?*
   (ii) How many of the arrangements begin with a vowel?
   (iii) How many arrangements begin with a vowel and end with a vowel?

9. In how many ways can the letters *A, B, C, D,* and *E* be arranged in a line if *D* is never first?

10. In how many different ways can the five letters of the word *ANGLE* be arranged?
    In how many of these arrangements do the two vowels come together?

    > See Worked Example 3.

11. In how many ways can the letters of the word *CARPET* be arranged?
    In how many of these arrangements are the letters *P* and *T* together?

12. How many 4-digit numbers can be formed using the digits 4, 5, 6 and 7, if no digit can be repeated in a number?
    (i)   How many of these numbers are greater than 6000?
    (ii)  Find the probability that the number is greater than 6000?

13. Two women A and B and two men C and D sit in a row for a photograph.
    (i)   How many different arrangements of the four people are possible?
    (ii)  Write out the four possible arrangements that have the two women in the middle.
    (iii) If the arrangement of the four people is chosen at random from all of the possible arrangements, what is the probability that the two women will be in the middle?

14. Shauna has five counters and she places them in a straight line.
    They are of five different colours: red, white, green, blue and yellow.
    (i)   How many different arrangements are possible?
    (ii)  In how many arrangements is the first counter blue?
    (iii) In how many arrangements is the first counter blue and the fifth counter green?

15. Evaluate each of the following:
    (i) 5!          (ii) 7!          (iii) $\dfrac{6!}{3!}$          (iv) $4! \times 3!$

16. (i) Is $7! = 4! \times 3!$?          (ii) Is $8! = 5! + 3!$?

17. Express 8! in the form
    (i) $p(7!)$          (ii) $q(6!)$

18. If $10! + 9! = k(9!)$, find the value of $k$.

# SECTION 4.10 Combinations

A selection of objects from a given set, without regard to the order is called a **combination**.
If we take the letters $A, B, C, D$ and select different groups of two letters we have:

   $AB, \quad AC, \quad AD, \quad BC, \quad BD, \quad CD, \quad$ i.e. 6 groups

The group $AB$ is the same as $BA$ in this case as order does not matter.

We use the notation $\binom{4}{2}$ to denote the number of ways 2 objects can be selected from 4 objects.

$$\binom{4}{2} = \frac{4 \times 3}{2 \times 1} \quad \text{... start at 4 and go down two terms} \\ \text{... 2! i.e. } 2 \times 1$$

Similarly $\binom{6}{3} = \dfrac{6 \times 5 \times 4}{3 \times 2 \times 1} = \dfrac{120}{6} = 20$ and $\binom{8}{4} = \dfrac{8 \times 7 \times 6 \times 5}{4 \times 3 \times 2 \times 1} = 70$

$\binom{8}{4}$ represents the number of ways 4 items can be chosen from 8 items.

In general $\binom{n}{r}$ is the number of ways in which $r$ objects can be selected from $n$ objects.

$\binom{n}{r}$ is pronounced 'n-c-r' or 'n choose r'.

Another word for **combination** is 'selection'.

$\binom{n}{r}$ may also be written as $^nC_r$ or $nCr$.

In electronic calculators it is written as $nCr$.

To find the value of $\binom{8}{4}$ on a calculator, key in

$$8 \boxed{nCr} \, 4 \boxed{=}$$

$$\binom{n}{r} = \frac{n(n-1)}{r!} \quad \begin{array}{l} \text{... start at } n \text{ and go down } r \text{ terms} \\ \text{... } r \text{ factorial} \end{array}$$

Again $\binom{8}{5} = \dfrac{8 \times 7 \times 6 \times 5 \times 4}{5 \times 4 \times 3 \times 2 \times 1} = 56$

and $\binom{8}{3} = \dfrac{8 \times 7 \times 6}{3 \times 2 \times 1} = 56.$

This shows that $\binom{8}{5} = \binom{8}{3}$ i.e. $\binom{8}{5} = \binom{8}{8-5}$

In general
$$\binom{n}{r} = \binom{n}{n-r}$$

Using the rule above, $\binom{10}{8} = \binom{10}{10-8} = \binom{10}{2} = \dfrac{10 \times 9}{2 \times 1} = 45.$

In practice, it is much shorter to work out $\binom{10}{2}$ than $\binom{10}{8}$.

$\binom{n}{n}$ and $\binom{n}{0}$

$\binom{8}{8} = \dfrac{8 \times 7 \times 6 \times 5 \times 4 \times 3 \times 2 \times 1}{8 \times 7 \times 6 \times 5 \times 4 \times 3 \times 2 \times 1} = 1$ and $\binom{8}{8} = \binom{8}{8-8} = \binom{8}{0} = 1$

These two examples illustrate, that:
$$\binom{n}{n} = 1$$
$$\binom{n}{0} = 1$$

---

### Example 1

How many different teams of 11 players can be selected from a panel of 14 players?
If the panel of 14 players includes the captain and one goalkeeper, how many teams can be selected if
  (i)   the goalkeeper has to be included
  (ii)  the goalkeeper and captain both have to be included?

The number of ways in which a team of 11 can be selected from 14 is $\binom{14}{11}$.

$$\binom{14}{11} = \binom{14}{3} = \frac{14 \times 13 \times 12}{3 \times 2 \times 1} = 364$$

(i) If the goalkeeper has to be included, then 10 players are selected from 13.

This can be done in $\binom{13}{10}$ ways.

$$\binom{13}{10} = \binom{13}{3} = \frac{13 \times 12 \times 11}{3 \times 2 \times 1} = 286$$

∴ 286 teams can be selected

(ii) If the goalkeeper and captain are included, then 9 players are selected from 12.

This can be done in $\binom{12}{9}$ ways.

$$\binom{12}{9} = \binom{12}{3} = \frac{12 \times 11 \times 10}{3 \times 2 \times 1} = 220$$

∴ 220 teams can be selected

## Selecting from Two Different Groups

There are 6 teachers and 8 students on a school council.

They want to select a delegation of 3 teachers and 3 students to meet the school principal.

In how many ways can this be done?

Here we have to select 3 teachers from 6 **AND** 3 students from 8.

3 teachers can be selected from 6 teachers in $\binom{6}{3}$ ways

3 students can be selected from 8 students in $\binom{8}{3}$ ways

Based on the **Fundamental Principle of Counting**, the word **AND** implies that the results of the two operations are **multiplied**.

> AND ⇒ Multiplication
> OR ⇒ Addition

Therefore the number of ways that three teachers and three students can be selected is

$$\binom{6}{3} \times \binom{8}{3}$$

$$\binom{6}{3} \times \binom{8}{3} = \frac{6 \times 5 \times 4}{3 \times 2 \times 1} \times \frac{8 \times 7 \times 6}{3 \times 2 \times 1} = 20 \times 56 = 1120.$$

### Example 2

A committee of 4 people is to be formed from a group of 7 men and 6 women.

(i) How many different committees can be formed?

(ii) On how many of these committees is there an equal number of men and women?

(i) Here we are selecting 4 people from 13.

This can be done in $\binom{13}{4}$ ways.

$$\binom{13}{4} = \frac{13 \times 12 \times 11 \times 10}{4 \times 3 \times 2 \times 1} = 715$$

∴ 715 committees can be formed.

(ii) If there is an equal number of men and women, the committee will consist of 2 men and 2 women.

We can select 2 men from 7 men and 2 women from 6 women in

$$\binom{7}{2} \times \binom{6}{2} \text{ ways}$$

$$\binom{7}{2} \times \binom{6}{2} = \frac{7 \times 6}{2 \times 1} \times \frac{6 \times 5}{2 \times 1} = 315$$

∴ 315 committees can be formed.

## Finding the value for $n$

$$\binom{8}{2} = \frac{8 \times 7}{2 \times 1} = 28. \text{ Similarly } \binom{n}{2} = \frac{n(n-1)}{2 \times 1} = \frac{n(n-1)}{2}$$

### Example 3

If $\binom{n}{2} = 45$, find the value of $n$, for $n \in N$.

$$\binom{n}{2} = \frac{n(n-1)}{2 \times 1} \quad \text{... go down 2 terms}$$
$$\qquad\qquad \text{... 2!}$$

$$\binom{n}{2} = 45 \quad \Rightarrow \quad \frac{n(n-1)}{2} = 45$$

$$\Rightarrow \quad n^2 - n = 90$$
$$\Rightarrow \quad n^2 - n - 90 = 0$$
$$\Rightarrow \quad (n - 10)(n + 9) = 0$$
$$\Rightarrow \quad n = 10, n = -9$$
$$\Rightarrow \quad n = 10, \text{ as } n \in N.$$

## Exercise 4.10

1. Evaluate each of the following:

   (i) $\binom{5}{2}$    (ii) $\binom{7}{3}$    (iii) $\binom{8}{4}$    (iv) $\binom{10}{3}$    (v) $\binom{10}{7}$    (vi) $\binom{16}{2}$

   Verify your answer by using a calculator.

**2.** Show that $\quad$ (i) $\binom{8}{3} + \binom{8}{2} = \binom{9}{3}$ $\qquad$ (ii) $\binom{10}{3} = \dfrac{10!}{3!7!}$

**3.** In how many ways can a committee of 6 persons be selected from 10 persons?

**4.** In how many ways can two class representatives be selected from a class of 20 students?

**5.** A student has to select six subjects for the Leaving Certificate course from twelve subjects being offered in the school.
   (i)   In how many ways can this be done?
   (ii)  In how many ways can this be done if maths must be included in each selection?

**6.** A football team manager has 11 players from which to select a team of 7 players.
   (i)   In how many ways can the team be chosen?
   (ii)  If the 11 players include one goalkeeper, how many teams can be selected if the goalkeeper must be included in each team?

**7.** Eight points lie on a circle, as shown. How many different line segments can be drawn by joining any two of the eight points?

**8.** How many different subsets of four letters can be made from the set $\{a, b, c, d, e, f\}$? How many of these subsets contain the letter $a$?

**9.** In how many ways can a committee of 5 persons be selected from 6 men and 4 women? How many committees consist of
   (i)   3 men and 2 women
   (ii)  2 men and 3 women?

**10.** Seven persons $A$, $B$, $C$, $D$, $E$, $F$ and $G$ are eligible for selection on a team of five persons.
   (i)    How many different teams can be selected?
   (ii)   In how many of the teams will $A$ be included?
   (iii)  In how many of the teams will $A$ and $B$ be included?

**11.** A school council consists of 6 teachers and 5 pupils.
   (i)   In how many ways can a committee of 4 be selected from this council?
   (ii)  How many committees can be selected if each committee consists of 2 teachers and 2 pupils?

**12.** Seven people take part in a tennis competition. How many matches will be played if each person must play each of the others?

**13.** A committee of 4 is to be chosen from 4 men and 5 women.
- (i) How many committees can be chosen?
- (ii) How many committees consist of 1 woman and 3 men?
- (iii) How many committees consist of 2 women and 2 men?

**14.** (i) If $\binom{n}{2} = 28$, find $n$ for $n \in N$.   (ii) If $\binom{n}{2} = 55$, find $n$ for $n \in N$.

**15.** A committee of 3 people is selected from a group of 15 doctors and 12 dentists.
In how many different ways can the 3 people be selected
- (i) if there are no restrictions
- (ii) if the selection must contain exactly 2 doctors.

**16.** There are 6 junior-cycle students and 5 senior-cycle students on the student council in a particular school.
A committee of 4 students is to be selected from the students on the council.
In how many different ways can the committee be selected if
- (i) there are no restrictions
- (ii) a particular student must be on the committee
- (iii) the committee must consist of 2 junior-cycle students and 2 senior-cycle students?
A committee of 4 students is chosen at random.
- (iv) Find the probability that all 4 students are junior-cycle students.

# TEST YOURSELF 4

**1.** The spinner has 8 equal sectors. Find the probability of
- (i) spinning a 5
- (ii) not spinning a 5
- (iii) spinning a 2
- (iv) spinning a 7
- (v) not spinning a 7.

**2.** Ben rolls a fair dice 300 times.
How many times would you expect him to roll
- (i) a 6
- (ii) an even number?

**3.** One letter is chosen at random from the letters of the word *DEALING*.
- (i) Find the probability that the letter chosen is G.
- (ii) Find the probability that the letter chosen is a vowel or G.

**4.** A bag contains 6 red beads, 4 blue beads and 2 green beads. If a bead is drawn at random from the bag, what is the probability that it is
- (i) green
- (ii) blue
- (iii) green or blue
- (iv) not red?

5. There are four possible results in a fairground game.
   The table shows the probability of each result.

   | Result | Probability |
   |---|---|
   | Top prize | $\frac{1}{20}$ |
   | Consolation prize | $\frac{1}{10}$ |
   | Your money back | ? |
   | Lose | $\frac{3}{5}$ |

   (i) What is the probability of getting your money back?
   (ii) What is the most likely result?
   (iii) What is the probability of not winning the top prize?
   (iv) How many times would you expect to lose if you played the game 100 times?

6. James takes a book from a shelf at random.
   The table shows the probability of getting different types of book.

   | Subject | Hardback | Paperback |
   |---|---|---|
   | Fiction | 0.1 | 0.3 |
   | Sport | 0.2 | 0 |
   | Computers | 0.1 | 0.15 |
   | Animals | 0.05 | 0.1 |

   What is the probability that the book chosen will be
   (i) a paperback
   (ii) a book about computers?
   If there are 120 books on the shelf altogether,
   (iii) how many of them are about animals?

7. A school snack bar offers a choice of four snacks.
   The four snacks are burgers, pizza, pasta and salad.
   Students can choose **one** of these four snacks.
   The table shows the probability that a student will choose burger or pizza or salad.

   | Snack | burger | pizza | pasta | salad |
   |---|---|---|---|---|
   | Probability | 0.35 | 0.15 | | 0.2 |

   300 students availed of the snack bar on Tuesday.
   Work out an estimate for the number of students who chose pasta.

8. Jane throws a red dice and a blue dice at the same time.
   Show all the possible outcomes in a sample space.
   Find the probability that Jane obtains
   (i) a total of 10
   (ii) a total of 12
   (iii) a total less than 6
   (iv) the same number on both dice.

9.  Cliona picks two cards at random from the 3, 4, 5 and 6 of hearts.
   Find the probability that the sum of the numbers on the two cards is more than 9.

10. Four friends, Ava, Brian, Cloe and Dara, each write their name on a card and the four cards are placed in a hat.
Ava chooses two cards to decide who does the maths homework that night.
List all the possible combinations.
What is the probability that Cloe and Dara have to do the homework?

11. These number cards are shuffled and put into a row.

John picks one card at random and does not replace it. He then picks a second card.
   (i)   If the first card was the '11', find the probability that John selects an even number with the second draw.
   (ii)  If the first card was the '8', find the probability that he selects a number higher than 9 with the second draw.

12. In a small school, a class consists of children of a variety of ages as given in the table.

| 5-year-old girls | 5-year-old boys | 6-year-old girls | 6-year-old boys | 7-year-old girls | 7-year-old boys |
|---|---|---|---|---|---|
| 3 | 4 | 6 | 8 | 5 | 2 |

A pupil is selected at random.
What is the probability that the pupil is
   (i)   a 6-year-old boy
   (ii)  a girl
   (iii) 6 or 7-year-old child
   (iv)  a boy or a 6-year-old child?

13. (i)  Aidan has a dice with 3 red faces, 2 blue faces and 1 green face.
        He throws the dice 300 times.
        The results are shown in the following table.

| Red | Blue | Green |
|---|---|---|
| 156 | 98 | 46 |

   (a)  What is the relative frequency of throwing a red?
   (b)  Do you think the dice is fair?
        Explain your answer.
   (ii) Emma has a dice with 4 red faces and 2 blue faces.
        She throws the dice 10 times and gets 2 reds.
        Emma says the dice is **not** fair.
        Explain why Emma could be wrong.

14. A coin is biased so that the probability of a head is $\frac{2}{3}$.
The coin is thrown three times.
Find the probability of obtaining
   (i)   tails on each of the first two throws
   (ii)  the first head on the third throw.

**15.** Here is a 4-sided spinner.

The sides of the spinner are labelled 1, 2, 3 and 4.

The spinner is biased.

The probability that the spinner will land on each of
the numbers 2 and 3 is given in the table below.

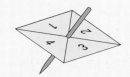

| Number | 1 | 2 | 3 | 4 |
|---|---|---|---|---|
| Probability | $x$ | 0.3 | 0.2 | $x$ |

The probability that the spinner will land on 1 is equal to the probability that it will
land on 4.

   (i)   Work out the value of $x$.

Sarah is going to spin the spinner 200 times.

   (ii)   Work out an estimate for the number of times it will land on 2.

**16.** Thirty students were asked to state the activities they
enjoyed from swimming (S), tennis (T) and hockey (H).
The numbers in each set are shown.
One student is randomly selected.

   (i)   Which of these pairs of events are mutually
         exclusive?

         (a)   'selecting a student from S', 'selecting a student from H'

         (b)   'selecting a student from S', 'selecting a student from T'.

   (ii)   What is the probability of selecting a student who enjoyed either hockey or tennis?

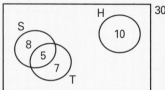

**17.** A dice has the numbers 1, 1, 1, 2, 2, 3 on its faces.

   (i)   What is the probability of scoring 2?

The dice is thrown three times.

   (ii)   What is the probability of getting a 2 on each
          of the first two throws?

   (iii)   What is the probability of getting the first 2 on the third throw?

**18.** Adam and Mandy are playing a game in which three coins are tossed.

Adam wins if there are no heads or one head.

Mandy wins if there are either two or three heads.

Is the game fair to both players? Explain your answer.

**19.** How many different 3-digit numbers can be formed using the digits 1, 2, 3, 4, 5 if no
digit is repeated in the number?

   (i)   How many of these numbers begin with 3?

   (ii)   How many of these numbers are greater than 300?

**20.** In how many ways can the letters of the word *GERMANY* be arranged in a line?

   (i)   How many of these arrangements begin with *G*?

   (ii)   What is the probability that the arrangement begins with *G*?

**21.** A fair dice and a biased dice are thrown together. The probabilities of throwing the numbers 1 to 6 are shown for the biased dice.

Fair      Biased

$P(6) = \frac{1}{4}$; $P(1) = \frac{1}{12}$

$P(2) = P(3) = P(4) = P(5) = \frac{1}{6}$

If the two dice are thrown, find the probability of getting

  (i)   a total of 2          (ii)   a total of 12          (iii)   a total of 3.

**22.** Marie made a five-sided spinner like the one shown in the diagram. She used it to play a board game with her friend Sarah. The girls thought that the spinner wasn't very fair as it seemed to land on some numbers more than others. They threw the spinner 200 times and recorded the results. The results are shown in the table.

| Side spinner lands on | 1 | 2 | 3 | 4 | 5 |
|---|---|---|---|---|---|
| Number of times | 20 | 28 | 32 | 50 | 70 |

  (i)   Work out the experimental probability of each number.

  (ii)   How many times would you expect each number to occur if the spinner is fair?

 (iii)   Do you think that the spinner is fair? Give a reason for your answer.

**23.**

**SWEET SIXTEEN**

START →

counter

|  |  |  |  |
|---|---|---|---|
| 1 | 2 | 3 |  |
| 8 | 7 |  | 5 |
| 9 |  | 11 | 12 |
| 16 | 15 | 14 | 13 |

'Sweet Sixteen' is a game for any number of players. To play the game, players take it in turns to throw a fair dice and then move their counter the number of places shown uppermost on the dice. If a player lands on one of the shaded squares the player must start again. The first player to land on square 16 is the winner. If a player would move past square 16 on a throw, the player is not allowed to move and misses that turn.

  (i)   What is the probability that a player lands on a shaded square on the first throw?

  (ii)   A player moves to square 3 on the first throw. What is the probability that the player lands on a shaded square on the second throw?

 (iii)  (a)   A player is on square 12 after three turns. Write, in the order thrown, three scores the player could have had.

       (b)   In how many different ways could a player have reached square 12 with three throws? Show your working to support your answer.

 (iv)  (a)   What is the minimum number of turns necessary to complete the game?

       (b)   What is the probability of this happening?

# Summary of key points

## Probability scale

The **probability** of an event is expressed as a number from 0 to 1 inclusive.

- If an event is **impossible**, its probability is 0.
- If an event is **certain**, its probability is 1.

## Theoretical probability

$$P(\text{event}) = \frac{\text{the number of ways the event can occur}}{\text{the total number of possible outcomes}}$$

## Mutually exclusive events

If two events cannot occur at the same time, they are **mutually exclusive**.

When events A and B are mutually exclusive, the probability of outcome A not happening is given by $P(\text{not A})$

$$P(\textbf{A or B}) = P(\textbf{A}) + P(\textbf{B})$$

$$P(\textbf{not A}) = 1 - P(\textbf{A})$$

## Relative frequency

$$\text{Relative frequency} = \frac{\text{number of successful trials}}{\text{total number of trials}}$$

$$\text{Expected frequency} = \text{probability} \times \text{number of trials}$$

## Independent events – The Multiplication Rule

Two events are independent if one does not affect the outcome of the other.

If events A and B are independent, then

$$P(\textbf{A and B}) = P(\textbf{A}) \times P(\textbf{B})$$

## Bernoulli trials

A **Bernoulli trial** is an experiment that consists of repeated trials satisfying these conditions:

- there are two possible outcomes, 'success' and 'failure'
- the probability of success is the same for each trial
- each outcome is independent of the outcomes of other trials.

## The Fundamental Principle of Counting

If one task can be done in $x$ ways, and following this, a second task can be done in $y$ ways, then the first task followed by the second task can be done in $xy$ ways.

## Arrangements (Permutations)

The number of arrangements of n different objects is n!, where

$$n! = n(n - 1)(n - 2) \ldots 3.2.1$$

## Combinations

The number of ways $r$ objects can be selected from $n$ objects is $\binom{n}{r}$.

$$\binom{n}{r} = \frac{n(n - 1)}{r!} \quad \begin{array}{l} \ldots \text{ start at } n \text{ and go down } r \text{ terms} \\ \ldots \text{ start with } r \text{ and go down to } 1 \end{array}$$

# chapter 5

# Coordinate Geometry – The Line

## Key Words

| Cartesian plane | origin | axis | quadrant | vertex | horizontal |

Cartesian plane  origin  axis  quadrant  vertex  horizontal

vertical  slope  parallel  perpendicular  positive  negative

linear equation  area  translation  intersection  collinear

## SECTION 5.1 Coordinating the Plane

The figure below shows the coordinated plane and the location of the points A, B, C, D and E.

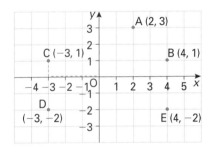

The horizontal line is called the **x-axis**.

The vertical line is called the **y-axis**.

The point (0, 0) is called the **origin** and is labelled O.

This coordinated plane is generally called the **Cartesian plane** in honour of the French mathematician, Rene Descartes (1596–1650).

### Example 1

Plot the points A(−1, 2), B(3, 2), C(3, −2) and D(−1, −2) on a coordinated plane.
 (i) Join the four points and name the figure you have drawn.
 (ii) Use the grid to write down the midpoint of [BC].

 (i) ABCD forms a square.
 (ii) The midpoint of [BC] is (3, 0).

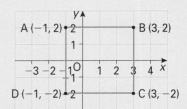

## Exercise 5.1

1. Write down the coordinates of each of the points marked in the coordinated plane on the right:

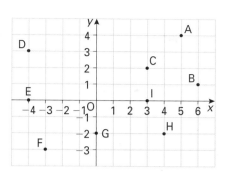

2. Draw a coordinated plane from $-5$ to $5$ on the $x$-axis and from $-4$ to $4$ on the $y$-axis. Now plot each of the following points:

   (i) A(3, 4)　　(ii) B($-1$, 3)　　(iii) C(4, $-3$)　　(iv) D($-4$, $-3$)　　(v) E(1, $-3$)

3. The four quadrants are shown on the right. In which quadrant does each of the following points lie?

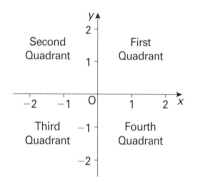

   (i) (3, 5)
   (ii) ($-2$, $-3$)
   (iii) (1, $-4$)
   (iv) ($-3$, 1)
   (v) (3, $-3$)
   (vi) ($-1$, $-3$).

4. On which axis does each of the following points lie?

   (i) (4, 0)　　(ii) ($-3$, 0)　　(iii) (0, 4)　　(iv) (0, $-3$)　　(v) (0, 0).

5. (i) Write down the coordinates of the points A, B, C and D shown on the given grid.
   (ii) What is the shortest distance between A and C if a person has to travel along the grid lines and each unit is 100 metres?
   (iii) What is the shortest distance between B and D if a person has to go through A and has to travel on grid lines only? [1 unit = 100 metres].

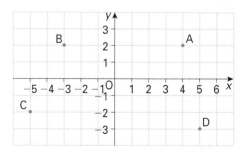

6. Look for a pattern in these coordinates.
   Use the pattern to find the missing coordinates.

   (i) (3, 5), (8, 0), (2, 6), (4, 4), ... (0, ...), (9, ...)
   (ii) (7, 8), (5, 10), (12, 3), (2, 13), ... (..., 11), (0, ...)
   (iii) (4, 4), (2, 6), (5, 3), ($-1$, 9), ... (7, ...), ($-3$, ...), (..., $-2$).

# SECTION 5.2  Distance between two points

The given diagram shows the points $A(x_1, y_1)$ and $B(x_2, y_2)$.

$$|BC| = y_2 - y_1 \quad \text{and} \quad |AC| = x_2 - x_1$$

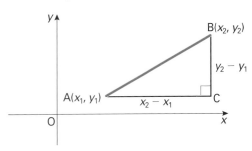

Using the Theorem of Pythagoras:

$$|AB|^2 = |AC|^2 + |BC|^2$$
$$= (x_2 - x_1)^2 + (y_2 - y_1)^2$$
$$\therefore \quad |AB| = \sqrt{(x_2 - x_1)^2 + (y_2 - y_1)^2}$$

> The distance between $A(x_1, y_1)$ and $B(x_2, y_2)$ is
> $$|AB| = \sqrt{(x_2 - x_1)^2 + (y_2 - y_1)^2}$$

## Example 1

Show that D(2, 4) is equidistant from E(−5, 1) and F(5, −3).

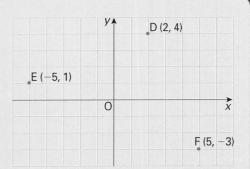

$$|DE| = \sqrt{(x_2 - x_1)^2 + (y_2 - y_1)^2}$$
$$= \sqrt{(-5 - 2)^2 + (1 - 4)^2}$$
$$= \sqrt{(-7)^2 + (-3)^2}$$
$$= \sqrt{49 + 9} = \sqrt{58}$$

$$
\begin{array}{cc}
D(2, 4) & E(-5, 1) \\
\downarrow & \downarrow \\
(x_1, y_1) & (x_2, y_2)
\end{array}
$$

Equidistant means the same distance.

$$|DF| = \sqrt{(x_2 - x_1)^2 + (y_2 - y_1)^2}$$
$$= \sqrt{(5 - 2)^2 + (-3 - 4)^2}$$
$$= \sqrt{(3)^2 + (-7)^2}$$
$$= \sqrt{9 + 49} = \sqrt{58}$$

$$
\begin{array}{cc}
D(2, 4) & F(5, -3) \\
\downarrow & \downarrow \\
(x_1, y_1) & (x_2, y_2)
\end{array}
$$

Since $|DE| = |DF| = \sqrt{58}$, D is equidistant from E and F.

## Example 2

If the distance between the points (2, 3) and (5, $k$) is $\sqrt{10}$, find two possible values of $k$.

$$\text{Distance} = \sqrt{(x_2 - x_1)^2 + (y_2 - y_1)^2}$$

$$= \sqrt{(5 - 2)^2 + (k - 3)^2}$$

$$= \sqrt{9 + k^2 - 6k + 9}$$

$$= \sqrt{k^2 - 6k + 18}$$

$(x_1, y_1)$    $(x_2, y_2)$
   ↓          ↓
(2, 3)      (5, $k$)

$$\text{Distance} = \sqrt{10} \Rightarrow \sqrt{k^2 - 6k + 18} = \sqrt{10}$$

$$\Rightarrow k^2 - 6k + 18 = 10$$

$$\Rightarrow k^2 - 6k + 8 = 0$$

$$\Rightarrow (k - 2)(k - 4) = 0$$

$$\Rightarrow k = 2 \quad \text{or} \quad k = 4$$

## Exercise 5.2

1. The points A, B, C and D are shown.
   Find  (i)  |AB|
          (ii)  |AC|
         (iii)  |AD|.
   Is |DC| = |BC|?

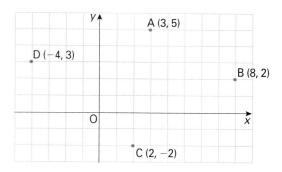

2. The given diagram shows the points D, E and F.
   (i)  Write down the lengths of [FE] and [ED].
   (ii)  Find |DF|.
   Use the Theorem of Pythagoras to show that the triangle DEF is right-angled.

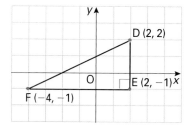

3. Find the distance between each of the following pairs of points:
     (i)  (2, 1) and (3, 4)      (ii)  (1, 5) and (2, 3)      (iii)  (−1, 4) and (2, 6)
    (iv)  (3, −2) and (−5, 3)    (v)  (−6, −1) and (1, −3)   (vi)  (4, −2) and (0, −5)

4. Find |AB| in each of the following:
     (i)  A = (2, −4), B = (3, 1)           (ii)  A = (0, 3), B = (−2, 5)
    (iii)  A = (0, −2), B = (3, −1)        (iv)  A = (5, −2), B = (3, −4)

5.  A(1, 1), B(3, 6) and C(5, 1) are the vertices of a triangle. Show that $|AB| = |BC|$.

6.  X(1, 6), Y(−3, −1) and Z(2, −2) are the vertices of a triangle.
    Find the lengths of the 3 sides and then state which two sides are equal in length.
    Hence, state what type of triangle is XYZ.

7.  A wire ABC is used to support a flag pole [BD],
    as shown on the right.

    Write down the coordinates of A, B, C and D.

    Calculate the length of wire needed to
    support the pole.

    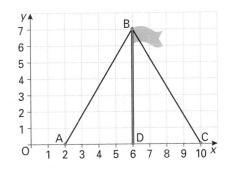

8.  The centre of a circle is (−3, 1) and (4, 3) is a point on the circle.
    Find the length of the radius of the circle.

9.  The points A(2, 1), B(6, 1), C(5, −2) and D(1, −2) are the vertices of a parallelogram.
    Plot the parallelogram on a coordinated plane.
    Find    (i) $|AC|$    (ii) $|BD|$.
    Are the diagonals equal in length?

10. The distance between the points (5, 2) and (4, $k$) is $\sqrt{2}$.
    Find two possible values for $k$.

11. X(3, $k$) and Y(−1, 2) are two points.
    If $|XY| = 5$, find two possible values for $k$.

12. Jordan lives (3 km West, 4 km South) of the centre of the
    town marked O in the given diagram,
    Michelle lives (2 km West, 3 km North) of Jordan's house.
    How far does Michelle live from the centre of town?

    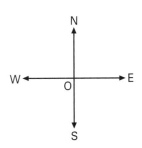

# SECTION 5.3  The midpoint of a line segment

Here is a line segment [AB].
The coordinates of A are (1, 1).
The coordinates of B are (7, 5).
M is the **midpoint** of the line segment [AB].
The coordinates of M are (4, 3).

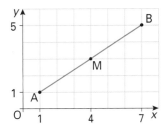

These coordinates are found as follows:

**1.** Add the $x$-coordinates of A and B and divide by 2, i.e. $\dfrac{1+7}{2} = 4$.

**2.** Add the $y$-coordinates of A and B and divide by 2, i.e. $\dfrac{1+5}{2} = 3$.

> The midpoint of the line segment joining $A(x_1, y_1)$ and $B(x_2, y_2)$ is
> $$\left(\frac{x_1 + x_2}{2}, \quad \frac{y_1 + y_2}{2}\right)$$

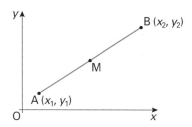

---

### Example 1

Find the midpoint of the line segment joining $A(-1, 3)$ and $B(5, 7)$.

$$\text{Midpoint of [AB]} = \left(\frac{x_1 + x_2}{2}, \frac{y_1 + y_2}{2}\right)$$

$$= \left(\frac{-1 + 5}{2}, \frac{3 + 7}{2}\right)$$

$$= \left(\frac{4}{2}, \frac{10}{2}\right) = (2, 5).$$

$$(-1, 3) \qquad (5, 7)$$
$$\downarrow \qquad\qquad \downarrow$$
$$(x_1, y_1) \qquad (x_2, y_2)$$

---

## Exercise 5.3

**1.** Find the midpoint of the line segment joining these points:
   (i)   (2, 4) and (6, 2)      (ii)   (2, 4) and (0, 2)      (iii)   (2, −1) and (4, 3)
   (iv)   (−2, 4) and (4, −2)      (v)   (2, −3) and (0, −1)      (vi)   (−3, 4) and (−1, −4).

**2.** Find the midpoint of the line segment joining (−3, 4) and (3, 7).
   On which axis does the midpoint lie?

**3.** The points (−2, 3) and (6, 5) are the end points of the diameter of a circle.
   Find the coordinates of the centre of the circle.

**4.** A(4, 3), B(1, −3), C(−2, −2) and D(1, 4) are the vertices of a parallelogram.
   Draw a sketch of this parallelogram.
   Find the midpoint of [AC].
   Verify that the midpoint of [AC] is also the midpoint of [BD].

**5.** Find M, the midpoint of the line segment joining $A(-3, 4)$ and $B(1, -6)$.
   Now show that $|AM| = |MB|$.

**6.** A(5, 2), and $B(x_1, y_1)$ are two points.
   If M(2, 4) is the midpoint of [AB], find the coordinates of B.

# SECTION 5.4  The slope of a line

The slope of the line AB is defined as

$$\frac{\text{the vertical change}}{\text{horizontal change}} \quad \text{or} \quad \frac{\text{rise}}{\text{run}}$$

The slope of AB $= \frac{3}{6} = \frac{1}{2}$.

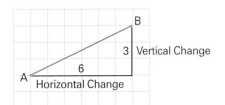

In the diagram on the right, the slope
of AB is found by getting the

$$\frac{\text{vertical change}}{\text{horizontal change}} = \frac{y_2 - y_1}{x_2 - x_1}$$

Thus the slope, $m$, of AB is $\dfrac{y_2 - y_1}{x_2 - x_1}$.

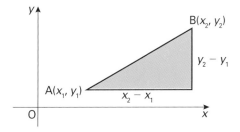

> The slope, $m$, of the line passing through $(x_1, y_1)$ and $(x_2, y_2)$ is
> $$m = \frac{y_2 - y_1}{x_2 - x_1}$$

## Positive and negative slopes

As we go from left to right, the slope is positive
if the line is rising and the slope is negative is
the line is falling.

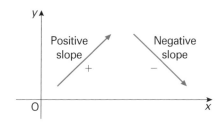

## Parallel lines

The lines $a$ and $b$ in the diagram below both have the slope $\frac{3}{2}$.

These lines are parallel.

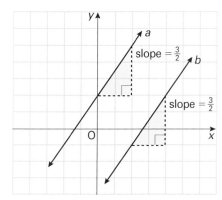

> Parallel lines have equal slopes.

## Perpendicular lines

The given lines $a$ and $b$ are perpendicular.

The slope of $a$ is $\frac{3}{2}$.

The slope of $b = -\frac{2}{3}$.

Notice that one slope is minus the reciprocal of the other.

Notice also that the product of the two slopes is $-1$, i.e.,

$$-\frac{2}{3} \times \frac{3}{2} = -1$$

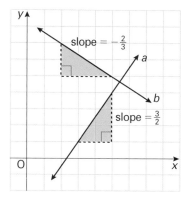

If two lines are perpendicular, the product of their slopes is $-1$, i.e.,

$$m_1 \times m_2 = -1$$

---

### Example 1

If $A = (3, -1)$ and $B = (5, 2)$, find the slope of the line AB.

$$m = \frac{y_2 - y_1}{x_2 - x_1}$$

$$= \frac{2 + 1}{5 - 3} = \frac{3}{2}$$

$$(3, -1) \qquad (5, 2)$$
$$\downarrow \qquad \downarrow$$
$$(x_1, y_1) \qquad (x_2, y_2)$$

The slopes of $AB = \frac{3}{2}$.

---

### Example 2

$A(-1, 0)$, $B(3, 2)$, $C(-1, 4)$ and $D(2, -2)$ are four points in the plane. Show that AB is perpendicular to CD.

Let $m_1$ be the slope of AB and $m_2$ be the slope of CD.

$$A(-1, 0) \qquad B(3, 2) \qquad\qquad C(-1, 4) \qquad D(2, -2)$$
$$\downarrow \qquad\qquad \downarrow \qquad\qquad\qquad \downarrow \qquad\qquad \downarrow$$
$$(x_1, y_1) \qquad (x_2, y_2) \qquad\qquad (x_1, y_1) \qquad (x_2, y_2)$$

$$m_1 = \frac{y_2 - y_1}{x_2 - x_1} \qquad\qquad m_2 = \frac{y_2 - y_1}{x_2 - x_1}$$

$$= \frac{2 - 0}{3 + 1} \qquad\qquad = \frac{-2 - 4}{2 + 1} = \frac{-6}{3}$$

$$= \frac{2}{4} = \frac{1}{2} \qquad\qquad = \frac{-6}{3} = -2$$

$$m_1 \times m_2 = \frac{1}{2} \times (-2)$$

$$= -1$$

AB is perpendicular to CD as the product of the slopes is $-1$.

## Exercise 5.4

1. The diagram shows four lines *a*, *b*, *c* and *d*
   (i) Which lines have positive slopes?
   (ii) Which lines have negative slopes?

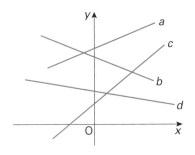

2. Three lines *a*, *b* and *c* are drawn on the grids below:

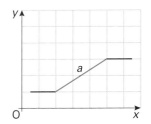 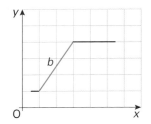 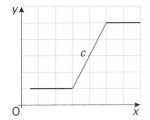

   (i) Which line has a slope of $\frac{3}{2}$?
   (ii) What is the slope of line *a*?
   (iii) What is the slope of line *c*?

3. Why is the slope of the given line negative?
   Use the grid to work out the slope of the line.

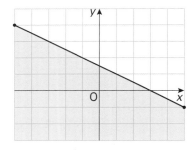

4. Find the slope of the line AB in each of the following:
   (i) A(3, 1) and B(5, 3)          (ii) A(−1, 2) and B(3, −4)
   (iii) A(−1, −3) and B(0, 5)      (iv) A(3, 0) and B(−1, −4)
   (v) A(−3, 2) and B(−5, 0)        (vi) A(−5, 1) and B(−2, 3).

5. Show that the line passing through A(−1, −2) and B(3, 0) has the same slope as the line passing through C(2, 3) and D(−2, 1).
   What can you say about the lines AB and CD?

6. ℓ contains the points (1, 1) and (2, 4).
   *m* contains the points (4, 1) and (3, −2).
   Investigate if ℓ is parallel to *m*.

7. A(−2, −4), B(5, −1), C(6, 4) and D(−1, 1) are the vertices of a quadrilateral.
   Draw a rough sketch of the figure.
   Now verify that AB∥CD and AD∥BC.

8. The given diagram shows three lines *a*, *b*, and *c*.
   Match the lines with these slopes:

   2,        $\frac{1}{2}$,        1.

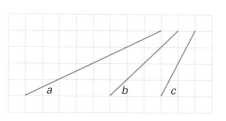

9. The slope of a line $\ell$ is $\frac{3}{4}$.
   (i)  Write down the slope of a line *m* if *m* is parallel to $\ell$.
   (ii) Write down the slope of a line *n* if *n* is perpendicular to $\ell$.

10. The slopes of five lines are given below.
    Write down the slope of a line that is perpendicular to each of these lines:
    (i)  $\frac{2}{3}$        (ii) $\frac{4}{5}$        (iii) $-\frac{3}{4}$        (iv) $-\frac{2}{5}$        (v) $-\frac{1}{2}$

11. A(−1, 1), B(1, 3), C(6, 2) and D(4, 4) are four points in the plane.
    Find the slope of      (i) AB      (ii) CD. Verify that AB ⊥ CD.

12. The line *m* contains the points (3, −1) and (4, −2).
    (i)  Find the slope of any line parallel to *m*.
    (ii) Find the slope of any line perpendicular to *m*.

13. If the slope of the line through the points (3, 2) and (8, *k*) is $\frac{3}{5}$, find the value of *k*.

14. The slope of the line through (3, −2) and (1, *k*) is $\frac{1}{3}$. Find the value of *k*.

15. The line $\ell$ contains the points (−2, 0) and (4, 3).
    The line *m* contains the points (1, −1) and (*k*, 1).
    (i)   Find the slope of $\ell$.
    (ii)  Find, in terms of *k*, the slope of *m*.
    (iii) If $\ell \| m$, find the value of *k*.

16. The diagram shows four lines $\ell$, *m*, *n* and *k*.
    (i)  Explain why the slopes of $\ell$, *m*, and
         *n* are negative.
    (ii) Match the lines with these slopes:
         $-\frac{1}{2}$,        0,        −2,        −1.

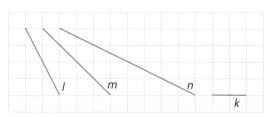

# SECTION 5.5  The equation of a line

In the given line $\ell$, the sum of the *x* and *y* values of
each point is 5, e.g. $2 + 3 = 5$.

For this reason we say that the equation of the line $\ell$ is

   $x + y = 5.$

$x + y = 5$ is called the **equation of a line**,
or a **linear equation**.

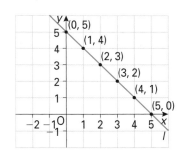

The equation was found by observing the relationship between the $x$ and $y$ values of each point and discovering that for all the points, $x + y = 5$.

We will now consider the figure below.

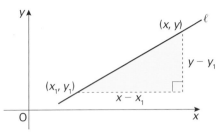

The line $\ell$ contains the point $(x_1, y_1)$ and has slope $m$.

Let $(x, y)$ be any other point on $\ell$.

From the diagram the slope is $\dfrac{y - y_1}{x - x_1} = m$.

If we multiply both sides by $(x - x_1)$ we get,

$$y - y_1 = m(x - x_1)$$

> The equation of the line through $(x_1, y_1)$ with slope $m$ is found by using
> $$y - y_1 = m(x - x_1)$$

---

### Example 1

Find the equation of the line containing the point $(-3, 2)$ and whose slope is $\frac{2}{3}$.

Equation of the line is: $y - y_1 = m(x - x_1)$ $\qquad\qquad m = \dfrac{2}{3}$

$$y - 2 = \frac{2}{3}(x + 3) \qquad\qquad (x_1, y_1) = (-3, 2)$$

$$y - 2 = \frac{2x}{3} + \frac{6}{3}$$

Multiply each term by 3: $\qquad\qquad\qquad 3y - 6 = 2x + 6$

Bring all terms to right-hand side. $\qquad 2x - 3y + 12 = 0$

$\therefore$ the equation of the line is: $\qquad 2x - 3y + 12 = 0$

---

## Equation of a line when given two points on the line

To find the equation of a line containing two points, we first find the slope of the line using the formula $\dfrac{y_2 - y_1}{x_2 - x_1}$.

We then use the formula $y - y_1 = m(x - x_1)$ to find the equation of the line.

You may use either of the two points as $(x_1, y_1)$.

## Example 2

Find the equation of the line containing the points $(-2, 3)$ and $(3, 1)$.

Slope of line: $m = \dfrac{y_2 - y_1}{x_2 - x_1}$

$\qquad\qquad = \dfrac{1 - 3}{3 + 2} = \dfrac{-2}{5}$

$$(-2, 3) \qquad (3, 1)$$
$$\downarrow \qquad\qquad \downarrow$$
$$(x_1, y_1) \qquad (x_2, y_2)$$

We now use the slope $-\dfrac{2}{5}$ and the point $(-2, 3)$...   you may use either of the 2 points

Equation of line: $y - y_1 = m(x - x_1)$

$$y - 3 = -\frac{2}{5}(x + 2)$$

$$y - 3 = -\frac{2x}{5} - \frac{4}{5}$$

$$5y - 15 = -2x - 4...\qquad \text{multiply each term by 5.}$$

$$\Rightarrow \quad 2x + 5y - 11 = 0 \text{ is the equation of the line.}$$

## Exercise 5.5

1. Find the equations of the following lines, given the slope and a point on the line in each case:
   (i)   slope = 2; point = (3, 4)
   (ii)  slope = 4; point = (1, 5)
   (iii) slope = 5; point = (−2, 3)
   (iv)  slope = −3; point = (−2, 0)
   (v)   slope = −5; point = (−3, −2)
   (vi)  slope = $\frac{2}{3}$; point = (3, −1).

2. Find the equations of the following lines, given the slope and a point on the line in each case:
   (i)  slope = $\frac{3}{4}$; point = (1, −4)
   (ii) slope = $\frac{3}{5}$; point = (−4, 2).

3. Find the equation of the line through $(-2, 3)$ with slope
   (i)  4
   (ii)  −2
   (iii)  $\frac{3}{4}$
   (iv)  $-\frac{2}{3}$

4. Find the equation of the line through $(0, 0)$ and whose slope is −3.

5. Find the equation of the line through $(0, 0)$ and whose slope is
   (i)  3
   (ii)  −5
   (iii)  $\frac{1}{3}$
   (iv)  $-\frac{3}{2}$
   What do you notice about the equation of each of these lines?

6. Find the slope of the line through A(3, −4) and B(1, 2).
   Hence, find the equation of the line AB.

7. Find the equations of the lines through the following pairs of points:
   (i)   (2, 3) and (4, 6)
   (ii)  (−1, 2) and (2, −4)
   (iii) (−5, 1) and (1, 0)
   (iv)  (−2, 3) and (3, −1)
   (v)   (2, 7) and (0, 5)
   (vi)  (−3, −5) and (−1, −1).

8. Find the equation of the line through $(-2, 3)$ and the midpoint of the line segment joining $(1, -3)$ and $(3, -1)$.

9. The given diagram shows the gable-end of a house.
Use the grid to write down
   - (i) the coordinates of the points marked A, B and C.
   - (ii) the slope of AB
   - (iii) the equation of AB.

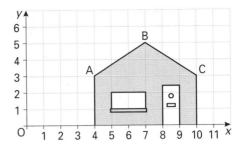

## SECTION 5.6 The equation $y = mx + c$

If the equation of a line is in the form

$$y = mx + c, \quad \text{then}$$

(i) the slope is $m$

(ii) the line intersects the $y$-axis at $(0, c)$.

The point $(0, c)$ is called the **y-intercept**.

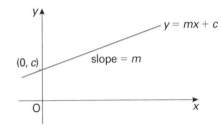

If a line is in the form $3x + 2y - 8 = 0$, change the equation to the form $y = mx + c$.

The slope is the value of $m$.

---

### Example 1

Find the slope of the line $3x - 2y - 9 = 0$.

We write the equation in the form $y = mx + c$.

$$3x - 2y - 9 = 0$$
$$\Rightarrow \quad -2y = -3x + 9 \ldots \quad \text{leave the } y \text{ term only on left-hand side}$$
$$\Rightarrow \quad 2y = 3x - 9 \ldots \quad \text{multiply each term by } -1$$
$$\Rightarrow \quad y = \frac{3}{2}x - \frac{9}{2} \ldots \quad \text{divide each term by 2}$$

$\therefore$ the slope of the line is $\frac{3}{2}$

---

### Example 2

$\ell$ is the line $2x - 3y + 6 = 0$ and $m$ is the line $3x + 2y - 4 = 0$.
Show that $\ell$ is perpendicular to $m$.

Slope of $\ell$:

$$2x - 3y + 6 = 0$$
$$\Rightarrow \quad -3y = -2x - 6$$
$$\Rightarrow \quad 3y = 2x + 6$$
$$\Rightarrow \quad y = \frac{2}{3}x + 2$$
$$\Rightarrow \quad \text{slope of } \ell = \frac{2}{3}$$

Slope of $m$:

$$3x + 2y - 4 = 0$$
$$\Rightarrow \quad 2y = -3x + 4$$
$$\Rightarrow \quad y = -\frac{3}{2}x + 2$$
$$\Rightarrow \quad \text{slope of } m = -\frac{3}{2}$$

Slope of $\ell$ × slope of $m = \dfrac{2}{3} \times \left(-\dfrac{3}{2}\right)$

$$= \dfrac{-6}{6} = -1$$

Since the product of the two slopes $= -1$, the lines are perpendicular.

## Exercise 5.6

1. Express each of the following lines in the form $y = mx + c$ and hence write down the slope of the line:
   (i)  $x + y - 4 = 0$
   (ii)  $3x + y - 5 = 0$
   (iii)  $2x + 3y - 7 = 0$
   (iv)  $5x - 2y + 3 = 0$
   (v)  $3x + 4y - 2 = 0$
   (vi)  $3x - 4y + 6 = 0.$

2. Express the line $\ell: 2x + 3y - 7 = 0$ in the form $y = mx + c$.
   (i)  Write down the slope of $\ell$.
   (ii)  What is the slope of any line parallel to $\ell$?
   (iii)  What is the slope of any line perpendicular to $\ell$?

3. Show that the lines, $x - 2y + 1 = 0$ and $3x - 6y - 7 = 0$ are parallel.
   What is the slope of any line perpendicular to these lines?

4. Show that the lines $2x + 3y - 4 = 0$ and $3x - 2y + 1 = 0$ are perpendicular to each other.

5. If the equation of the line $\ell$ is $y = 3x - 4$, write down the equation of any line, in the form $y = mx + c$, that is
   (i)  parallel to $\ell$
   (ii)  perpendicular to $\ell$.

6. Investigate if the lines $y = \dfrac{2}{3}x + 4$ and $2x - 3y - 5 = 0$ are parallel.

7. The equation of the line $m$ is $y = 3x - 2$.
   Find  (i)  the slope of $m$
          (ii)  the point at which $m$ intersects the $y$-axis.

8. The equations of six lines are given below:
   a:  $y = 2x - 3$
   c:  $y = x + 3$
   e:  $y = -\dfrac{1}{2}x + 4$
   b:  $y = \dfrac{1}{2}x + 5$
   d:  $y = -2x - 4$
   f:  $y = 2x - 2$
   (i)  Name a pair of parallel lines.
   (ii)  Name a pair of perpendicular lines.
   (iii)  Which line crosses the $y$-axis at $(0, 4)$?
   (iv)  Which line crosses the $y$-axis at $(0, -3)$?

9. By finding the slope and $y$-intercept, write down the equation of the given line.

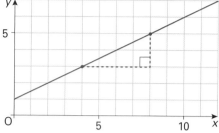

10. If the line $x + 2y - 6 = 0$ is parallel to the line $2x + ky - 5 = 0$, find the value of $k$.

11. If the line $2x - 3y + 7 = 0$ is perpendicular to the line $3x + ky - 4 = 0$, find the value of $k$.

12. For what value of $k$ is the line $2x + ky - 4 = 0$ parallel to the line $x + 3y + 7 = 0$?

# SECTION 5.7  Parallel and Perpendicular lines

If we are given the equation of a line, $\ell$, such as $2x + 3y - 4 = 0$, we can find the slope of the line by expressing the equation in the form $y = mx + c$.

If we are also given a point $(x_1, y_1)$, we can then find the equation of a line through $(x_1, y_1)$ and which is parallel to or perpendicular to $\ell$.

## Example 1

Find the equation of the line through the point $(-2, 3)$ which is perpendicular to the line $2x - y + 5 = 0$.

To find the slope of $2x - y + 5 = 0$, we express it in the form $y = mx + c$.

$$2x - y + 5 = 0$$
$$\Rightarrow \quad -y = -2x - 5$$
$$\Rightarrow \quad y = 2x + 5 \ldots \qquad \text{multiply each term by } -1$$
$$\Rightarrow \quad \text{the slope is 2.}$$

The slope of the line perpendicular to this line is $-\dfrac{1}{2}$.

Equation of line through $(-2, 3)$ with slope $-\dfrac{1}{2}$ is:

$$y - y_1 = m(x - x_1) \qquad (x_1, y_1) = (-2, 3)$$
$$y - 3 = -\frac{1}{2}(x + 2) \qquad m = -\frac{1}{2}$$
$$y - 3 = \frac{-x}{2} - 1$$
$$\Rightarrow \quad 2y - 6 = -x - 2 \ldots \quad \text{multiply each term by 2}$$
$$\Rightarrow \quad x + 2y - 4 = 0 \text{ is the required equation.}$$

## Exercise 5.7

1. Find the slope of the line $2x + y - 4 = 0$.
   Now find the equation of the line through the point $(2, 4)$ and which is parallel to the line $2x + y - 4 = 0$.

2. Find the equation of the line through the point $(1, -6)$ and which is parallel to the line $3x - y + 4 = 0$.

3. Find the slope of the line $2x - 3y + 1 = 0$.
   What is the slope of any line perpendicular to $2x - 3y + 1 = 0$?
   Now find the equation of the line through the point $(4, -1)$ and which is perpendicular to the line $2x - 3y + 1 = 0$.

4. Find the equation of the line through $(-2, 1)$ and which is perpendicular to the line $3x + 2y - 4 = 0$.

5. Find the equation of the line through $(-4, 0)$ and which is parallel to the line $y = 3x - 5$.

6. A line passes through the origin and is perpendicular to the line whose equation is $3x - y - 2 = 0$. Find the equation of the line.

7. The point A has coordinates $(1, 7)$ and the point B has coordinates $(3, 1)$.
   The midpoint of [AB] is P.
   Find the coordinates of P.
   Now find the equation of the line which passes through P and which is perpendicular to the line $x + 5y - 7 = 0$.

8. The given diagram shows the points $A(-1, 5)$, $B(2, -1)$ and $C(0, 5)$.
   The line $\ell$ is parallel to AB and contains the point C.
   Find the equation of $\ell$.

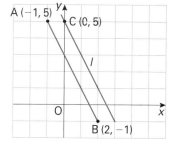

9. A line is perpendicular to the line whose equation is $y = 4x - 3$.
   Find the equation of the line if it crosses the $y$-axis at $(0, 7)$.

10. Which one of the following lines is parallel to $3x + y - 4 = 0$?
    A: $y = 3x - 2$     B: $y = \frac{1}{3}x + 4$     C: $6x + 2y + 7 = 0$     D: $x + 3y + 2 = 0$

11. The line $y = 2x + 5$ intersects the $y$-axis at the point P.
    Find the equation of the line through P and which is perpendicular to $y = 2x + 5$.

12. The equation of the line AB is $5x - 3y = 26$.
    (i) Find the slope of AB.
    (ii) The point A has coordinates $(4, -2)$ and a point C has coordinates $(-6, 4)$.
        (a) Prove that AC is perpendicular to AB.
        (b) Find the equation of the line AC, expressing your answer in the form $ax + by = c$.

# SECTION 5.8 Graphing lines

To draw a line such as $2x + 3y = 6$, we need to know at least two points on the line.

The easiest points to find are those at which the line crosses the $x$-axis and $y$-axis.

On the $x$-axis, $y = 0$; on the $y$-axis, $x = 0$.

Take the line $2x + 3y = 6$

When $x = 0$, then $2(0) + 3y = 6$
$$3y = 6$$
$$\Rightarrow \quad y = 2$$

$\therefore$ $(0, 2)$ is one point on the line

When $y = 0$, then $2x + 3(0) = 6$
$$2x = 6$$
$$x = 3$$

$\therefore$ $(3, 0)$ is a second point on the line

A sketch of the line is shown on the right.

Sketch of line $2x + 3y = 6$

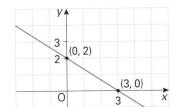

## Lines parallel to the axes

The lines $x = 2$ and $x = 4$ are shown.

Notice that the $x$-value of all points on the line $x = 4$ is 4.

Similarly, the $x$-value of each point on the line $x = 2$ is 2.

All lines with equations of the form $x = a$ will be parallel to the $y$-axis.

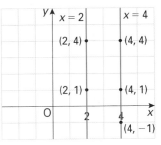

The diagram on the right shows the line $y = 2$.

Again notice that all the $y$-values of the points on this line are 2.

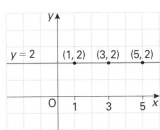

## Lines containing the origin

A line such as $x + 2y = 0$, with no independent term, always contains the origin $(0, 0)$.

To plot the line $x + 2y = 0$, we know that it contains the origin.

To find a second point, we select a value for $x$ and then find the corresponding $y$-value.

Let $x = 2$: $\quad 2 + 2y = 0$
$$2y = -2$$
$$y = -1$$

$\therefore$ $(2, -1)$ is a second point on the line.

A sketch of the line containing $(0, 0)$ and $(2, -1)$ is shown.

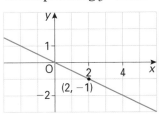

## To verify that a point is on a given line

To investigate if the point $(3, -2)$ is on the line $x + 2y + 1 = 0$, we substitute 3 for $x$ and $-2$ for $y$ in the equation.

$$x + 2y + 1 = 0$$
$x = 3; y = -2$:    $3 + 2(-2) + 1$
$$= 3 - 4 + 1$$
$$= 4 - 4 = 0$$

> If a point is on a line, then the coordinates of the point will satisfy the equation of the line.

Since $(3, -2)$ **satisfies** the equation $x + 2y + 1 = 0$, it shows that the point is on the line.

However, $(-3, 4)$ is not on the line $x - 3y + 7 = 0$, since $-3 - 12 + 7 \neq 0$, i.e. it does not satisfy the equation.

---

**Example 1**

If the point $(k, 3)$ is on the line $4x - 3y + 1 = 0$, find the value of $k$.

We substitute $k$ for $x$ and 3 for $y$ in the equation $4x - 3y + 1 = 0$.
$$\Rightarrow \quad 4k - 3(3) + 1 = 0$$
$$\Rightarrow \quad 4k - 9 + 1 = 0$$
$$\Rightarrow \quad 4k - 8 = 0$$
$$\Rightarrow \quad 4k = 8 \Rightarrow k = 2.$$

---

## Exercise 5.8

1. Write down the equations of the lines $a$, $b$, $c$ and $d$ shown on the right.

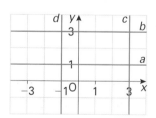

2. Draw a pair of axes and sketch these four lines:
   (i)   $x = 4$       (ii)   $y = 2$       (iii)   $x = -2$       (iv)   $y = -3$.

3. Use the graph of the line $2x + y = 6$ to write down
   (i)   the value of $x$ when $y = 0$
   (ii)  the coordinates of the point where the line crosses the $y$-axis
   (iii) the value of $y$ when $x = 1$
   (iv)  the value of $x$ when $y = 2$
   (v)   the area of the triangle formed by the line, the $x$-axis and the $y$-axis.

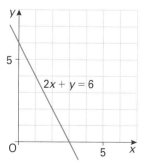

4. Find the coordinates of the points at which the line $x - 2y - 6 = 0$ intersects the $x$-axis and $y$-axis.
   Now use these points to draw a sketch of the line.

**5.** On separate diagrams draw rough sketches of the following lines:

    (i)   $x - y - 4 = 0$         (ii)   $2x + y + 2 = 0$        (iii)   $x - 2y + 4 = 0$

**6.** Find the coordinates of the points where the line $x - 2y = 5$ intersects the $x$-axis and $y$-axis. Hence draw a sketch of the line.

**7.** Draw a sketch of the line $2x - y + 6 = 0$.
Hence write down the area of the triangle formed by the $x$-axis, the $y$-axis and the line.

**8.** On separate diagrams draw rough sketches of the following lines:

    (i)   $2x - y = 7$           (ii)   $4x - y - 4 = 0$        (iii)   $x - 3y - 6 = 0$

**9.** The equations of the lines A and B are:

    A: $y = \frac{2}{3}x + 2$

    B: $3x + 5y - 15 = 0$

    (i)   Which line intersects the $y$-axis at $(0, 2)$?

    (ii)   Which line intersects the $x$-axis at $(5, 0)$?

    (iii)   Use the slopes of the two lines to investigate whether the lines are perpendicular to each other.

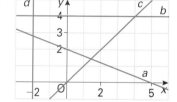

    (iv)   Write down the area of the triangle formed by the line $3x + 5y - 15 = 0$, the $x$-axis and the $y$-axis.

**10.** Each of the following lines contain the origin $(0, 0)$.
By taking a value for $x$ and then finding the corresponding $y$-value, sketch each of the lines on separate diagrams:

    (i)   $x - 2y = 0$      (ii)   $x + 3y = 0$       (iii)   $3x - y = 0$       (iv)   $x - 4y = 0$.

**11.** The lines $a$, $b$, $c$ and $d$ are graphed in the given diagram.
Match each line with one of these equations:

    (i)   $x = -2$

    (ii)   $x - y = 0$

    (iii)   $2x + 5y = 10$

    (iv)   $y = 4$

**12.**    (i)   Verify that $(2, -5)$ is on the line $2x + y + 1 = 0$.

    (ii)   Verify that $(2, -3)$ is on the line $y = x - 5$.

    (iii)   Show that $(-3, 1)$ is not on the line $x - 3y + 1 = 0$.

    (iv)   Investigate if $(2, 0)$ is on the line $2x - y + 3 = 0$.

**13.** Show that $(-3, 1)$ is on the line $2x + 4y + 2 = 0$.

**14.** If $(1, 4)$ is on the line $2x + y + k = 0$, find the value of $k$.

**15.** If $(2, -3)$ is on the line $x + ky + 7 = 0$, find the value of $k$.

**16.**    (i)   Find the value of $k$ if the line $2x + ky - 8 = 0$ contains the point $(3, 1)$.

    (ii)   If $(1, t)$ lies on the line $y = 2x + 3$, find the value of $t$.

# SECTION 5.9 Intersection of two lines

A sketch of the lines $x + y = 4$ and $x + 3y = 6$ is shown on the right.

The point of intersection of the two lines can be read from the diagram.

This point is $(3, 1)$.

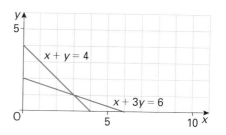

The point of intersection of any two lines can be found by sketching the lines on a grid and then reading their point of intersection from this grid.

However, the point of intersection of two lines may be found more easily by using simultaneous equations, as shown in the following example.

> Simultaneous equations can be used to find the point of intersection of two lines.

---

**Example 1**

Use simultaneous equations to find the point of intersection of the lines
$$x + y = 5 \quad \text{and} \quad 2x - y = 4.$$

$$x + y = 5 \ldots ①$$
$$\underline{2x - y = 4 \ldots ②}$$

Adding: $\quad 3x \quad = 9 \implies x = 3$

From ①: $\quad 3 + y = 5 \implies y = 2$

$\therefore$ the point of intersection is $(3, 2)$.

---

## Exercise 5.9

1. Using the one diagram, sketch the lines
   $x + y = 5 \quad \text{and} \quad x + 4y = 8$.
   Use your sketch to write down the point of intersection of the two lines.

2. A sketch of the lines $2x + y = 6$ and $x + y = 5$ is shown.
   Use the sketch to write down the point of intersection of the two lines.
   Now use simultaneous equations to verify your answer.

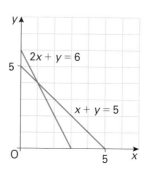

Use simultaneous equations to find the point of intersection of the following pairs of lines:

3.  $x + y = 5$
    $2x - y = 1$

4.  $x - y = 2$
    $2x + y = 7$

5.  $2x + 5y = 1$
    $x - 3y = -5$

6.  $x + 2y = -1$
    $2x - 3y = -9$

7.  $x + 3y = 7$
    $2x - y = -7$

8.  $x - 7y = 4$
    $3x - y = -8$

9.  $2x - 3y = 4$
    $2x + 3y = -8$

10.  $3x - 2y = 17$
    $4x + 3y = 0$

11.  $x + 3y = 13$
    $2x + 5y = 21$

12.  Use simultaneous equations to verify that the lines
    $$2x + 3y = 12 \quad \text{and} \quad 3x - 4y = 1$$
    intersect at the point (3, 2).

# SECTION 5.10  Area of a triangle

The diagram on the right shows a triangle with vertices $(0, 0)$, $(x_1, y_1)$ and $(x_2, y_2)$.

The area of this triangle is given by

$$\frac{1}{2} |x_1 y_2 - x_2 y_1|$$

The two vertical lines || indicate that we take the positive value of the result.

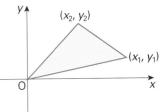

---

**Example 1**

Find the area of the triangle with vertices (0, 0), (−2, 1) and (3, 4).

Area $= \frac{1}{2} |x_1 y_2 - x_2 y_1|$  $(x_1, y_1)$  $(x_2, y_2)$

$= \frac{1}{2} |(-2)(4) - (3)(1)|$   $\downarrow$      $\downarrow$

$= \frac{1}{2} |-8 - 3|$     $(-2, 1)$   $(3, 4)$

$= \frac{1}{2} |-11|$

$= 5\frac{1}{2}$ square units

---

**Note:**  If none of the vertices of the triangle is at the origin, then the triangle has to be moved (translated) until one of the vertices is $(0, 0)$.

Let  $(2, 4) \rightarrow (0, 0)$
     $(7, 3) \rightarrow (5, -1)$
     $(4, 1) \rightarrow (2, -3)$

Here we take 2 from each *x*-value and 4 from each *y*-value for each of the points.

Find the area of the triangle with vertices $(2, 4)$, $(-3, 1)$ and $(3, -5)$.

Let $\quad(2, 4) \to (0, 0)$
$\quad\quad(-3, 1) \to (-5, -3)$
$\quad\quad(3, -5) \to (1, -9)$

> Here we take 2 from each $x$-value and 4 from each $y$-value.

Area of triangle $\quad= \frac{1}{2}|x_1 y_2 - x_2 y_1|$

$\quad\quad\quad\quad= \frac{1}{2}|(-5)(-9) - (1)(-3)|$

$\quad\quad\quad\quad= \frac{1}{2}|45 + 3|$

$\quad\quad\quad\quad= \frac{1}{2}|48|$

$\quad\quad\quad\quad= 24$ square units

$\quad\quad(x_1, y_1) \quad\quad (x_2, y_2)$
$\quad\quad\quad\downarrow \quad\quad\quad\quad\downarrow$
$\quad\quad(-5, -3) \quad (1, -9)$

## Exercise 5.10

1. Find the area of the triangle whose vertices are
   (i) $(0, 0)$, $(2, 1)$, $(3, 4)$
   (ii) $(0, 0)$, $(5, 1)$, $(3, 6)$
   (iii) $(0, 0)$, $(-2, 3)$, $(1, -4)$
   (iv) $(0, 0)$, $(3, 4)$, $(-2, -6)$
   (v) $(2, -1)$, $(-2, 4)$, $(0, 0)$
   (vi) $(0, 0)$, $(6, 0)$, $(-2, 3)$.

2. $A(2, 3)$, $B(-5, 1)$ and $C(3, 1)$ are the vertices of a triangle.
   By using the translation $A(2, 3) \to (0, 0)$, find the images of B and C under this translation.
   Hence find the area of the triangle ABC.

3. By translating one of the vertices to $(0, 0)$, find the area of each of the triangles whose vertices are
   (i) $(2, 3)$, $(5, 1)$ and $(2, 0)$
   (ii) $(-2, 3)$, $(4, 0)$ and $(1, -4)$
   (iii) $(-2, 1)$, $(3, 6)$ and $(0, -3)$
   (iv) $(5, 1)$, $(2, -3)$ and $(7, 1)$.

4. The area of a triangle is *half length of base multiplied by perpendicular height*.
   Use this to write down the area of each of the triangles shown below.

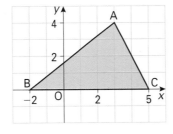 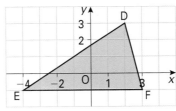

5. $A(0, 0)$, $B(4, -1)$, $C(2, 3)$ and $D(-2, 4)$ are the vertices of a quadrilateral.
   Find the area of the quadrilateral by dividing it into the two triangles ABC and ACD.

6. Find the area of the quadrilateral with vertices $A(0, 0)$, $B(2, -3)$, $C(4, 0)$ and $D(0, 4)$.

7. The line $2x - y - 4 = 0$ intersects the $x$-axis at A and the $y$-axis at B.
   Find the area of the $\triangle OAB$, where O is the origin.

8. Find the area of the triangle whose vertices are (0, 0), (1, 3) and (2, 6).
   What conclusion can you draw from your answer?

9. Find the value of $k$ if the area of the given triangle is
   7 square units.

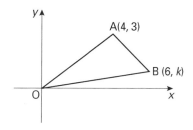

# TEST YOURSELF 5

1. A(−1, 4) and B(2, 5) are two points in the plane.
   Find  (i) |AB|    (ii) the slope of AB.

2. P is the point (1, 2) and Q is the point (−2, 6).
   (i)   Plot P and Q on graph paper.
   (ii)  Find the slope of PQ.
   (iii) Find the equation of PQ.

3. The equation of a line is $y = 2x − 4$.
   (i)   Write down the slope of this line.
   (ii)  At what point does the line intersect the $y$-axis?
   (iii) At what point does the line intersect the $x$-axis?
   (iv)  What is the slope of any line that is perpendicular to $y = 2x − 4$?

4. (i)   Verify that the point (2, 3) is on the line $2x − 3y + 5 = 0$.
   (ii)  If the point (1, $k$) is on the line $2x − 3y + 7 = 0$, find the value of $k$.

5. A(−3, 1) and B(3, 9) are two points in the plane.
   (i)   Find M, the midpoint of [AB].
         On which axis does M lie?
   (ii)  Find the slope of AB.
   (iii) Write down the slope of any line perpendicular to AB.
   (iv)  Now find the equation of the line through the origin and which is perpendicular to
         AB.

6. Use the grid on the right to write down the slope of the line $p$.
   Now write down the equation of $p$ in the form $y = mx + c$.

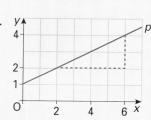

7.  $\ell$ is the line $y - 6 = -2x - 2$.
   (i)   Write down the slope of $\ell$.
   (ii)  Verify that $(1, 2)$ is a point on $\ell$.
   (iii) $\ell$ intersects the $y$-axis at T.
         Find the coordinates of T.
   (iv)  Show the line $\ell$ on a coordinate diagram.

8.  The equation of the line $k$ is $x - 2y + 10 = 0$.
   (i)   Verify that $T(2, 6) \in k$.
   (ii)  Find the slope of $k$.
   (iii) Find the equation of the line which contains t and is perpendicular to the line $k$.

9.  (i)   If the line $2x + y - 7 = 0$ is parallel to the line $4x + ky - 3 = 0$, find the value of $k$.
   (ii)  The line $2x + 3y - 6 = 0$ intersects the $x$-axis at A and the $y$-axis at B.
         Find the coordinates of A and B and hence find the area of the triangle OAB,
         where O is the origin.

10. To clean the upstairs window on the side of a house,
    it is necessary to position the ladder so that it just
    touches the edge of the lean-to shed as shown in the
    diagram. The coordinates represent distances from O
    in metres, in the $x$ and $y$ directions shown.
    Find (i)   the equation of the line of the ladder
       (ii)  the height of the point A reached by the top
             of the ladder
       (iii) the length of the ladder in metres, correct to
             one decimal place.

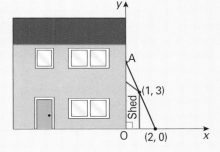

11. $\ell$ is the line $x - 2y + 2 = 0$.
    $m$ is the line $3x + y - 8 = 0$.
    Use simultaneous equations to find the coordinates of P, the point of intersection of $\ell$
    and $m$.

12. A line $\ell$ has slope $-2$ and passes through the point $(3, 6)$.
   (i)   Find the equation of $\ell$.
   (ii)  Find the coordinates of the points at which the line intersects the $x$-axis and
         $y$-axis.
   (iii) Find the area of the triangle formed by $\ell$, the $x$-axis and the $y$-axis.

13. (i)   Find the equation of the straight line through $(0, 1)$ and $(3, 7)$.
   (ii)  Another line has equation $y = 7 - 2x$.
         Without drawing the lines, explain how you can tell whether or not this line is
         perpendicular to the line in part (i).

**14.** The given graph shows three lines *a*, *b* and *c*.

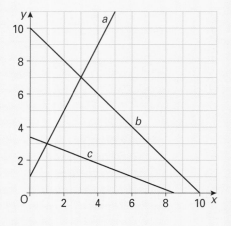

   (i)   Which line(s) have negative slopes?

   (ii)  Use the grid to find the slope of the line *a*.

   (iii)  Associate each of the lines with one of these
         equations:

              D:  $y = 2x + 1$

              E:  $x + y = 10$

              F:  $2x + 5y = 17$.

**15.** *p* is the line $3x + 2y + c = 0$.

   (i)   If $(3, -1)$ is a point on *p*, find the value of *c*.

   (ii)  The line *q* is parallel to *p* and passes through the point $(-2, 5)$.
         Find the equation of *q*.

**16.** A(4, 2), B(−2, 0) and C(0, 4) are three points.

   (i)   Prove that AC is perpendicular to BC.

   (ii)  Show that |AC| = |BC|.

   (iii)  Find the area of the triangle ABC.

**17.** The linear graph below shows the relationship between degrees Celsius and degrees
Fahrenheit.

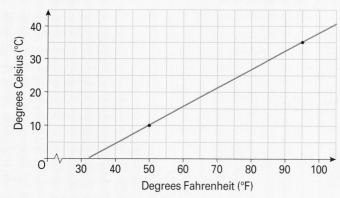

Use the graph to convert approximately

   (i)   35°C to Fahrenheit          (ii)   15°C to Fahrenheit

   (iii)  50°F to Celsius            (iv)  100°F to Celsius.

Use the two marked points on the graph to find the equation of the line in the form
$ax + by + c = 0$.

## Summary of Key Points

For any two points $A(x_1, y_1)$ and $B(x_2, y_2)$:

**1. Length of [AB]** $= \sqrt{(x_2 - x_1)^2 + (y_2 - y_1)^2}$

**2. Midpoint of [AB]** $= \left( \dfrac{x_1 + x_2}{2}, \ \dfrac{y_1 + y_2}{2} \right)$

**3. Slope of AB($m$)** $\quad m = \dfrac{y_2 - y_1}{x_2 - x_1} = \dfrac{\text{difference in } y\text{-values}}{\text{difference in } x\text{-values}}$

### The equation of a line

The line $y = mx + c$ has slope $m$ and intersects the $y$-axis at $(0, c)$.

The equation of the line which contains $(x_1, y_1)$ and has slope $m$ is

$$y - y_1 = m(x - x_1)$$

### Parallel and perpendicular lines

If the line $\ell$ has slope $m_1$ and the line $k$ has slope $m_2$, then

1. $\ell$ is parallel to $k$ if $m_1 = m_2$.
2. $\ell$ is perpendicular to $k$ if $m_1 \times m_2 = -1$.

If the slope of $\ell = \frac{3}{4}$ and $\ell \perp k$, then the slope of $k = -\frac{4}{3}$.

### Graphing lines

To graph the line $2x - 3y = 6$:

1. Let $x = 0$ and find the corresponding $y$-value, i.e. $(0, -2)$.
2. Let $y = 0$ and find the corresponding $x$-value, i.e. $(3, 0)$.
3. Draw a line through $(0, -2)$ and $(3, 0)$.

Lines parallel to the $x$-axis will take the form $y = a$.

Lines parallel to the $y$-axis will take the form $x = b$.

Lines through the origin will have no independent term, e.g. $x = 2y$.

### Point of intersection of two lines

The point of intersection of two lines is found by solving their simultaneous equations.

### Area of a triangle

The area of the triangle with vertices $(0, 0)$, $(x_1, y_1)$ and $(x_2, y_2)$ is given by

$$\text{Area} = \tfrac{1}{2} \left| x_1 y_2 - x_2 y_1 \right|.$$

## Key Words

centre    radius    diameter    equation    inside    outside
element of    intersection    tangent    horizontal    perpendicular

## SECTION 6.1   Equation of a circle with centre (0, 0)

The diagram below shows a circle with centre (0, 0) and radius $r$.

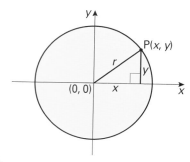

P($x$, $y$) is any point on the circle.

From the right-angled triangle, we see that

$$x^2 + y^2 = r^2$$

We say that $x^2 + y^2 = r^2$ is the equation of the circle.

To find the equation of a circle, we need to know
  (i)   the centre of the circle
  (ii)  the length of the radius.

> The equation of the circle with centre (0, 0) and radius $r$ is $x^2 + y^2 = r^2$.

### Example 1

Find the equation of the circle with centre (0, 0) and radius   (i) 3   (ii) $1\frac{1}{4}$.

(i)   The equation is  $x^2 + y^2 = r^2$
$$\Rightarrow \quad x^2 + y^2 = 9 \dots (r = 3)$$

(ii)  Here  $r = 1\frac{1}{4} = \frac{5}{4}$
$$\Rightarrow \quad x^2 + y^2 = \left(\frac{5}{4}\right)^2$$
$$\Rightarrow \quad x^2 + y^2 = \frac{25}{16}$$
$$\Rightarrow \quad 16x^2 + 16y^2 = 25 \dots \text{multiply both sides by 16}$$

## Example 2

Find the equation of the circle with centre $(0, 0)$ and which contains the point $(4, -1)$.

The radius of the circle is the distance from $(0, 0)$ to $(4, -1)$.

$\Rightarrow \quad r = \sqrt{(4 - 0)^2 + (-1 - 0)^2}$

$\qquad = \sqrt{16 + 1} = \sqrt{17}$

Equation is $x^2 + y^2 = r^2$

$\qquad \Rightarrow \quad x^2 + y^2 = (\sqrt{17})^2$

$\qquad$ i.e. $x^2 + y^2 = 17$

$\qquad (x_1, y_1) \qquad (x_2, y_2)$
$\qquad \quad \downarrow \qquad\qquad \downarrow$
$\qquad \;\, (0, 0) \qquad (4, -1)$

$(\sqrt{8})^2 = 8$
$(\sqrt{a})^2 = a$

## Finding the radius when given the equation

The circle whose equation is $x^2 + y^2 = r^2$ has centre $(0, 0)$ and radius $= r$.

$\Rightarrow \quad$ the circle $x^2 + y^2 = 16$ has (i) centre at $(0, 0)$ (ii) radius $= \sqrt{16} = 4$

However, if the equation of the circle is $4x^2 + 4y^2 = 9$, first divide each term by 4 so that the equation is in the form $x^2 + y^2 = r^2$.

$\Rightarrow \quad 4x^2 + 4y^2 = 9 \quad \Rightarrow \quad x^2 + y^2 = \dfrac{9}{4}$

$\Rightarrow \quad$ the length of the radius $= \sqrt{\dfrac{9}{4}} = \dfrac{\sqrt{9}}{\sqrt{4}} = \dfrac{3}{2}$

## Example 3

Find the length of the radius of these circles:

(i) $x^2 + y^2 = 8$ 　　　　　　(ii) $9x^2 + 9y^2 = 16$

(i) $x^2 + y^2 = 8$

$\Rightarrow \quad r = \sqrt{8}$

$\qquad = \sqrt{4}.\sqrt{2}$

$\Rightarrow \quad r = 2\sqrt{2}$

(ii) $9x^2 + 9y^2 = 16$

$\Rightarrow \quad x^2 + y^2 = \dfrac{16}{9}$ ... divide both sides by 9

$\Rightarrow \quad r = \sqrt{\dfrac{16}{9}}$

$\Rightarrow \quad r = \dfrac{4}{3}$

## Exercise 6.1

1. Write down the equation of the circle with centre $(0, 0)$ and radius:
   (i) 2 　　　(ii) 3 　　　(iii) 1 　　　(iv) 5 　　　(v) $\sqrt{2}$

2. Write down the equation of the circle with centre $(0, 0)$ and radius:
   (i) $\sqrt{8}$ 　　　(ii) $2\sqrt{2}$ 　　　(iii) $3\sqrt{2}$ 　　　(iv) $\dfrac{2}{3}$ 　　　(v) $\dfrac{4}{3}$

3. Find the distance from $(0, 0)$ to $(-3, 4)$.
   Hence write down the equation of the circle with centre $(0, 0)$ and which contains the point $(-3, 4)$.

**4.** Find the equation of the circle with centre (0, 0) and which passes through the point
   (i)  (2, 3)          (ii)  (−1, 2)          (iii)  (4, −3)          (iv)  (4, 0)

**5.** The given diagram shows two circles $a$ and $b$,
   both with centres (0, 0).
   $a$ contains the point (5, 0).
   $b$ contains the point (3, 0).
     (i)   Write down the equation of circle $a$.
     (ii)   Write down the equation of circle $b$.
    (iii)   Write down the coordinates of the points
           where circle $a$ intersects the $y$-axis.
    (iv)   Write down the coordinates of the points
           where circle $b$ intersects the $x$-axis.

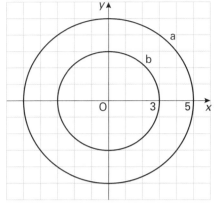

**6.** Draw a sketch of the circle $x^2 + y^2 = 16$.
   Mark on it the coordinates of the points where it crosses the $x$-axis and $y$-axis.

**7.** Express in terms of $\pi$, the area of the circle $x^2 + y^2 = 36$.    Area of circle $= \pi r^2$.

**8.** Write down the radius of each of these circles:
     (i)   $x^2 + y^2 = 9$          (ii)   $x^2 + y^2 = 49$          (iii)   $x^2 + y^2 = 1$
    (iv)   $x^2 + y^2 = 12$          (v)   $x^2 + y^2 = 27$          (vi)   $x^2 + y^2 = 5$

**9.** Express each of the following circles in the form $x^2 + y^2 = k$.
   Hence, write down the length of the radius of each circle:
     (i)   $4x^2 + 4y^2 = 9$          (ii)   $9x^2 + 9y^2 = 25$          (iii)   $4x^2 + 4y^2 = 49$

**10.** The points (4, 3) and (−4, −3) are the end points
   of the diameter of a circle.
   Find (i)   the coordinates of the centre of the circle
        (ii)   the length of the radius
       (iii)   the equation of the circle.

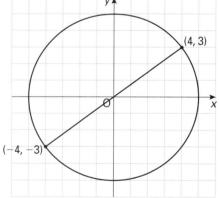

**11.** Find the length of the diameter of the
   circle $x^2 + y^2 = 81$.

**12.** Verify that $(2\sqrt{5})^2 = 20$.
   Hence write down the equation of the circle with centre (0, 0) and radius $= 2\sqrt{5}$.

**13.** Write down the equation of the circle with centre (0, 0) and radius of length
     (i)   $\sqrt{6}$          (ii)   $2\sqrt{6}$          (iii)   $3\sqrt{2}$          (iv)   $2\sqrt{3}$          (v)   $3\sqrt{5}$.

**14.** The equation of a circle, $c$, is $x^2 + y^2 = 9$.
   Find the equation of the circle, $d$, with centre (0, 0) and radius equal in length to the
   diameter of $c$.

# SECTION 6.2 Points and Circles

A given point may be inside, on or outside a circle.

  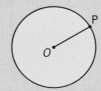  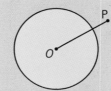

| A point P is **inside** a circle if the distance from the centre of the circle to the point P is **less** than the radius. | A point P is **on a circle** if the distance from the centre of the circle to the point P is **equal** to the radius. | A point P is **outside** a circle if the distance from the centre of the circle to the point P is **greater than** the radius. |

## Example 1

Are the points
   (i)   (1, −3) and (ii) (3, −2) inside, outside or on the circle $x^2 + y^2 = 13$?

The length of the radius of the circle is $\sqrt{13}$.
   (i)   The distance from the centre (0, 0) to (1, −3) is
$$\sqrt{(1 - 0)^2 + (-3 - 0)^2} = \sqrt{1 + 9} = \sqrt{10}$$
   Since $\sqrt{10} < \sqrt{13} \Rightarrow (1, -3)$ is inside the circle.
   (ii)  The distance from (0, 0) to (3, −2) is
$$\sqrt{(3 - 0)^2 + (-2 - 0)^2} = \sqrt{9 + 4} = \sqrt{13}$$
   Since $\sqrt{13}$ is equal to the length of the radius of the circle,
   $\Rightarrow (3, -2)$ is on the circle.

## Another method

Another method of determining whether a point is inside, on or outside a circle is to substitute the coordinates of the point into the given equation of the circle.

> If $x^2 + y^2 < r^2$, the point is **inside** the circle.
> If $x^2 + y^2 = r^2$, the point is **on** the circle.
> If $x^2 + y^2 > r^2$, the point is **outside** the circle.

## Example 2

Investigate if the point (−3, 4) is inside, on or outside the circle $x^2 + y^2 = 16$.

Substituting −3 for $x$ and 4 for $y$ in the equation $x^2 + y^2 = 16$, we get
   $(-3)^2 + 4^2 : 16$
   $9 + 16 > 16$
   i.e.   $25 > 16$ ... (greater than $r^2$)
   $\therefore$  (−3, 4) is outside the circle.

## Exercise 6.2

1.  (i)   Show that the point $(3, -1)$ is on the circle $x^2 + y^2 = 10$.
    (ii)  Show that the point $(5, -1)$ is outside the circle $x^2 + y^2 = 20$.
    (iii) Show that the point $(1, 2)$ is inside the circle $x^2 + y^2 = 8$.

2.  Investigate whether the point $(3, 2)$ is inside, on or outside the circle $x^2 + y^2 = 10$.

3.  Verify that the point $(3, 4)$ is on the circle $x^2 + y^2 = 25$.
    Write down the coordinates of the four points at which this circle intersects the $x$-axis and $y$-axis.

4.  Show that the following points are on the given circles:
    (i)   $(2, 1)$:    $x^2 + y^2 = 5$           (ii)   $(-2, 5)$:    $x^2 + y^2 = 29$
    (iii) $(-4, 0)$: $x^2 + y^2 = 16$       (iv)   $(\sqrt{5}, \sqrt{5})$: $x^2 + y^2 = 10$

5.  Investigate if each of the following points is inside, outside or on the given circle:
    (i)   $(1, -4)$: $x^2 + y^2 = 16$       (ii)   $(-2, 3)$:    $x^2 + y^2 = 13$
    (iii) $(-5, 2)$: $x^2 + y^2 = 26$      (iv)   $(-3, 1)$:    $x^2 + y^2 = 12$

6.  Which one of the following points is outside the circle $x^2 + y^2 = 34$?
    (i)   $(5, -2)$              (ii)   $(-5, 3)$             (iii)   $(-4, 5)$

7.  Draw a sketch of the circle $x^2 + y^2 = 16$.
    The circle intersects the $y$-axis at the points P and Q.
    (i)   Find the coordinates of P and Q.     (ii)   Find $|PQ|$.

8.  $x^2 + y^2 = 18$.
    The point $(4, k)$ is outside the circle. Find the least value of $k$, if $k \in N$.

## SECTION 6.3

# The equation of a circle with centre $(h, k)$ and radius $r$

The diagram on the right shows a circle with centre $C(h, k)$ and radius $r$.

Let $P(x, y)$ be any point on the circle.
The distance from C to P is equal to the radius.

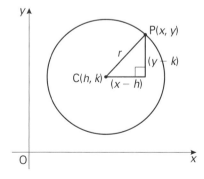

Using the distance formula we have:

$|CP| = \sqrt{(x - h)^2 + (y - k)^2} = r$

$\Rightarrow (x - h)^2 + (y - k)^2 = r^2$

This is the equation of the circle of centre $(h, k)$ and radius $r$.

To use the formula above to find the equation of a circle, we need
(i)   the centre of the circle, $(h, k)$
(ii)  the radius of the circle, $r$.

> The equation of the circle with centre $(h, k)$ and radius $r$ is
> $$(x - h)^2 + (y - k)^2 = r^2.$$

## Example 1

Find the equation of the circle with centre $(2, -3)$ and radius 5.

The equation is

$(h, k) \qquad r = 5$
$\downarrow$
$(2, -3)$

$(x - h)^2 + (y - k)^2 = r^2$

$\Rightarrow \ (x - 2)^2 + (y + 3)^2 = (5)^2$

$\Rightarrow \ (x - 2)^2 + (y + 3)^2 = 25$ is the equation

## Finding the centre and radius when given the equation

In the equation $(x - h)^2 + (y - k)^2 = r^2$, centre $= (h, k)$ and radius $= r$.

In the equation $(x - 2)^2 + (y + 3)^2 = 16$,

we can see that $h = 2$ and $k = -3$;   also $r = \sqrt{16} = 4$.

$\Rightarrow$   centre $= (2, -3)$ and radius $= 4$.

## Example 2

Find the centre and radius of the circle $(x + 3)^2 + (y - 4)^2 = 8$.

Comparing the equations  $(x - h)^2 + (y - k)^2 = r^2$

and  $(x + 3)^2 + (y - 4)^2 = 8$

we have $h = -3$, $k = 4$ and $r^2 = 8$

$\Rightarrow \ r = \sqrt{8}$

$\therefore$   the centre $= (-3, 4)$ and radius $= \sqrt{8}$

## Example 3

The circle with centre $(1, 3)$ passes through the point $(3, 5)$.
Find the equation of the circle.

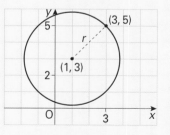

The radius is the distance from $(1, 3)$ to $(3, 5)$.

Radius $= \sqrt{(x_2 - x_1)^2 + (y_2 - y_1)^2}$

$= \sqrt{(3 - 1)^2 + (5 - 3)^2}$

$= \sqrt{4 + 4} = \sqrt{8}$

Equation of circle is: $(x - h)^2 + (y - k)^2 = r^2$

$(h, k) \qquad r = \sqrt{8}$
$\downarrow$
$(1, 3)$

$\Rightarrow \ (x - 1)^2 + (y - 3)^2 = (\sqrt{8})^2$

$\Rightarrow \ (x - 1)^2 + (y - 3)^2 = 8$

# Exercise 6.3

1. Find the equations of the following circles, given the centre and radius in each case:
   (i)   centre = (3, 1); radius = 2
   (ii)  centre = (3, 4); radius = 3
   (iii) centre = (1, −4); radius = 5
   (iv)  centre = (−3, 5); radius = 4
   (v)   centre = (−3, −2); radius = 1
   (vi)  centre = (3, 0); radius = 6
   (vii) centre = (−3, −5); radius = $\sqrt{10}$
   (viii) centre = (0, −2); radius = $2\sqrt{2}$

2. The centre of a circle is (2, 4) and it contains the point (−1, 3).
   Find   (i)  the length of the radius      (ii)  the equation of the circle.

3. Find the equation of the circle which passes through the point (−1, 5) and whose centre is (5, −2).

4. The given circle has centre (2, 2).
   If the circle contains the point (5, 1),
   find its equation.

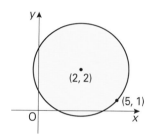

5. The line segment joining (3, 5) and (−1, 1) is the diameter of a circle.
   Find (i)   the centre of the circle
        (ii)  the length of the radius of the circle
        (iii) the equation of the circle.

Find the centre and radius of each of the following circles:

6. $(x − 2)^2 + (y − 3)^2 = 16$

7. $(x − 4)^2 + (y + 3)^2 = 9$

8. $(x + 2)^2 + (y + 5)^2 = 64$

9. $(x + 5)^2 + (y − 1)^2 = 81$

10. $x^2 + (y − 4)^2 = 25$

11. $(x − 3)^2 + y^2 = 9$

12. $(x − 1)^2 + (y + 5)^2 = \frac{16}{9}$

12. $x^2 + (y − 2)^2 = 12$

14. The given circle touches both the x-axis and y-axis.
    If the radius of the circle is 3, write down the coordinates
    of C, the centre.
    Hence write down the equation of the circle.

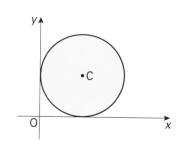

**15.** The diagram shows two circles $C_1$ and $C_2$.
The centre of $C_1$ is on the $x$-axis and its radius is 4.

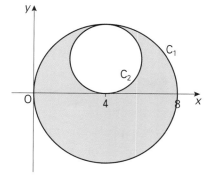

  (i)   Write down the coordinates of the centre of $C_1$.
  (ii)  Write down the equation of $C_1$.
  (iii)  What is the length of the radius of $C_2$.
  (iv)  Find the coordinates of the centre of $C_2$.
  (v)   Write down the equation of $C_2$.
  (vi)  Write down the coordinates of the point that is
       common to $C_1$ and $C_2$.

**16.** The diagram shows four circles of equal radius length.
The circles are touching as shown.
The equation of $k_1$ is $x^2 + y^2 = 4$.

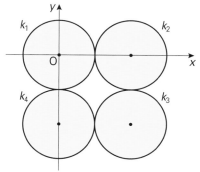

  (i)   Write down the radius of $k_1$.
  (ii)  Write down the coordinates of the centre of $k_3$.
  (iii)  Write down the equation of $k_3$.
  (iv)  Is $x^2 + (y + 4)^2 = 4$ the equation of $k_2$ or $k_4$?
       Explain your answer.

**17.** A$(-1, 2)$ and B$(5, 4)$ are the end points of the diameter of a circle $k$.
Find the coordinates of the centre of $k$ and hence write down its equation.

**18.** The point $(4, 3)$ is the centre of a circle $c$. If the $x$-axis is a tangent to $c$ find
  (i)   the length of the radius of $c$       (ii)  the equation of $c$.

**19.** The given diagram shows four semicircles.
The centres all lie on the $x$-axis.
The radius length of the three smaller semicircles is 2.

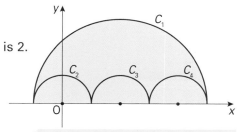

  (i)   Find the coordinates of the centre of $C_3$.
  (ii)  Write down the equation of $C_3$.
  (iii)  Find the equation of $C_1$.
  (iv)  Investigate whether the circumference
       of the semicircle $C_1$ is equal to the
       sum of the circumferences of the
       three smaller semicircles.

> You are finding the equation
> of the full circle in each case.

**20.** The diagram shows three semicircles $C_1$, $C_2$ and $C_3$.
Each semicircle has radius length 1 unit.
The centres of the circles are P, Q and R, as shown.

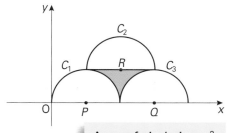

  (i)   Write down the equation of the circle, $C_1$.
  (ii)  Write down the coordinates of R.
  (iii)  Find the equation of the circle, $C_2$.
  (iv)  Express in terms of $\pi$ the area of
       the shaded region in the diagram.

> Area of circle is $\pi r^2$.

# SECTION 6.4 Intersection of a line and a circle

The diagram on the right shows a line $\ell$ intersecting a circle at the points A and B.

The line $t$ intersects the circle at one point only. This line is said to be a **tangent** to the circle.

To find the point(s) of intersection of a line and circle, we express the line in the form

$$y = \ldots \qquad \text{or} \qquad x = \ldots$$

When selecting $y = \ldots$ or $x = \ldots$, avoid fractions if possible.

We then use simultaneous equations to find the point(s) of intersection of the line and circle.

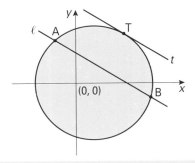

If a line is a tangent to a circle, it will intersect the circle at one point only.

---

### Example 1

Find the points of intersection of the line $x + 3y - 5 = 0$ and the circle $x^2 + y^2 = 5$.

**Step 1**  Express $x$ in terms of $y$ in the equation of the line.
$$x + 3y - 5 = 0 \quad \Rightarrow \quad x = -3y + 5 \ldots \text{①}$$

**Step 2**  Substitute $(-3y + 5)$ for $x$ in the equation of the circle.
$$\Rightarrow \quad x^2 + y^2 = 5 \text{ now becomes}$$
$$(-3y + 5)^2 + y^2 = 5$$
$$\Rightarrow \quad 9y^2 - 30y + 25 + y^2 = 5$$
$$\Rightarrow \quad 10y^2 - 30y + 20 = 0$$
$$\Rightarrow \quad y^2 - 3y + 2 = 0 \ldots \text{ divide each term by 10.}$$
$$\Rightarrow \quad (y - 2)(y - 1) = 0$$
$$\Rightarrow \quad y = 2 \text{ or } y = 1$$

Substituting these values for $y$ in equation ① we get:
$$y = 2 \Rightarrow x = -3(2) + 5 \Rightarrow x = -1 \qquad \text{i.e. the point } (-1, 2)$$
$$y = 1 \Rightarrow x = -3(1) + 5 \Rightarrow x = 2 \qquad \text{i.e. the point } (2, 1)$$

Thus the two points of intersection are $(-1, 2)$ and $(2, 1)$.

---

### Example 2

Show that the line $3x + y + 10 = 0$ is a tangent to the circle $x^2 + y^2 = 10$ and find the point of contact.

Here we express $y$ in terms of $x$ to avoid fractions.

If $3x + y + 10 = 0 \Rightarrow y = -3x - 10 \ldots \text{①}$

Substituting $(-3x - 10)$ for $y$ in the equation of the circle we get:
$$x^2 + (-3x - 10)^2 = 10$$
$$\Rightarrow \quad x^2 + 9x^2 + 60x + 100 = 10$$
$$\Rightarrow \quad 10x^2 + 60x + 90 = 0$$
$$\Rightarrow \quad x^2 + 6x + 9 = 0 \ldots \quad \text{divide each term by 10}$$
$$\Rightarrow \quad (x + 3)(x + 3) = 0$$
$$\Rightarrow \quad x = -3 \ldots \quad \text{notice that there is only one value for } x$$

We now substitute $-3$ for $x$ in equation ①

$$x = -3 \Rightarrow y = -3(-3) - 10$$
$$= 9 - 10 = -1 \qquad \text{i.e. the point } (-3, -1)$$

Therefore the point of intersection is $(-3, -1)$.

Since there is only one point of contact, the line is a tangent to the circle.

## Exercise 6.4

1. Find the points of intersection of the line $\ell$ and the circle $c$ in each of the following:
   (i) $\ell: x - y = 1$;          $c: x^2 + y^2 = 13$
   (ii) $\ell: x + y - 4 = 0$;     $c: x^2 + y^2 = 10$
   (iii) $\ell: x - 2y - 5 = 0$;   $c: x^2 + y^2 = 25$
   (iv) $\ell: x + 3y - 10 = 0$;   $c: x^2 + y^2 = 20$

2. Find the point of intersection of the line $2x - y - 5 = 0$ and the circle $x^2 + y^2 = 5$.

3. Show that the line $\ell$ is a tangent to the circle $k$ in each of the following.
   Find the point of contact in each case:
   (i) $\ell: x + y - 2 = 0$;      $k: x^2 + y^2 = 2$
   (ii) $\ell: x - 3y - 10 = 0$;   $k: x^2 + y^2 = 10$
   (iii) $\ell: x - y - 4 = 0$;      $k: x^2 + y^2 = 8$

4. Find the point(s) of intersection of the line $x - y - 3 = 0$ and the circle $x^2 + y^2 = 9$.
   Is the line a tangent to the circle? Explain your answer.

5. Find the points of intersection of the line $x - 2y = 0$ and $x^2 + y^2 = 20$.

6. Find the equation of the circle of centre $(0, 0)$ and which contains the point $(3, 1)$.
   Find the coordinates of the points of intersection of this circle and the line $x + y + 4 = 0$.

7. $A(4, -1)$ and $B(-1, 4)$ are two points.
   Find the equation of AB.
   Now find the coordinates of the points of intersection of the line AB and the circle $x^2 + y^2 = 5$.

8. Show that the line $x - 2y + 10 = 0$ is a tangent to the circle $x^2 + y^2 = 20$ by finding the point of contact.

9. The diagram shows a circle of centre C and radius length 3.
   The circle touches the $x$-axis and $y$-axis.
   (i) Write down the coordinates of C.
   (ii) Write down the equation of the circle.
   (iii) The line $t_1$ is a tangent to the circle and is parallel to the $x$-axis. Write down the equation of $t_1$.
   (iv) The line $t_2$ is also a tangent to the circle and is parallel to the $y$-axis. Find the equation of $t_2$.
   (v) Write down the coordinates of the point of intersection of $t_1$ and $t_2$.

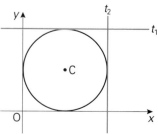

# SECTION 6.5  A circle intersecting the axes

The circle shown intersects the x-axis at $(-1, 0)$ and $(4, 0)$.

In each of the points, the y-value is zero.

In general, when any line or circle intersects the x-axis, the y-values of the points of intersection will be zero.

Similarly, a line or circle intersects the y-axis at the points where $x = 0$.

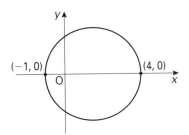

---

### Example 1

Find the coordinates of the points at which
  (i)   the circle $x^2 + y^2 = 16$ intersects the x-axis
  (ii)  the circle $(x + 3)^2 + (y - 2)^2 = 10$ intersects the y-axis.

(i)  $x^2 + y^2 = 16$ intersects the x-axis at the points where $y = 0$.

$$y = 0 \Rightarrow x^2 + 0 = 16$$
$$\Rightarrow x^2 = 16 \Rightarrow x = \pm 4$$
$$\Rightarrow x^2 + y^2 = 16 \text{ intersects the x-axis at } (4, 0) \text{ and } (-4, 0).$$

(ii)  $(x + 3)^2 + (y - 2)^2 = 10$ intersects the y-axis at the points where $x = 0$.

$$x = 0 \Rightarrow (0 + 3)^2 + (y - 2)^2 = 10$$
$$\Rightarrow \quad 9 + y^2 - 4y + 4 = 10$$
$$\Rightarrow \qquad y^2 - 4y + 3 = 0$$
$$\Rightarrow \qquad (y - 1)(y - 3) = 0$$
$$\Rightarrow \qquad y = 1 \quad \text{or} \quad y = 3$$
$$\Rightarrow \quad (x + 3)^2 + (y - 2)^2 = 10 \text{ intersects the y-axis at } (0, 1) \text{ and } (0, 3).$$

---

## Exercise 6.5

1. Find the coordinates of the points where each of these circles intersect the x-axis:
   (i)  $x^2 + y^2 = 4$      (ii)  $x^2 + y^2 = 25$      (iii)  $x^2 + y^2 = 81$.

2. Find the coordinates of the points where the circle $x^2 + y^2 = 49$ intersects the y-axis.

3. Find the coordinates of the points where each of these circles intersect the x-axis:
   (i)  $(x - 5)^2 + (y + 4)^2 = 25$      (ii)  $(x - 2)^2 + (y - 3)^2 = 25$

4. Find the coordinates of the points where the circle $(x - 2)^2 + (y + 3)^2 = 20$ intersects the y-axis.

5. Show that the point $(3, 2)$ is on the circle $(x - 6)^2 + (y - 6)^2 = 25$.

6. Write down the centre and radius length of the circle
   $$(x + 4)^2 + (y - 1)^2 = 9$$
   Now show that the point $(-3, 0)$ is inside the circle.

**7.** Investigate if the point $(3, 2)$ is inside, on or outside the circle
$$(x - 2)^2 + (y + 1)^2 = 4.$$

**8.** The end points of a diameter of a circle are $(-2, -3)$ and $(-4, 3)$.
Find the equation of the circle.
The circle cuts the $y$-axis at the points A and B.
Find $|AB|$.

**9.** The $x$-axis is a tangent to the circle with centre $(-2, 4)$.
   (i)   What is the length of the radius of the circle?
   (ii)  Write down the equation of the circle.

# TEST YOURSELF 6

**1.** The circle $c$ has equation $x^2 + y^2 = 49$.
   (i)   Write down the centre and radius of $c$.
   (ii)  Verify that the point $(5, -5)$ is outside the circle $c$.

**2.** A circle $k$ has centre $(0, 0)$ and it contains the point $(3, 4)$.
Find the equation of $k$.
Now write down the coordinates of the points where the circle $k$ intersects the $x$-axis.

**3.** The circle $c$ has equation $x^2 + y^2 = 36$.
   (i)   Write down the length of the radius of $c$.
   (ii)  Another circle has centre $(0, 0)$ and a radius that is twice the length of the radius of $c$.
         Write down the equation of this circle.

**4.** Find the equation of the circle with centre $(2, -3)$ and radius 4.

**5.** The equation of the circle $c$ is $(x - 3)^2 + (y - 4)^2 = 25$.
   (i)   Write down the centre and radius length of $c$.
   (ii)  Show that the point $(6, 0)$ lies on the circle $c$.

**6.** Show that the line $x - 3y = 10$ is a tangent to the circle $x^2 + y^2 = 10$ by finding the point of intersection.

**7.** The equation of a circle is $x^2 + y^2 = 36$.
   (i)   Find the length of the radius of the circle.
   (ii)  Show, by calculation, that the point $(7, 1)$ is outside the circle.
   (iii) Find the coordinates of the points where the circle intersects the $y$-axis.

**8.** The diagram on the right shows three circles a, b and c
with centres A, O and C respectively on the *x*-axis.
The radius of circle a and the radius of circle
c are both equal to the diameter of circle b.
Circles a and c touch circle b, as shown.
If the equation of b is $x^2 + y^2 = 9$, find

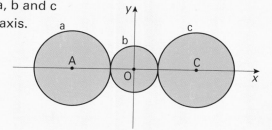

   (i)   the coordinates of A and C.

   (ii)  the equations of the circles a and c

  (iii)  the equations of the two tangents common to a and c but which do not touch b.

**9.** The line $y = 10 - 2x$ intersects the circle $x^2 + y^2 = 40$ at the points A and B.

   (i)  Find the coordinates of A and the coordinates of B.

  (ii)  Show the line, the circle and the points of intersection on a coordinate diagram.

**10.** The points $(-1, -1)$ and $(3, -3)$ are the end points of a diameter of a circle, *s*.

   (i)  Find the centre and radius length of *s*.

  (ii)  Find the equation of *s*.

  (iii)  Show, by calculation, that the point $(1, -1)$ lies inside the circle.

**11.** $A(-1, 0)$ and $B(5, 0)$ are the end points of a diameter of the
circle *k* with C as centre, as shown.

   (i)  Write down the coordinates of C and the radius
length of *k*.

  (ii)  Find the equation of *k*.

  (iii)  The lines $t_1$ and $t_2$ are tangents to the circle *k* and are
parallel to the *x*-axis.
Write down the equations of $t_1$ and $t_2$.

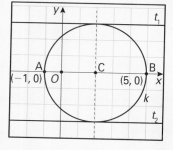

**12.** The line $x - 3y = 0$ intersects the circle $x^2 + y^2 = 10$ at the points A and B.

   (i)  Find the coordinates of A and the coordinates of B.

  (ii)  Show that [AB] is a diameter of the circle.

**13.** Write down the centre and radius length of the circle
$$(x - 3)^2 + (y - 4)^2 = 20.$$
The circle intersects the *x*-axis at A and B.
Find the coordinates of A and B.
Hence write down |AB|.

**14.** $A(0, -1)$ and $B(8, -1)$ is a diameter of a circle,
as shown.

   (i)  Find the centre and radius length of the circle.

  (ii)  Write down the equation of the circle.

The line $\ell$ intersects the circle at A and E.

The slope of $\ell$ is $-\frac{4}{5}$.

  (iii)  Write down the slope of EB.
Explain your answer.

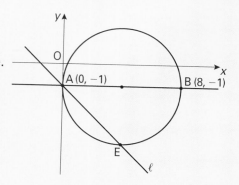

15. The circle $k$ has equation $(x + 2)^2 + (y - 3)^2 = 25$.
    P and Q are the endpoints of a diameter of $k$ and PQ is horizontal.
    (i) Write down the coordinates of the centre of $k$ and its radius length.
    (ii) Draw a sketch of $k$ on the coordinate plane.
    (iii) Find the coordinates of P and the coordinates of Q.
    (iv) Write down the equations of two vertical tangents to $k$.
    (v) Another circle also has these two vertical lines as tangents.
        The centre of this circle is on the $x$-axis.
        Find the equation of this circle.

16. A circle has equation $x^2 + y^2 = 13$.
    The points A(2, −3), B(−2, 3) and C(3, 2) are on the circle.
    (i) Verify that [AB] is a diameter of the circle.
    (ii) Verify that $|\angle ACB|$ is a right angle.

17. In the given diagram $k_1$ is the circle of centre A(0, 2) and radius 2.
    $k_2$ is the circle of centre B(0, −2) and radius 2.
    Write down the equations of $k_1$ and $k_2$.
    $k_3$ is the circle of centre (0, 0) which touches $k_1$ at C
    and $k_2$ at D.
    Write down the equation of $k_3$.
    Write down also the equation of the tangent
    common to $k_1$ and $k_3$ at the point C.

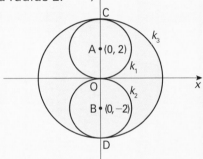

18. The circle $k$ has equation $(x + 4)^2 + (y - 3)^2 = 36$.
    (i) Write down the coordinates of the centre of $k$ and its radius length.
    (ii) Draw a sketch of $k$ on a coordinate plane.
    (iii) The point (2, 3) is one end-point of a diameter of $k$.
         Find the coordinates of the other end-point.

19. $c$ is the circle with centre (−1, 2) and radius 5.
    Write down the equation of $c$.
    The circle $k$ has equation $(x - 8)^2 + (y - 14)^2 = 100$.
    Show that P(2, 6) is on the circle $k$.
    Show also that P(2, 6) is on the line which joins the centres of the two circles.

# Summary of key points

## The equation of a circle

The equation of the circle with centre $(0, 0)$ and radius $r$ is

$$x^2 + y^2 = r^2$$

The equation of the circle with centre $(h, k)$ and radius $r$ is

$$(x - h)^2 + (y - k)^2 = r^2$$

## Finding the centre and radius from the equation

For the circle $x^2 + y^2 = a^2$, centre $= (0, 0)$, radius $= a$.

For the circle $(x - h)^2 + (y - k)^2 = a^2$, centre $= (h, k)$, radius $= a$.

## Points and circles

Point inside if
$|OP| <$ radius

Point on if
$|OP| =$ radius

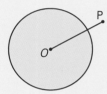

Point outside if
$|OP| >$ radius

## Intersection of a line and a circle

Simultaneous equations are used to find the point(s) of intersection of a line and a circle.

To find the points of intersection of the line $x + 3y - 5 = 0$ and the circle $x^2 + y^2 = 5$,

(i)   express $x$ in terms of $y$ in the equation of the line,

      i.e.   $x = -3y + 5$

(ii)  substitute this value for $x$ into the equation of the circle,

      i.e.   $(-3y + 5)^2 + y^2 = 5$

(iii) solve this equation to find two values for $y$

(iv)  find the two corresponding values for $x$.

## A circle intersecting axes

A circle intersects the $x$-axis at the points where $y = 0$.

A circle intersects the $y$-axis at the points where $x = 0$.

## Proving a line is a tangent to a circle

A line is a tangent to a circle if there is only one point of intersection.

## Key Words

| | | | | |
|---|---|---|---|---|
| **Pythagoras** | **right-angled triangle** | **sine** | **cosine** | **tangent** |
| **opposite side** | **adjacent side** | **hypotenuse** | **sine rule** | **cosine rule** |
| **compass** | **sector** **arc** | **quadrants** | **reference angle** | **surd form** |

## SECTION 7.1   The Theorem of Pythagoras

The given figure shows a right-angled triangle.

The side opposite the right angle is called the **hypotenuse**.

A Greek mathematician named Pythagoras is credited with the proof of a very important theorem involving right-angled triangles.

It is known as the **Theorem of Pythagoras** and is given below.

**Theorem of Pythagoras**
In a right-angled triangle, the area of the square drawn on the hypotenuse is equal to the sum of the squares on the other two sides.

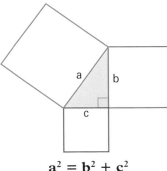

$$a^2 = b^2 + c^2$$

### Example 1

Find the length of the side marked $x$ in this right-angled triangle.

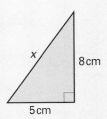

$x^2 = 8^2 + 5^2$
$x^2 = 64 + 25$
$x^2 = 89$
$x = \sqrt{89}$
$x = 9.4\,\text{cm}$

## Exercise 7.1

1. The area of square A is 23 cm² and the area of square C is 35 cm².
   Find the area of square B.

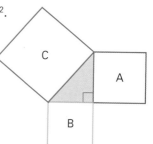

2. Use the figure in Question 1 to find the area of square C if square A is 17 cm² and square B is 14 cm².

3. Three squares have areas of 18 cm², 21 cm² and 39 cm².
   Will the squares fit exactly along the sides of a right-angled triangle?
   Explain your answer.

4. Calculate the length of the side marked with a letter in each of the following triangles:
   (Give answer correct to one decimal place where necessary.)

   (i)

   *a*  3 cm
   2 cm

   (ii)

   *b*  11 cm
   6 cm

   (iii)

   9 cm
   3 cm  *c*

   (iv)

   *d*
   6 cm  4 cm

   (v)

   *e*  12 cm
   9 cm

   (vi)

   *f*  13 cm
   5 cm

   (vii)

   9 cm  *g*
   13 cm

   (viii)

   5.2 cm
   3.8 cm  *h*

   (ix)

   14 cm
   10.8 cm  *i*

5. A rectangle is 10 cm long and 8 cm wide.
   Calculate the length of the diagonal.
   Give your answer in centimetres correct to one decimal place.

   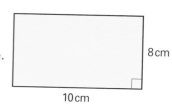

   8 cm

   10 cm

**6.** Use the given grid to write down the lengths of [PR] and [QR].
Hence find the length of [PQ], correct to one decimal place.

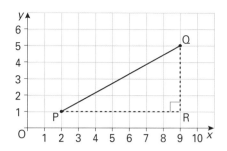

**7.** A golf flag casts a shadow 3 m long.
If the distance from the top of the flag pole to the end of the shadow is 4 m, find the height, f, in metres, correct to one decimal place.

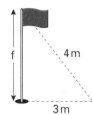

**8.** In the given figure, $|AB| = 10$ cm, $|AD| = 5$ cm and $|DC| = 6$ cm.
The angles at A and D are right angles.
Find the length of [BC].

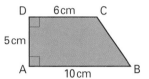

**9.** The diagram shows a right-angled triangle ABC.
   (i)   Find the length of [BD].
   (ii)   Find the length [AD] in centimetres, correct to one decimal place.

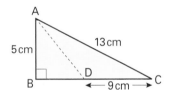

**10.** In the given figure the two right angles are marked.
Find the lengths of $c$ and $d$.

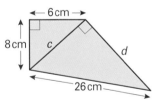

**11.** The diagram shows a horizontal shelf [AB].
The shelf is fixed to a vertical wall at A.
The support [CD] is fixed to the wall at C and to the shelf at D.
$|AB| = 23$ cm, $|AC| = 20$ cm and $|BD| = 8$ cm.
Calculate the length of [CD].

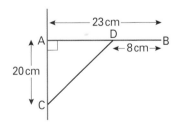

**12.** Find the missing dimension to work out the perimeter of the room shown.
Give your answer in metres, correct to one decimal place.

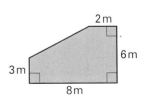

# SECTION 7.2  Sine, Cosine and Tangent ratios

One of the most common uses of trigonometry is in working out lengths and angles in right-angled triangles. Three very special ratios connecting angles and sides are given below.

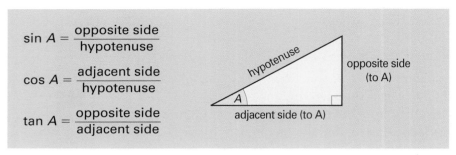

$$\sin A = \frac{\text{opposite side}}{\text{hypotenuse}}$$

$$\cos A = \frac{\text{adjacent side}}{\text{hypotenuse}}$$

$$\tan A = \frac{\text{opposite side}}{\text{adjacent side}}$$

A useful memory aid is SOHCAHTOA

If we are given $\cos A = \frac{3}{4}$, we can draw a sketch of a right-angled triangle in which the side adjacent to $A$ is 3 and the hypotenuse is 4.

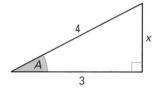

We now find the third side by using the Theorem of Pythagoras.

Let the third side $= x$.
$$x^2 + 3^2 = 4^2$$
$$x^2 + 9 = 16$$
$$x^2 = 7$$
$$x = \sqrt{7}$$

---

### Example 1

If $\tan B = \frac{\sqrt{5}}{2}$, find the value of $\sin B$ and $\cos B$.

$\tan B = \frac{\sqrt{5}}{2} \Rightarrow$ opposite side to $B$ is $\sqrt{5}$ and adjacent side is 2.

Now draw a rough sketch of a right-angled triangle.
Let $x$ be the length of the hypotenuse.

$$x^2 = 2^2 + (\sqrt{5})^2 \ldots (\sqrt{5})^2 = 5$$
$$x^2 = 4 + 5$$
$$x^2 = 9 \Rightarrow x = 3$$

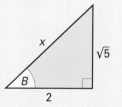

From the triangle: $\sin B = \frac{\sqrt{5}}{3}$  and  $\cos B = \frac{2}{3}$.

---

## Exercise 7.2

1.  In the given triangle, state which of the ratios sine, cosine or tangent
    (i)   connects 3, 4 and the angle A
    (ii)  connects 4, 5 and the angle A
    (iii) connects 3, 5 and the angle A.

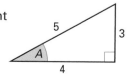

2. Find the sin, cos and tan of the angle marked with a capital letter in each of the following triangles:

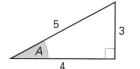 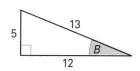 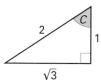

3. Find the length of the side marked $x$ in the given right-angled triangle. Hence write down the value of
   (i)   sin $A$
   (ii)   cos $A$
   (iii)   tan $A$.

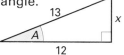

4. Find the value of $a$ in the given right-angled triangle. Hence write down the value of
   (i)   sin $B$
   (ii)   cos $B$
   (iii)   tan $B$.

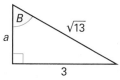

5. The angle $\theta$ and three sides of a right-angled triangle are shown in the given diagram.
   State whether each of these ratios represent sin $\theta$, cos $\theta$ or tan $\theta$.
   (i)   $\dfrac{4}{5}$
   (ii)   $\dfrac{4}{\sqrt{41}}$
   (iii)   $\dfrac{5}{\sqrt{41}}$.

6. Given that cos $B = \frac{5}{13}$, draw a rough sketch of a right-angled triangle and use it to write down the ratios, sin $B$ and tan $B$.

7. (i) If tan $A = \frac{1}{2}$, find sin $A$.          (ii)   If cos $B = \frac{2}{5}$, find tan $B$.

8. If tan $C = \dfrac{1}{\sqrt{3}}$, find the values of sin $C$ and cos $C$.

9. If tan $A = \frac{3}{4}$, find the value of (sin² $A$ + cos² $A$).

10. From the given triangle, write down the value of
    (i)   sin² $A$ + cos² $A$                    (ii)   sin² $B$ + cos² $B$.
    If you have done your calculations correctly, you have verified a very important fact about any angle, i.e.,

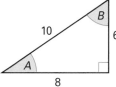

sin² $A$ + cos² $A$ = 1.

# SECTION 7.3  Using a calculator

We use the ⌨sin , ⌨cos and ⌨tan keys on an electronic calculator to find the sine, cosine and tangent of any angle.

To find sin 35°, key in ⌨sin 35 ⌨= .

The result is 0.573576... = 0.5736, correct to 4 decimal places.

## Parts of a degree

A degree can be divided into 60 parts.

$$1° = 60'$$

Each part is called 1 **minute**, written $1'$.

To find tan 34.5° or 34°30′ on your calculator, you may use either of these methods

Thus 34.5° = 34°30′.

**1.** For tan 34.5°

key in [ tan ] 34.5 [ = ]

Result = 0.6873

**2.** For tan 34°30′

key in [ tan ] 34 [ °‚‚‚ ] 30 [ °‚‚‚ ] [ = ]

Result = 0.6873

## Using the [ sin⁻¹ ] [ cos⁻¹ ] and [ tan⁻¹ ] keys

If we are given that sin $A$ = 0.8661, we can find the angle $A$ by using the [ sin⁻¹ ] key.

The [ sin⁻¹ ] key is got by keying in [ SHIFT ] [ sin ].

Thus if sin $A$ = 0.8661, we find $A$ by keying in [ SHIFT ] [ sin ] 0.8661 [ = ].

The result is 60.008° = 60°.

Similarly, if tan $B$ = 1.2734, we find the angle $B$ by keying in [ SHIFT ] [ tan ] 1.2734 [ = ].

The result is 51.86°… correct to 2 decimal places.

---

### Example 1

(i)   Find cos 72°18′, correct to 4 decimal places.
(ii)  If sin $A$ = 0.5216, find $A$ correct to the nearest degree.

Notice that the [ °‚‚‚ ] key is used twice.

(i)   To find cos 72°18′, key in [ cos ] 72 [ °‚‚‚ ] 18 [ °‚‚‚ ] [ = ]

The result is 0.3040.

$$\text{Or } 18' = \frac{18°}{60} = 0.3° \Rightarrow 72°18' = 72.3°$$

Thus to find 72.3°, key in [ cos ] 72.3 [ = ]

(ii)  If sin $A$ = 0.5216, we find $A$ by keying in

[ SHIFT ] [ sin ] 0.5216 [ = ]

The result is 31.44°.   $\Rightarrow$   $A$ = 31°, to the nearest degree.

---

**Note:** If you are given sin $A = \frac{4}{7}$, you can find the angle $A$ by keying in

[ SHIFT ] [ sin ] 4 [ ÷ ] 7 [ = ]

The result is 34.8°.

## Exercise 7.3

**1.** Use your calculator to evaluate each of the following, correct to 4 decimal places:

(i)   sin 48°     (ii)   cos 74°     (iii)   tan 15°     (iv)   sin 72°     (v)   cos 28.5°.

**2.** Use your calculator to evaluate the following, correct to 4 decimal places:

    (i)  sin 32°18′      (ii)  cos 43°24′      (iii)  tan 30°36′      (iv)  cos 73°54′

**3.** Use your calculator to find the measure of each of these angles, correct to the nearest degree:

    (i)  sin $A = 0.7453$      (ii)  cos $B = 0.3521$      (iii)  tan $C = 1.4538$

    (iv)  cos $A = 0.2154$      (v)  tan $B = 0.8923$      (vi)  sin $C = 0.2132$

**4.** Find the value of $A$ in each of the following.

Give your answer in degrees, correct to one decimal place.

    (i)  sin $A = 0.6$                     (ii)  cos $A = 0.7534$

    (iii)  tan $A = 3.84$               (iv)  cos $A = 0.2715$

**5.** Find the measure of the angle $\theta$, correct to the nearest degree in each of the following:

    (i)  sin $\theta = \frac{2}{3}$      (ii)  cos $\theta = \frac{3}{5}$      (iii)  tan $\theta = \frac{7}{8}$      (iv)  sin $\theta = \frac{2}{5}$

    (v)  tan $\theta = \frac{6}{11}$      (vi)  sin $\theta = \frac{1}{5}$      (vii)  cos $\theta = \frac{9}{11}$      (viii)  tan $\theta = 1\frac{3}{5}$

**6.** If cos $A = 0.5484$ and $A < 90°$, find $A$ and hence find the value of sin $A$, correct to 2 decimal places.

**7.** Find, correct to the nearest degree, the size of the angles marked $A$, $B$ and $C$ in the triangles below:

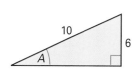  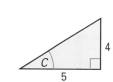

# SECTION 7.4  Solving right-angled triangles

In this section we will use the sine, cosine and tangent ratios to find an unknown side or an unknown angle in a right-angled triangle.

When using your calculator to find the sine, cosine or tangent of an angle, write the value correct to 4 decimal places.

---

### Example 1

Find the length of the side marked $x$ in the given triangle.

tan $32° = \dfrac{x}{14}$

    $x = 14 \times$ tan $32°$

    $x = 14 \times 0.6249$

    $x = 8.75$, correct to two decimal places.

---

## Example 2

In the given triangle, |AB| = 9 and |BC| = 13.
Find |∠ACB|, correct to the nearest degree.

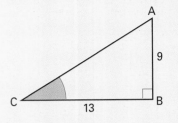

$\tan \angle ACB = \frac{9}{13}$

$|\angle ACB| = \tan^{-1} \frac{9}{13}$

$|\angle ACB| = 34.695°$   Key in ⎡SHIFT⎤ ⎡tan⎤ 9 ⎡÷⎤ 13 ⎡=⎤

$= 35°$, correct to the nearest degree

## Exercise 7.4

1. Write down which trigonometric ratio is needed to calculate the length of the side marked *x* in each of these triangles:

   (i)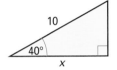

   (ii)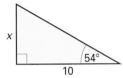

   (iii)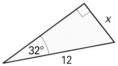

2. In each of the following triangles, work out the length of the side marked with a letter. Give each answer correct to 1 decimal place.

   (i)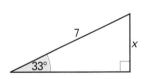

   (ii)

   (iii)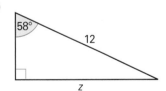

3. Find the length of the side marked *x* in these triangles:
   Give your answers correct to one decimal place.

   (i)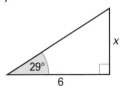

   (ii)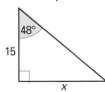

   (iii)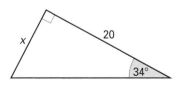

4. Find the size of the angle marked *A* in each of these triangles:
   Give your answers correct to the nearest degree.

   (i)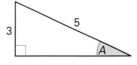

   (ii)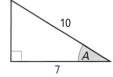

   (iii)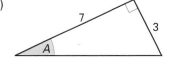

**5.** Find the measure of the angles marked *p*, *q* and *r* in each of these triangles:
Give each answer correct to the nearest degree.

(i)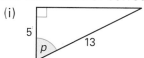

(ii)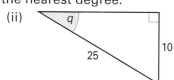

(iii)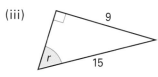

**6.** Copy and complete the following to find the length of the side marked *x*.

$$\frac{8}{x} = \cos 32°$$

$$x \times \cos 32° = 8$$

$$x = \frac{8}{\cos 32°}$$

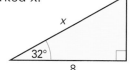

**7.** Find the length of the hypotenuse marked *x* in each of these triangles:

(i)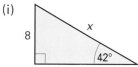

(ii)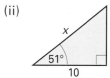

(iii)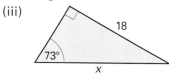

Give each answer correct to 1 decimal place.

**8.** Find the values of *x* and *y*, correct to the nearest whole number in the given triangle.

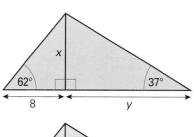

**9.** In the given triangle, find
 (i) *x*, correct to 1 decimal place
 (ii) the angle *A* correct to the nearest degree.

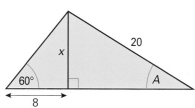

**10.** ABCD is a rectangle as, shown.
If |DC| = 11 cm and |∠BDC| = 28°, find the length of the diagonal [DB].
Give your answer in centimetres, correct to one decimal place.

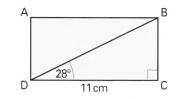

**11.** In the given triangle ABC, |AB| = 5 cm and |∠ABC| = 90°.
D is a point on [CB] and |AD| = |CD|.
If |DB| = 12 cm, find
 (i) |AD|
 (ii) |∠ACB|, correct to the nearest degree.

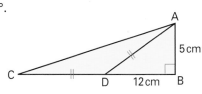

**12.** In the given diagram, |AD| = 6 cm, |DB| = 9 cm,
|∠CAD| = 35° and CD⊥AB.
  Find  (i)  |CD|, correct to 1 decimal place
       (ii)  |∠CBD|, correct to the nearest degree.

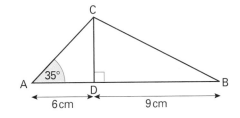

**13.** Paula stands at point P on the bank of a river.
Vertically across from her on the other bank is a tree, T.
She walks 25 metres along the bank to a point Q.
She measures the angle between QT and QP and
finds that it is 38°.
Find the width of the river correct to the nearest metre.

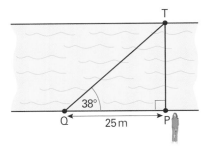

**14.** From a point on the ground 20 m from the base of a tree,
the angle of elevation to the top of the tree is 47°.
Calculate the height of the tree, correct to the
nearest metre.

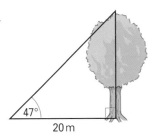

**15.** From a point on the ground 10 m from a block of flats, the angle of elevation to the top of
the block is 76°. Calculate the height of the block of flats, correct to the nearest metre.

**16.** The diagram shows the cross-section of a roof
with sides 7.5 m in length.
Both sides are inclined at an angle of 32° to
the horizontal.
  (i)  Find the height marked *h*.
  (ii)  Find the width, *w*, of the roof support.
  Give each answer in metres, correct to 1 decimal place.

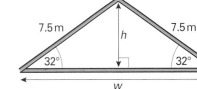

**17.** The diagram below shows the cross-section ABCD of a valley.

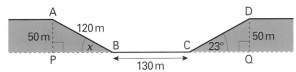

  Calculate (i)  the angle *x*, correct to the nearest degree
           (ii)  |PB|, in metres correct to the nearest metre
          (iii)  |CQ| correct to the nearest metre
           (iv)  the distance straight across the valley from A to D, correct to the
                nearest metre.

**18.** Ryan and Emily are estimating the height of a phone mast.

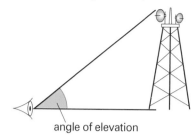

angle of elevation

Ryan stands 15 m from the mast and measures the angle of elevation to the top as 60°.
Emily stands 25 m from the mast and measures the angle of elevation to the top as 46°.
Can they both be correct? Discuss.

**19.** In the given triangle, $|AB| = 10$ m, $|BD| = 2$ m and $|\angle ABC| = 53°$.
   (i)  Write down $|\angle BAC|$.
   (ii)  Find $|BC|$ and hence find $|DC|$.

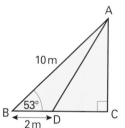

**20.** The total angle of swing of a particular pendulum is 44° (22° each way).
Work out the difference in height of the bottom of the pendulum at
the lowest and highest point in the swing.
Give your answer correct to the nearest centimetre.

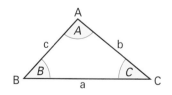

# SECTION 7.5 The area of a triangle

The diagram shows a triangle ABC.

We use capital letters to denote the angles at the
vertices $A$, $B$ and $C$.

We use the lower-case letters a, b and c to represent the sides
opposite the angles A, B and C.

The area of the given triangle is $\frac{1}{2} \times$ base $\times$ perpendicular height

$$= \frac{1}{2} \times a \times h$$

But   $\dfrac{h}{c} = \sin B$

$\Rightarrow \quad h = c \times \sin B$

Now area $\frac{1}{2} \times a \times h$ becomes $\frac{1}{2} \times a \times c \times \sin B$

    **Area $= \frac{1}{2}ac \sin B$**

This is a very useful formula for finding the area of a triangle if we know two sides and the angle between these sides.

**Area of a triangle**

Area $= \frac{1}{2}ab \sin C$

In words: Area = Half the product of any two sides multiplied by the sine of the angle between them.

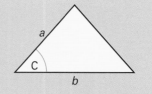

---

**Example 1**

Find the area of the triangle shown on the right.

Here we have 2 sides and the angle between them.

Area $= \frac{1}{2}(7)(8) \sin 46°$

$= (0.5)(7)(8) \sin 46°$

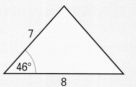

Using a calculator, key in $0.5 \times 7 \times 8 \times$ [ sin ] 46 [ = ].

The answer is 20.14 sq. units, correct to 2 decimal places.

---

**Example 2**

If the area of the given triangle is 40 cm², find the angle $A$ correct to the nearest degree.

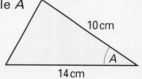

Area of $\triangle = \frac{1}{2}(10)(14) \sin A$

$\Rightarrow \quad \frac{1}{2}(10)(14) \sin A = 40$

$\Rightarrow \quad 70 \sin A = 40$

$\Rightarrow \quad \sin A = \frac{40}{70}$

$\Rightarrow \quad A = \sin^{-1} \frac{40}{70}$

To find $A$ key in [ SHIFT ] [ sin ] 40 [ ÷ ] 70 [ = ]

The result is 34.85°

∴ $A = 35°$, correct to the nearest degree.

---

## Exercise 7.5

**1.** Find the area of each of the triangles shown below.
Give your answers in cm², correct to one decimal place.

(i)

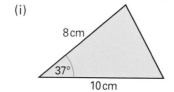

(ii)

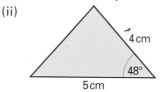

(ii)

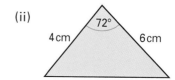

**2.** Find the area of each of these triangles, in cm², correct to the nearest whole number.

(i)

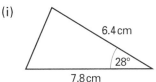

(ii)

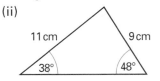

(iii)

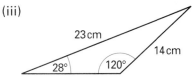

**3.** Find the area of the figure ABCD.
Give your answer correct to
the nearest integer.

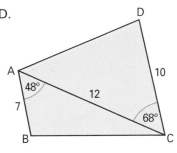

**4.** Find the area of this parallelogram, correct to the nearest cm².

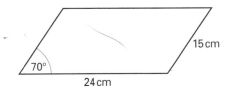

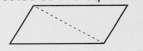

A parallelogram can be
treated as two equal triangles.

**5.** Find the area of the given triangle if sin $\theta$ = 0.7.
Give your answer to the nearest cm².

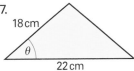

**6.** The area of each of the triangles below is given.
Find the measure of the angle marked with a letter.
Give your answer correct to the nearest degree in each case.

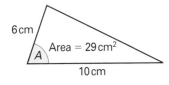

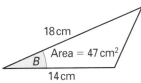

**7.** The area of the triangle shown is 30 square units.
Find the length of the side marked *x*,
correct to 1 decimal place.

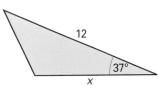

**8.** The area of an equilateral triangle is 43.3 cm².
Find the length of the side of the triangle.

**9.** In the given triangle, cos A = $\frac{4}{5}$.
Without using a calculator, find the value of sin A.
Hence find the area of the triangle.

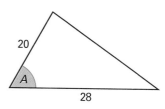

**10.** A farmer wants to give a triangular plot of land
to his daughter to build a house. The plot is
bounded on two sides by a hedge and a road.
The hedge makes an angle of 78° with the road.
If the road frontage of the plot is
20 metres, how far along the hedge should the
plot extend if the area of the plot is 1500 m²?
Give your answer correct to the
nearest metre.

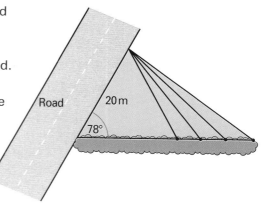

**11.** RST is a triangular plot of land in which |RT| = 18 m and |TS| = 23 m.
The area of the plot is 207 m².
  (i) Draw a rough sketch of this plot.     (ii) Find |∠RTS|.
  (iii) If the lengths of the sides of the plot are doubled but the measure of ∠RTS
        remains unchanged, investigate if the area of the plot is also doubled.
        Explain your answer.

**12.** In the given triangle ABC, cos ∠BAC = $\frac{1}{5}$.
  (i) Find sin ∠BAC in surd form.
  (ii) Show that the area of the triangle ABC
       can be written in the form $k\sqrt{k}$, $k \in N$.
       Hence write down the value of $k$.

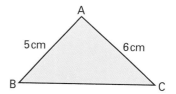

# SECTION 7.6  The Sine Rule

In our study of trigonometry so far we have dealt mainly with right-angled triangles.
In this section we will deal with the Sine Rule which enables us to find sides and angles of a
triangle which does not contain a right angle.

### The Sine Rule

For any triangle $ABC$,

$$\frac{a}{\sin A} = \frac{b}{\sin B} = \frac{c}{\sin C}$$

or  $$\frac{\sin A}{a} = \frac{\sin B}{b} = \frac{\sin C}{c}$$

The Sine Rule may also be stated in words, as shown.

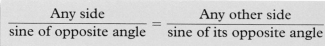

$$\frac{\text{Any side}}{\text{sine of opposite angle}} = \frac{\text{Any other side}}{\text{sine of its opposite angle}}$$

To use the Sine Rule to solve a triangle, we need to know one side and the angle opposite this side as well as one other angle or side.

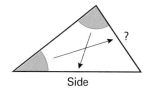

In practice two parts of the Sine Rule only are used when solving problems, i.e.,

$$\frac{a}{\sin A} = \frac{b}{\sin B} \text{ or } \frac{\sin A}{a} = \frac{\sin B}{b}$$

To find a side have the sides on top.
To find an angle have the angles on top.

## Example 1

Find, correct to the nearest whole number, the length of the side marked $x$ in the given triangle.

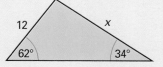

Here we have a side of length 12 and the opposite angle is 34°.
Using the Sine Rule we have:

$$\frac{x}{\sin 62°} = \frac{12}{\sin 34°}$$

$$\Rightarrow \frac{x}{0.8829} = \frac{12}{0.5592} \qquad \text{key in } \boxed{\text{SIN}} \text{ 62 and } \boxed{\text{SIN}} \text{ 34}$$

$$\Rightarrow x(0.5592) = 12(0.8829)$$

$$\Rightarrow x = \frac{12(0.8829)}{0.5592} = 18.946 \Rightarrow x = 19$$

## Example 2

Find the measure of the angle $A$, correct to the nearest degree.
Hence find the area of the triangle ABC.

$$\frac{12}{\sin 53°} = \frac{14}{\sin A}$$

$$\Rightarrow \frac{12}{0.7986} = \frac{14}{\sin A}$$

$$\Rightarrow 12 \sin A = 14(0.7986)$$

$$\Rightarrow \sin A = \frac{14(0.7986)}{12} = 0.9317$$

$$\Rightarrow A = \sin^{-1} 0.9317$$

To find $A$ key in $\boxed{\text{SHIFT}}$ $\boxed{\text{sin}}$ 0.9317 $\boxed{=}$.

The result is 68.70°

$\therefore$ $A = 69°$, correct to the nearest degree

We now find the angle $B$ to get the area of $\triangle ABC$.

$B = 180° - 53° - 69° \Rightarrow B = 58°$

Area of $\triangle ABC = \frac{1}{2}|AB|.|BC| \sin B$

$= (0.5)(12)(14) \sin 58°$

$= 71.236$

Area $= 71.2 \text{ cm}^2$

## Exercise 7.6

**1.** Find, correct to 1 decimal place, the length of the side marked $x$ in each of these triangles.

(i)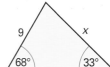

(ii)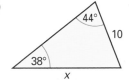

(iii)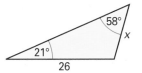

**2.** Find the measure of the angle marked with a letter in each of these triangles.
Give each angle correct to the nearest degree.

(i)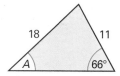

(ii)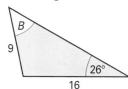

(iii)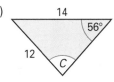

**3.** In the given triangle, $|\angle BAC| = 71°$, $|BC| = 22$ cm and $|AC| = 15$ cm.

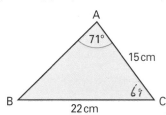

Find (i) $|\angle ABC|$, correct to the nearest degree
(ii) $|AB|$, correct to the nearest cm.

**4.** In the given triangle, $|AB| = 22$, $|\angle BAC| = 65°$ and $|\angle ABC| = 71°$.
Find, correct to the nearest integer,
(i) $|BC|$
(ii) the area of the triangle ABC.

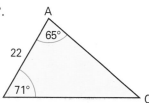

5. In the given triangle, $|CD| = 15$ m, $|\angle ADC| = 30°$, $|\angle CAD| = 23°$ and $|\angle ABC| = 90°$.
   Find, in metres, correct to 1 decimal place,
   (i) $|AC|$
   (ii) $|AB|$.

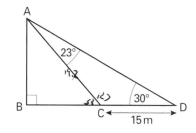

6. From a point A on level ground the angle of elevation of the top of a tower $|BC|$ is 40°. On walking 50 m towards the tower, the angle of elevation is now 60°.
   Find, correct to the nearest metre
   (i) $|CD|$
   (ii) the height of the tower $|BC|$.

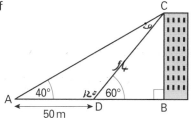

7. Two lighthouse P and Q are 73 km apart.
   Another lighthouse, R, is situated 52 km from Q.
   If $|\angle RPQ| = 31.5°$, find
   (i) $|\angle PRQ|$, correct to the nearest degree
   (ii) $|PR|$, correct to the nearest kilometre.

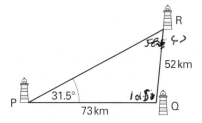

8. ABC is a triangle and D is on the line BC.
   If $|BD| = 4$ cm, $|AC| = 6$ cm, $|\angle ACD| = 65°$ and $|\angle DAC| = 70°$, find
   (i) $|DC|$, correct to the nearest cm
   (ii) the area of $\triangle ABC$, correct to the nearest cm$^2$.

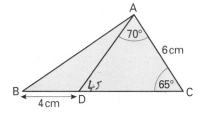

9. The diagram shows two parallel banks of a river.

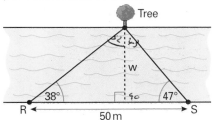

The angles from two points R and S on one bank to a tree on the opposite bank are 38° and 47°, as shown.
Find correct to the nearest metre
   (i) the distance from R to the tree   (ii) the width, w, of the river.

**10.** A farmer makes a triangular pen bounded by a fence 59 metres long, a hedge 68 metres long and a wall.

The angle between the wall and the hedge is 49°.

Draw a rough sketch of the triangle.

   (i)   Find the measure of the angle between the fence and the wall, correct to the nearest degree.

 (ii)   Find the length of the wall, correct to the nearest metre.

(iii)   Find the area of the pen, correct to the nearest m².

# SECTION 7.7  The Cosine Rule

In each of the triangles shown below, we are given 3 pieces of information.

In triangle A we are given two sides and the included angle (i.e. the angle between them).

In triangle B we are given the lengths of the three sides.

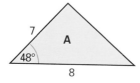 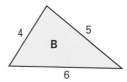

In neither of these triangles can the Sine Rule be used to find the remaining sides and angles.

To solve these triangles we use another rule, called the **Cosine Rule**, which is given below.

> For any triangle, ABC
> $$a^2 = b^2 + c^2 - 2bc \cos A$$
> or $\quad b^2 = c^2 + a^2 - 2ca \cos B$
> or $\quad c^2 = a^2 + b^2 - 2ab \cos C$

**The Cosine Rule is used**

**1.** to find an angle when three sides are given

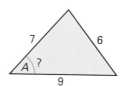

**2.** to find the third side when two sides and the included angle are given.

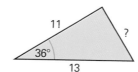

## Example 1

In the given triangle, $|AB| = 6$, $|AC| = 8$ and $|\angle BAC| = 48°$.
Find $|BC|$, correct to the nearest integer.

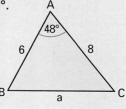

Let $[BC] = a$.
To find the side $a$, we use the *Cosine Rule*
beginning with $a^2$.

$$a^2 = b^2 + c^2 - 2bc \cos A \dots (b = 8 \text{ and } c = 6)$$
$$= 8^2 + 6^2 - 2.8.6 \cos 48°$$
$$= 64 + 36 - 96(0.6691)$$
$$= 35.77$$
$$\Rightarrow \quad a = 5.98 \quad \text{i.e. } |BC| = 5.98 = 6, \text{ correct to the nearest integer.}$$

$b = 8$
$c = 6$

## Example 2

Find $|\angle ABC|$, in the given triangle.

$\angle ABC = B$
To find the angle $B$ we use the Cosine Rule
beginning with $b^2$.

$$b^2 = c^2 + a^2 - 2ca \cos B$$
$$\Rightarrow \quad 25 = 16 + 36 - 2(4)(6) \cos B$$
$$25 = 52 - 48 \cos B$$
$$25 - 52 = -48 \cos B$$
$$-27 = -48 \cos B$$
$$48 \cos B = 27$$
$$\cos B = \frac{27}{48}$$
$$B = \cos^{-1} \frac{27}{48} \dots [\text{key in } \boxed{\text{SHIFT}} \ \boxed{\cos} \ 27 \ \boxed{\div} \ 48 \ \boxed{=} ]$$
$$B = 55.77°$$
$$\therefore \quad |\angle ABC| = 56°, \text{ correct to the nearest degree.}$$

$a = 6$
$b = 5$
$c = 4$

**Note:**  1. When solving a triangle, we generally try to use the *Sine Rule* first.
  If the *Sine Rule* cannot be used, we then use the Cosine Rule.
  2. If the cosine of an angle in a triangle is negative, the angle will lie between 90° and 180°.

## Compass Directions

The diagram on the right shows some compass directions.
Compass directions begin with N (for North) or
S (for South) and then a given number of degrees East or West.

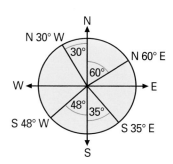

# Exercise 7.7

1. Find the length, correct to one decimal place, of the side marked with a letter in each of the following triangles:

(i)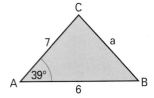

(ii)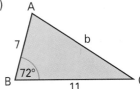

(iii)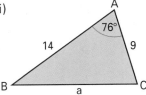

2. Find, correct to the nearest whole number, the length of the side marked with a letter in each of these triangles:

(i)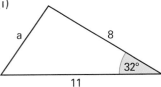

(ii)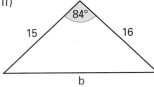

(iii)

3. Find the measure of the angle marked with a letter in each of the following triangles. Give each angle correct to the nearest degree.

(i)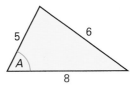

(ii)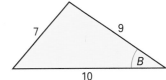

(iii)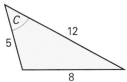

4. Find the measure of the smallest angle in the given triangle. Give your answer correct to the nearest degree.

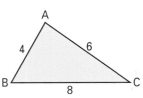

5. In the given triangle, $|PQ| = 15$ cm, $|PR| = 12$ cm and $|RQ| = 5$ cm. Find $|\angle PQR|$, correct to the nearest degree.

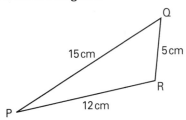

**6.** The distance from the tee to the pin on the green
is 190 metres.
A golfer hits a shot at an angle of 20° away
from the direct line to the hole.
If the ball travels 170 m, find the distance
between the ball and the hole.
Give your answer correct to the nearest metre.

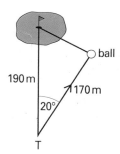

**7.** Use the information in the given figure to find

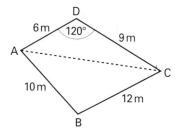

    (i)   |AC|, correct to the nearest metre.

    (ii)  Use this length of [AC] to find |∠ABC|, correct to the nearest degree.

**8.** On a snooker table the cue ball and
black ball are situated as shown in
the diagram.
Find the distance the cue ball has
to travel before hitting the black ball.
Give your answer correct to the
nearest centimetre.

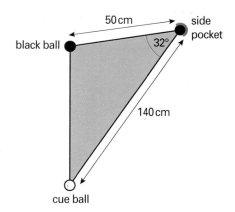

**9.** Two ships S and T leave a port P at the same time.
S travels in a direction N 80° E at a speed of 24 km/hr.
T travels in a direction S 60° E at a speed of 32 km/hr.
How far apart are the ships one hour after leaving port?
Give your answer correct to the nearest kilometre.

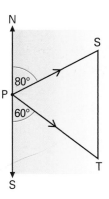

**The following problems may involve the use of the *Sine Rule* as well as the *Cosine Rule*.**

**10.** In the given triangle ABC, D is a point on [BC].
|BD| = 6 cm, |AC| = 9 cm, |∠DCA| = 80° and |∠CAD| = 50°.
    (i)  Find |DC|,
    (ii)  Find |AB|, correct to the nearest cm.

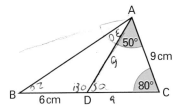

**11.** In the triangle XYZ, |XY| = 22 cm, |YZ| = 15 cm and |∠XYZ| = 74°.
    Find (i)  |XZ|, correct to the nearest cm.
        (ii)  |∠YXZ|, correct to the nearest degree.

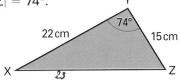

**12.** In the quadrilateral ABCD, |AC| = 5, |BC| = 4, |∠BCA| = 110°,
|∠ACD| = 33° and |∠CDA| = 23°.
Find, correct to two decimal places
    (i)  |AB|
    (ii)  |CD|.

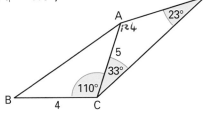

**13.** The diagram shows wires attached to a communications antenna.
Find the length *h*, correct to the nearest metre.

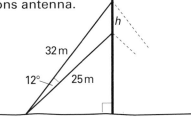

**14.** In the given triangle ABC, |BC| = 60 m and |∠ACB| = 150°.
If the area of △ABC = 450 m², find
    (i)  |AC|,
    (ii)  the perimeter of the triangle ABC,
        correct to the nearest metre.

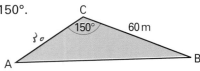

**15.** In the triangle PQR, |PR| = 7 cm, QR = 13 cm and |∠PRQ| = 80°.
    (i)  Find the length of [PQ] in centimetres, correct
        to one decimal place.
    (ii)  Find |∠QPR|, correct to the nearest degree.

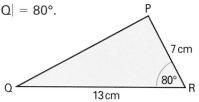

**16.** S and T are two points 300 metres apart on a straight path due north.
A pillar, P, is N 40° E of S.
The pillar is N 70° E of T.

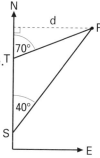

   (i)   Find the distance from T to the pillar, correct to the nearest metre.

   (ii)  Find the shortest distance, d, from the path to the pillar,
        correct to the nearest metre.

**17.** From a point A on the same level as the base of a radio mast, the angle of elevation
of the top of the mast is 25°. From a point B, 20 metres closer to the mast, and on the
same level, the angle of elevation is 32°. Find the height of the radio mast in metres,
correct to the nearest metre.

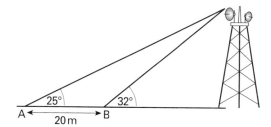

**18.** The diagram shows a point A, which lies 10 km due south
of a point B.
A straight road AD is such that D is N 43° E of A.
P and Q are two points on this road which are both
8 km from B.

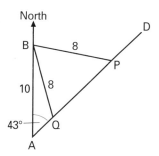

   (i)   Find $|\angle BPA|$, correct to the nearest degree.

   (ii)  Find $|\angle ABP|$, correct to the nearest degree.

# SECTION 7.8  The angles 30°, 45° and 60°

The angles 30°, 45° and 60° are used very frequently and we will use triangles to express the
sine, cosine and tangent ratios of these angles as fractions or surds.

### The 45° angle

The triangle on the right is isosceles where the equal sides are 1 unit in length.

The hypotenuse is $\sqrt{2}$ units in length.

The sine, cosine and tangent ratios can be read from the triangle.

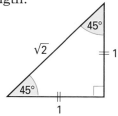

$$\sin 45° = \frac{1}{\sqrt{2}} \qquad \cos 45° = \frac{1}{\sqrt{2}} \qquad \tan 45° = 1$$

## The angles 30° and 60°

The given right-angled triangle has angles of 60° and 30°.

We can use this triangle to write down the trigonometric ratios of these two angles.

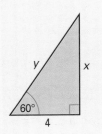

$$\sin 60° = \frac{\sqrt{3}}{2} \qquad \cos 60° = \frac{1}{2} \qquad \tan 60° = \sqrt{3}$$

$$\sin 30° = \frac{1}{2} \qquad \cos 30° = \frac{\sqrt{3}}{2} \qquad \tan 30° = \frac{1}{\sqrt{3}}$$

**Note:** The sine, cosine and tangent ratios for 30°, 45° and 60° are given on page 13 of *Formulae and Tables*.

### Example 1

Without using a calculator, find the values of $x$ and $y$ in the given right-angled triangle.

$$\frac{x}{4} = \tan 60° \qquad\qquad \frac{4}{y} = \cos 60°$$

$$\Rightarrow \quad \frac{x}{4} = \frac{\sqrt{3}}{1} \qquad\qquad \frac{4}{y} = \frac{1}{2}$$

$$\Rightarrow \quad x = 4\sqrt{3} \qquad\qquad \Rightarrow \quad y = 8$$

## Exercise 7.8

Without using a calculator, write the value of each of the following as a simple fraction or as a surd:

1. $\cos 60°$
2. $\tan 45°$
3. $\sin 30°$
4. $\cos 45°$
5. $\sin^2 30°$

6. $\cos 30°$
7. $\sin 60°$
8. $\cos^2 45°$
9. $\sin^2 60°$
10. $\tan^2 30°$

11. Show that (i) $1 - \sin^2 30° = \cos^2 30°$  (ii) $\sin 60° = 2 \sin 30° \cos 30°$

12. Without using a calculator, find the values of $x$ and $y$ in the given triangle.

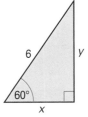

13. Find the values of $x$ and $y$ in the given triangle, without using a calculator.

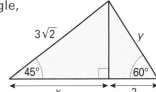

**14.** Find the values of $x$, $y$ and $z$ in the given diagram, without using a calculator.

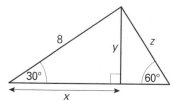

**15.** A field is in the shape of an equilateral triangle, as shown.
Each side is 40 m in length.
Suggest two methods of finding the area of this field without using a calculator.
Find the area using each of these methods.
Give your answer in surd form.

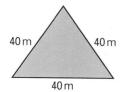

# SECTION 7.9  Area of sector – Length of arc

You will have already learned how to find the circumference and area of a circle.

The formulae for these are given below.

**Circumference** of a circle $= 2\pi r$

**Area** of a circle $= \pi r^2$

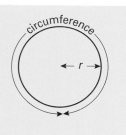

In this section we will learn how to find
  (i)  the length of an arc of a circle
  (ii)  the area of a sector of a circle.

The diagram below shows a circle with O as centre.

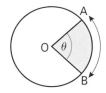

OAB is a sector of the circle, where $|\angle AOB| = \theta$.

AB is called the **minor arc**.

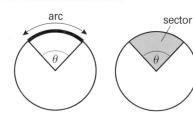

Area of sector AOB $= \dfrac{\theta}{360°} \times \pi r^2$

Length of minor arc AB $= \dfrac{\theta}{360°} \times 2\pi r$

## Example 1

The given circle has radius 9 cm, and $|\angle AOB| = 120°$.
Taking $\pi = \frac{22}{7}$, find

   (i)   the length of the minor arc AB

   (ii)  the area of the shaded sector AOB

   (i)   Length of arc $AB = \dfrac{120°}{360°} \times 2\pi r$

$$= \frac{120}{360} \times \frac{2}{1} \times \frac{22}{7} \times \frac{9}{1}$$

$$= 18.86 \text{ cm}$$

   (ii)  Area of sector $AOB = \dfrac{120°}{360°} \times \pi r^2$

$$= \frac{120}{360} \times \frac{22}{7} \times \frac{9^2}{1} = 84.86 \text{ cm}^2$$

## Example 2

The area of the sector AOB = 205 cm$^2$.
Find the length of the radius of the circle.

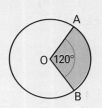

Let $r$ be the radius

$$\text{Area of AOB} = \frac{120}{360} \times \pi r^2 = 205$$

$$\Rightarrow \quad \frac{\pi r^2}{3} = 205$$

$$\Rightarrow \quad \pi r^2 = 205 \times 3 \dots \quad \text{multiply both sides by 3}$$

$$\Rightarrow \quad r^2 = \frac{205 \times 3}{\pi}$$

$$= 195.76 \dots \quad \text{use } \pi \text{ key on your calculator}$$

$$\Rightarrow \quad r = \sqrt{195.76} = 13.99$$

$$\Rightarrow \quad \text{radius} = 14 \text{ cm, correct to the nearest cm.}$$

## Exercise 7.9

**1.** Find the area of each of these sectors, correct to the nearest cm$^2$:

(i)

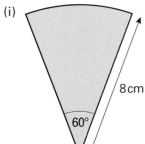

8 cm

60°

(ii)

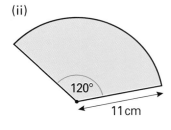

120°

11 cm

(iii)

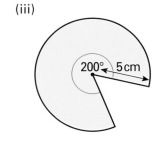

200°  5 cm

2. Find the length of the arc in each of the sectors in question 1 on the previous page. Give your answer in centimetres, correct to one decimal place.

3. Find, correct to one decimal place
   (i) the area of the sector AOB
   (ii) the length of the arc AB in the given diagram.

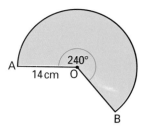

4. The radius of the given circle is 18 cm.
   The measure of ∠AOB = 75°.
   (i) Find the length of the arc AB, correct to the nearest centimetre.
   (ii) Find the area of the sector AOB, correct to the nearest cm².

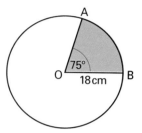

5. Find the length of the radius of the circle if the area of the given sector is 77 cm².

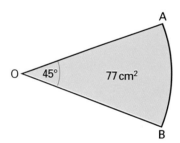

6. In the given sector, |∠AOB| = 140° and its area is 276 cm². Find the length of the radius of the circle, correct to the nearest cm.

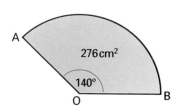

7. A golfer can hit a ball 220 m with an accuracy of 15° either side of his intended direction.
   Find the length of the arc along which he might find his ball, correct to the nearest metre.

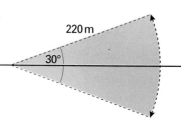

**8.** A coastguard radar makes a sweep of 55° from its base, B. If the range of the radar is 3.5 km, find the area of the sector swept by the radar. Give your answer in km², correct to one decimal place.

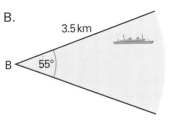

**9.** *OPQ* is a sector of a circle with radius 20 cm. *X* is the midpoint of [*OP*] and *Y* is the midpoint of [*OQ*]. Angle *POQ* = 65°.

Calculate
  (i) the area *XPQY*,
  (ii) the perimeter of *XPQY*.
Give each answer correct to the nearest whole number.

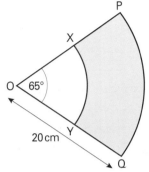

**10.** The given sector has a radius of 18 cm. The angle in the sector is 80°. Find, correct to the nearest whole number in each case,
  (i) the length of the arc AB
  (ii) the length of the chord [AB]
  (Hint: Use the Cosine Rule)
  (iii) the area of the sector OAB
  (iv) the area of the triangle OAB
  (v) the area of the shaded region.

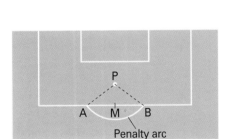

**11.** The diagram shows part of a football pitch. The penalty arc is part of a circle, radius 10 metres, with centre P.
M is the midpoint of [AB] and [PM] = 6 metres.
  (i) Find the measure of the ∠APB, correct to the nearest degree.
  (ii) Calculate the length of the penalty arc, correct to one decimal place.

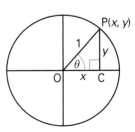

# SECTION 7.10  Ratios of angles greater than 90°

## 1. The Unit Circle

The circle on the right has centre at (0, 0) and radius 1 unit in length. It is generally referred to as the unit circle.

Let P($x$, $y$) be any point on the circle, as shown.

From the triangle OPC,

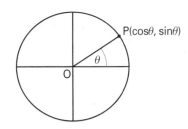

$$\frac{x}{1} = \cos \theta \qquad x = \frac{y}{1} = \sin \theta$$

$$\Rightarrow \quad x = \cos \theta \qquad \Rightarrow \quad y = \sin \theta$$

$\therefore$ the coordinates of P are $(\cos \theta, \sin \theta)$

> The coordinates of any point on
> the unit circle are $(\cos \theta, \sin \theta)$.

The unit circle shown crosses the $x$-axis
and $y$-axis at the indicated points.

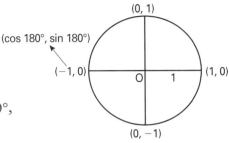

We can use these points to write down the
value of $\sin \theta$ and $\cos \theta$ for the angles $0°$,
$90°$, $180°$, $270°$ and $360°$.

Thus $(-1, 0)$ gives the values of $\cos 180°$ and $\sin 180°$,

i.e. $\cos 180° = -1$ and $\sin 180° = 0$.

## 2. The Four Quadrants

The $x$-axis and $y$-axis divide a full
rotation of $360°$ into 4 quadrants
as shown on the right.

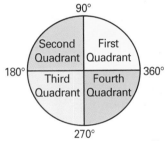

The unit circle on the right shows an angle, $\theta$,
in each of the four quadrants. The signs shown
in each triangle determine whether a ratio is
positive or negative.

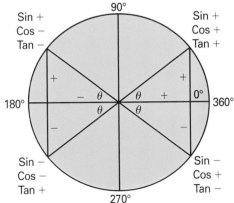

The positive ratios in the four quadrants are
shown in the highlighted section below.

(i)   In the 1st quadrant, all (A) positive
(ii)  In the 2nd quadrant, sin(S) only positive
(iii) In the 3rd quadrant, tan(T) only positive
(iv)  In the 4th quadrant, cos(C) only positive

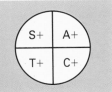

## 3. Finding the ratio of an angle between 90° and 360°

An electronic calculator will give the sine, cosine and tangent of any angle, including the negative sign, if it exists. However, if we need the ratio of a certain angle as a fraction or as a surd, the following steps must be followed:

1. Make a rough sketch of the angle to determine in which quadrant it lies.

2. Use  to determine whether the ratio is positive or negative.

3. Determine the angle (<90°) between the rotated line and the **x-axis**. This angle is known as the **reference angle**.

4. Use a calculator or the 30°, 45° and 60° triangles to find the required ratio.
   Use the diagram in **2** above to determine the sign of the ratio.

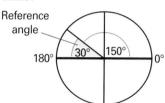

---

#### Example 1

Find in surd form    (i) sin 120°    (ii) cos 225°

(i) sin 120°:

     120° is in the second quadrant

     ⇒ the sine ratio is positive

     The reference angle is 180° − 120° = 60°.

     Using the triangle shown,

     $\sin 60° = \dfrac{\sqrt{3}}{2}$ ⇒ $\sin 120° = \dfrac{\sqrt{3}}{2}$

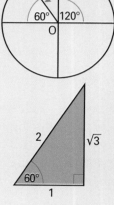

(ii) cos 225°:

     225° is in the third quadrant

     ⇒ the cosine ratio is negative

     The reference angle is 225° − 180° = 45°.

     Using the 45° triangle shown,

     $\cos 45° = \dfrac{1}{\sqrt{2}}$ ⇒ $\cos 225° = -\dfrac{1}{\sqrt{2}}$.

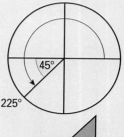

## Example 2

Given $\cos A = -0.4153$ and $0° \leqslant A \leqslant 360°$.

Use your calculator to find the values of $A$ in degrees, correct to one decimal place.

$\cos A = -0.4153$

Disregard the negative sign and find the reference angle.

To find this reference angle, key in $\boxed{\text{SHIFT}}$ $\boxed{\cos}$ 0.4153 $\boxed{=}$

The result is $65.46°$

         $= 65.5°$, correct to one decimal place.

The cosine is negative in the second and third quadrants.

Therefore, the two values of $A$ are,

     $180° - 65.5°$ and $180° + 65.5°$

∴   $A = 114.5°$ and $245.5°$

## Exercise 7.10

1. Use the unit circle on the right to write down the value of
    - (i)   $\sin 50°$
    - (ii)   $\cos 220°$
    - (iii)   $\cos 50°$
    - (iv)   $\sin 220°$

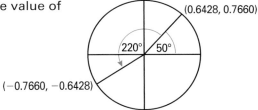

2. Use a calculator to write down, correct to four decimal places, the value of each of these ratios:
    - (i)   $\sin 138°$
    - (ii)   $\cos 212°$
    - (iii)   $\tan 318°$
    - (iv)   $\cos 159°$
    - (v)   $\tan 193°$
    - (vi)   $\sin 236°$
    - (vii)   $\cos 317°$
    - (viii)   $\tan 254°$

3. If $\cos 120° = -\cos 60°$, copy and complete the following in the same way:
    - (i)   $\sin 130° = \ldots$
    - (ii)   $\cos 115° = \ldots$
    - (iii)   $\tan 160° = \ldots$
    - (iv)   $\cos 220° = \ldots$
    - (v)   $\sin 250° = \ldots$
    - (vi)   $\tan 300° = \ldots$

4. Use the triangles on the right to express each of the following as a fraction or as a surd:
    - (i)   $\sin 120°$
    - (ii)   $\cos 135°$
    - (iii)   $\sin 240°$
    - (iv)   $\sin 210°$
    - (v)   $\cos 330°$
    - (vi)   $\tan 225°$
    - (vii)   $\cos 150°$
    - (viii)   $\sin 300°$
    - (ix)   $\tan 150°$

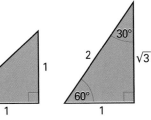

5. Find, correct to the nearest degree, the two values of $A$ if $\sin A = 0.2167$ and $0° \leqslant A \leqslant 360°$.

6. Find, correct to the nearest degree, the two values of $B$ for $0° \leqslant B \leqslant 360°$, given that
   (i) $\cos B = -0.8428$               (ii)    $\tan B = -1.2464$.

7. If $\sin \theta = \frac{1}{2}$, find 2 values for $\theta$, if $0° \leqslant \theta \leqslant 360°$.

8. If $\cos \theta = \dfrac{1}{\sqrt{2}}$, find 2 values for $\tan \theta$, if $0° \leqslant \theta \leqslant 360°$.

9. If $\tan A = \dfrac{1}{\sqrt{3}}$, find 2 values for $\cos A$, if $0° \leqslant A \leqslant 360°$.

10. If $\sin \theta = -\dfrac{\sqrt{3}}{2}$, find two values for $\cos \theta$ without using a calculator if $0° \leqslant \theta \leqslant 360°$.

11. Find $A$, correct to the nearest degree, if $\sin A = -\frac{4}{5}$ and $\cos A = -\frac{3}{5}$ for $A \leqslant 360°$.

12. If $\sin B = \frac{3}{5}$ and $\cos B = -\frac{4}{5}$, find the value of $\tan B$ without using a calculator if $0° \leqslant B \leqslant 360°$.

13. If $\tan B = \dfrac{1}{\sqrt{3}}$ and $\sin B = -\frac{1}{2}$, express $\cos B$ as a surd.

14. If $\tan A = \frac{1}{2}$ and $180° < A < 270°$, find $\sin A$ in surd form.

# TEST YOURSELF 7

1. Use the given right-angled triangle to write down
   (i) $\sin A$                 (ii) $\tan A$
   Now find the measure of the angle $A$, correct to the nearest degree.

   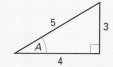

2. Find the length of the side marked $x$ in the given triangle.
   Hence write down as fractions
   (i) $\tan A$                 (ii) $\cos A$.

   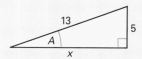

3. In the given triangle, $|\angle ACB| = 34°$, $|\angle ABC| = 90°$, and $|AB| = 12$ cm.
   Find $|BC|$, in cm, correct to one decimal place.

   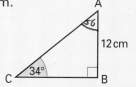

4. In the given triangle, $|AB| = 12$ cm, $|CD| = 20$ cm,
   $|\angle ABC| = 43°$ and $|\angle ACD| = 90°$.
   (i) Find $|AC|$, correct to the nearest cm.
   (ii) Find $|\angle ADC|$, correct to the nearest degree.

   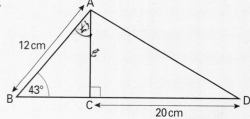

**5.** In the given triangle ABC, |AB| = 5 cm, |AC| = 8 cm and
|∠BAC| = 52°.
Find, correct to the nearest whole number in each case
  (i)   the area of the triangle ABC
  (ii)  the length of [BC]
  (iii) |∠BCA|.

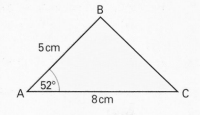

**6.** In the given diagram, |AD| = 6 cm, |DB| = 9 cm, |∠CAD| = 35°
and CD is perpendicular to AB.
  (i)   Find |CD|, in cm, correct to one decimal place.
  (ii)  Find |∠CBD|, correct to the nearest degree.

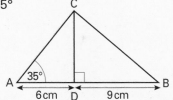

**7.**   (i)   Find the measure of the angle *A* in the given figure.
            Give your answer in degrees,
            correct to one decimal place.

  (ii)  The area of the given triangle is 51 cm².
        Find the the measure of the angle *A*,
        correct to the nearest degree.

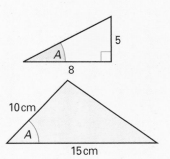

**8.** The radius of the given circle is 7 cm and |∠AOB| = 95°.
  (i)   Find the area of the sector AOB in cm²,
        correct to the nearest whole number.
  (ii)  Find the length of the arc AB in centimetres,
        correct to one decimal place.

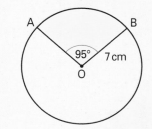

**9.** In the given figure, |YZ| = 15 m, |∠XYW| = 40°,
|∠YZW| = 20° and |∠WXY| = 90°.
Find, in metres, correct to one decimal place
  (i)   |WY|
  (ii)  |WX|.

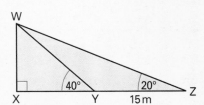

**10.** In the given figure, OAB is a sector of radius 8 cm and
|∠AOB| = 40°.
Find, in cm², correct to one decimal place
  (i)   the area of the sector OAB
  (ii)  the area of the shaded region.

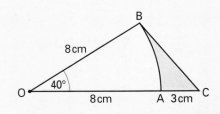

11. In the triangle PQR, $|PQ| = |PR|$, $|QR| = 15$ cm and $|\angle RPQ| = 40°$.

    (i) Find $|PR|$, correct to the nearest centimetre.

    (ii) S is a point on the line QR such that $|RS| = 10$ cm. Find $|PS|$, correct to the nearest centimetre.

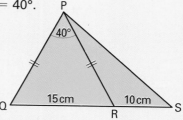

12. (i) If $\sin A = -0.8660$, find two values for $A$, for $0° \leqslant A \leqslant 360°$.

    (ii) Use the triangle on the right to write the value of $\sin^2 60° + \cos^2 30°$ in the form $\frac{a}{b}$, $a, b \in N$.

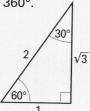

13. In the quadrilateral ABCD, $|\angle BAD| = 90°$, $|\angle BDC| = 63°$, $|AB| = 12$ cm, $|AD| = 9$ cm and $|DC| = 14$ cm. Find, correct to the nearest integer,

    (i) the length of [BD]

    (ii) the area of ABCD.

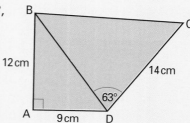

14. The diagram shows a tower.
    At $A$ the angle of elevation to the top of the tower is 43°.
    At $B$ the angle of elevation to the top of the tower is 74°.
    The distance $|AB|$ is 10 m.
    Calculate the height of the tower, in metres, correct to one decimal place.

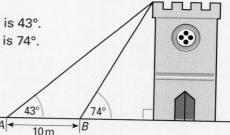

15. The area of the triangle ABC is 66 cm².
    $|AB| = 16$ cm and $|\angle BAC| = 55°$.

    (i) Find $|BC|$, in centimetres, correct to one decimal place.

    (ii) Find $|\angle ABC|$, correct to the nearest degree.

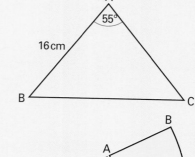

16. In the given sectors, $|\angle BOC| = 40°$, $|OD| = 5$ cm and $|OC| = 9$ cm.
    Find, correct to the nearest whole number,

    (i) the area of ABCD

    (ii) the perimeter of ABCD.

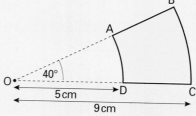

**17.** If the area of the triangle PQR is 42 cm², find |PR|, in centimetres, correct to one decimal place.
Given also that |RQ| = 11 cm, use the value you have found for |PR| to find the measure of the angle RQP, correct to the nearest degree.

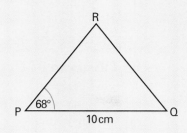

**18.** Two radar manufacturers are trying to sell their products to the coastguard.
The specifications of the two different products, A and B, are given below:

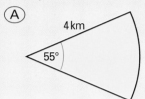
Range = 4 km
Sweep = 55°

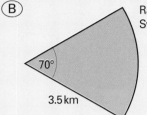
Range = 3.5 km
Sweep = 70°

   (i) If the most important feature is the area of the sector covered by the radar, which radar should be chosen. Explain your answer.
   (ii) If radar A costs €75 000 and radar B costs €73 500, which radar gives the best value for money?
   Explain your answer.

**19.** (i) If $\cos A = -\dfrac{\sqrt{3}}{2}$, find the two values for $A$, $0 \leqslant A \leqslant 360°$, without using a calculator.

   (ii) Find the values of $a$ and $b$ in the given diagram where the right angles are indicated.
   Give each answer as a surd.

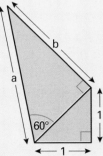

**20.** A surveyor wishes to estimate the area of a triangular patch of woodland.
A sketch is made showing the given measurements.
Estimate the area of the woodland in km², correct to 1 decimal place.

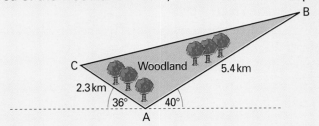

# Summary of Key Points

## The Theorem of Pythagoras

In a right-angled triangle, the square on the hypotenuse is equal to the sum of the squares on the other two sides.

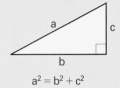

$$a^2 = b^2 + c^2$$

## Sine, cosine and tangent ratios

$$\sin \theta = \frac{\text{opposite}}{\text{hypotenuse}} \qquad \tan \theta = \frac{\text{opposite}}{\text{adjacent}}$$

$$\cos \theta = \frac{\text{adjacent}}{\text{hypotenuse}}$$

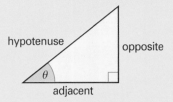

## Area of a triangle

The area of the triangle ABC:

Area $= \frac{1}{2} ab \sin C$

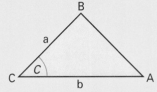

## The Sine Rule

$$\frac{a}{\sin A} = \frac{b}{\sin B} = \frac{c}{\sin C}$$

or $\quad \dfrac{\sin A}{a} = \dfrac{\sin B}{b} = \dfrac{\sin C}{c}$

## The Cosine Rule

$$a^2 = b^2 + c^2 - 2bc \cos A$$

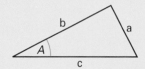

## Ratios of 30°, 45° and 60°

The values of the trigonometric ratios for the angles 30°, 45° and 60° can be found from the triangles on the right.

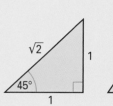

## Sector of a circle

Area of sector AOB $= \dfrac{\theta}{360°} \times \pi r^2$

Length of arc AB $= \dfrac{\theta}{360°} \times 2\pi r$

## Ratios of angles greater than 90°

The diagram shows the positive ratios in the four quadrants.

(i)   In the first quadrant, all (A) positive
(ii)  In the second quadrant, sin(S) only positive
(iii) In the third quadrant, tan(T) only positive
(iv)  In the fourth quadrant, cos(C) only positive.

## SECTION 8.1  Revision of angles and triangles

The diagrams shown below will remind us of some of the results we have encountered in our study of Geometry so far.

### Names and types of angles

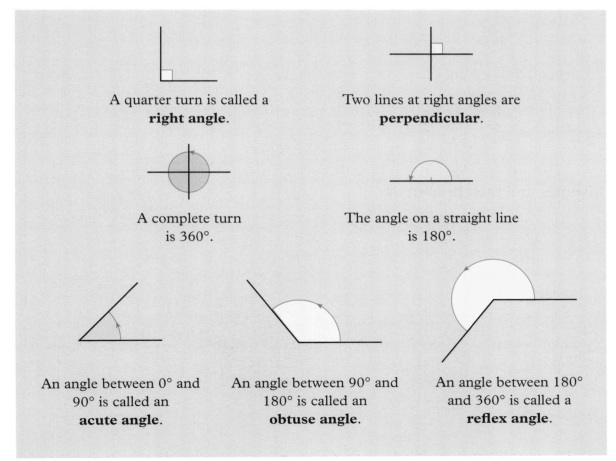

A quarter turn is called a **right angle**.

Two lines at right angles are **perpendicular**.

A complete turn is 360°.

The angle on a straight line is 180°.

An angle between 0° and 90° is called an **acute angle**.

An angle between 90° and 180° is called an **obtuse angle**.

An angle between 180° and 360° is called a **reflex angle**.

## Properties of angles

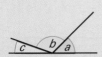

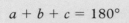

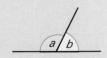

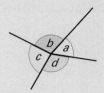

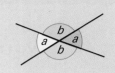

$a + b + c = 180°$

Angles which meet at a point on a straight line add up to 180°.

$a + b = 180°$

A pair of angles that add together to make 180° are called **supplementary angles**.

$a + b + c + d = 360°$

Angles which meet at a point add up to 360°.

Two straight lines which cross at a point form two pairs of **vertically opposite angles**. Vertically opposite angles are **equal**.

Angles formed when a straight line crosses a pair of parallel lines have the following properties:

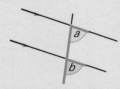

**Corresponding angles** are equal. So $a = b$. You can find them by looking for an F shape.

**Alternate angles** are equal. So $a = b$. Look for a Z shape.

The **interior angles** $x$ and $y$ sum to 180°. $x + y = 180°$.

## Triangles and their properties

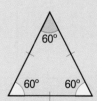

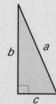

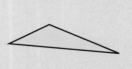

An **equilateral triangle** has:
3 sides equal
3 interior angles equal (60°)

An **isosceles triangle** has:
2 sides equal
base angles equal

A **right-angled triangle** has:
1 angle of 90°
$a^2 = b^2 + c^2$

Triangles without any of these properties are called **scalene triangles**.

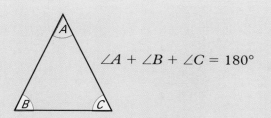 $\angle A + \angle B + \angle C = 180°$

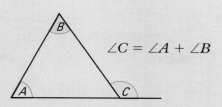 $\angle C = \angle A + \angle B$

The angles of a triangle sum to 180°.

The **exterior angle** of a triangle is equal to the sum of the interior opposite angles.

## Congruent triangles

Triangles are congruent if one of these conditions is true:

 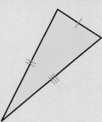

 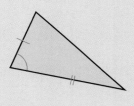

Three pairs of sides are equal (**SSS**).

Two pairs of sides are equal and the angles between them (the included angle) are equal (**SAS**).

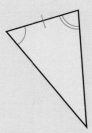 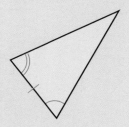

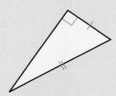 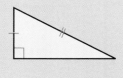

Two pairs of angles are equal and the sides between them are equal (**ASA**).

Both triangles have a right angle, the hypotenuses are equal and one pair of corresponding sides is equal (**RHS**).

# Exercise 8.1

1. Write down the size of the angles marked with letters in each of the following diagrams where arrows indicate parallel lines.

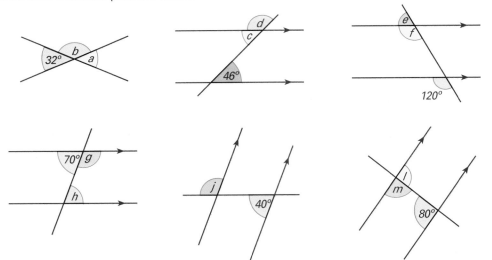

2. Find the size of the angle marked with a letter in each of the following triangles:

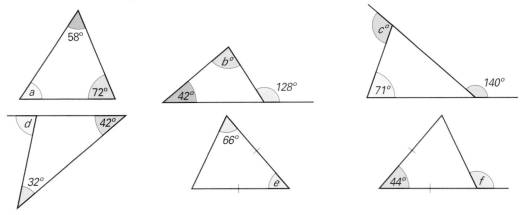

3. Find the size of the angle marked with a letter in the following figures:

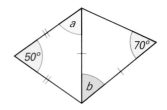 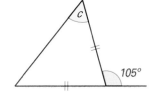 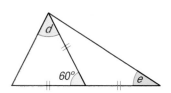

4. Find the measure of the angles marked x and y in the given diagram if the line ℓ is parallel to the line m.

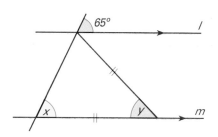

5. Find the values of a, b, c and d in the following triangles:

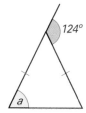 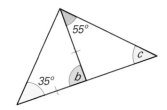 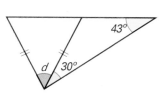

6. In the given triangle, BC∥DEF. Find |∠DAE|.

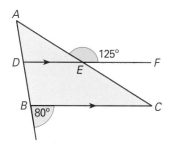

7. In the given diagram, AC is parallel to BE. If |∠BCA| = 80° and |∠CAB| = 55°, find
   (i)  x
   (ii) y.

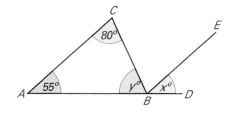

8. In the given diagram, |AB| = |AC| and |∠BAD| = 104°.
   (i)  Find |∠CAB|.
   (ii) Find |∠ABC|.

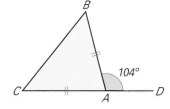

**9.** Find the measure of the angle marked with a letter in each of the following diagrams, where the arrows indicate parallel lines:

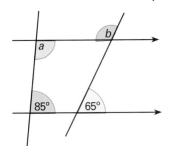 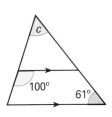 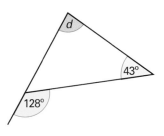

**10.** Find the values of *x* and *y* in the following triangles:

(i)    (ii) 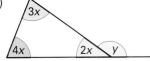   (iii)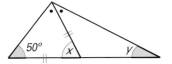

**11.** Use the *Theorem of Pythagoras* to find the length of the side marked with a letter in each of these triangles:

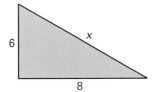 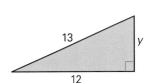 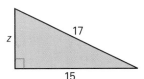

**12.** Find |AB| in the given right-angled triangle.
Now find the area of the triangle ABC.

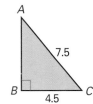

**13.** In the given figure, the angles ACB and ABD are both right angles.
If |AC| = 3, |CB| = 4 and |BD| = 12, find
    (i)  |AB|              (ii)  |AD|.

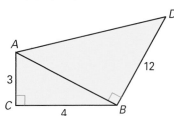

**14.** Find the length of the side marked *x* in each of the following right-angled triangles:

(i)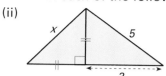

(ii)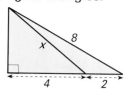

(iii)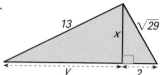

**15.** Find the values of *x* and *y* in the given diagram.
[Remember: $[\sqrt{5}]^2 = 5$.]

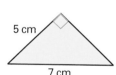

**16.** Explain why the two triangles below are congruent.

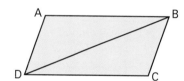

**17.** ABCD is a parallelogram.
Explain why the triangles ABD and
BCD are congruent.

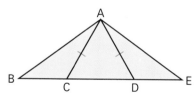

**18.** In the given diagram, |AC| = |AD| and |BD| = |CE|.

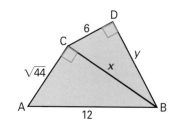

Prove that the triangles ABC and ADE are congruent.

**19.** In the given figure, |∠ACB| = |∠CDB| = 90°.
Find the lengths of the sides marked *x* and *y*.

# SECTION 8.2  Area of triangles and parallelograms ─

The diagrams below show two identical triangles.

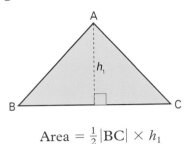

$$\text{Area} = \tfrac{1}{2}|BC| \times h_1$$

In this triangle, the base is [BC] and the perpendicular height is $h_1$.

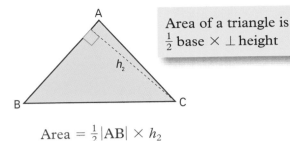

Area of a triangle is $\tfrac{1}{2}$ base $\times \perp$ height

$$\text{Area} = \tfrac{1}{2}|AB| \times h_2$$

In this triangle, the base is [AB] and the perpendicular height is $h_2$.

Since both triangles are identical, their areas are equal.

The areas were found by using different bases and different perpendicular heights.

This illustrates an important theorem about the area of a triangle, as given on the right.

**Theorem**

For any triangle, base times height does not depend on the choice of the base.

---

### Example 1

In the given triangle, $|BC| = 16\,\text{cm}$,
$|AB| = 12\,\text{cm}$ and $[AD] = 10\,\text{cm}$.
Find   (i)   the area of $\triangle ABC$
        (ii)   $|EC|$.

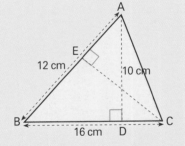

(i)    Area of $\triangle ABC = \tfrac{1}{2}$ base $\times$ perpendicular height

$$= \tfrac{1}{2} \times 16\,\text{cm} \times 10\,\text{cm} \quad \text{... base is [BC]}$$

$$= 80\,\text{cm}^2$$

(ii)   Area is also $\tfrac{1}{2}|AB| \times |EC|$.

$$\therefore \quad \tfrac{1}{2}|AB| \times |EC| = 80\,\text{cm}^2$$

$$\tfrac{1}{2}(12) \times |EC| = 80$$

$$6|EC| = 80$$

$$|EC| = \tfrac{80}{6} = \tfrac{40}{3} = 13\tfrac{1}{3}$$

$$|EC| = 13\tfrac{1}{3}\,\text{cm}$$

# Area of a parallelogram

The figure on the right shows a parallelogram ABCD. In a parallelogram, the opposite sides are parallel and equal in length.

The diagonal [DB] divides the parallelogram into two triangles, ABD and BCD.

These triangles are congruent because the three sides in △ABD are equal in length to the three sides in △BCD.

**Theorem**
A diagonal of a parallelogram bisects the area.

Since the triangles are congruent, they are equal in area.

This shows that the diagonal [DB] bisects the area of the parallelogram ABCD.

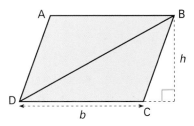

In the given parallelogram,

$$\text{area of } \triangle DCB = \tfrac{1}{2} \times \text{base} \times \text{height}$$
$$= \tfrac{1}{2} \times |DC| \times h$$
$$= \tfrac{1}{2} b \times h$$

Area of ABCD = twice area of △DCB.

$$\therefore \quad \text{Area of ABCD} = 2\left[\tfrac{1}{2} b \times h\right]$$
$$= b \times h$$

**Theorem**
Area of a parallelogram is the base multiplied by the perpendicular height.

---

### Example 2

(i) Find the area of the given parallelogram ABCD.

(ii) If $|BC| = 9\,\text{cm}$, find the perpendicular height, $h$, from A to [BC].

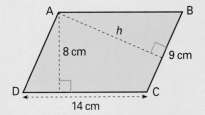

(i)  Area of ABCD = base × perpendicular height
$$= 14 \times 8$$
$$= 112\,\text{cm}^2$$

(ii) Area of ABCD is also $|BC| \times h$
$$= 9\,\text{cm} \times h$$
$$= 9h\,\text{cm}^2$$

But area of ABCD = $112\,\text{cm}^2$   ... from (i) above

$$\therefore \quad 9h = 112$$
$$h = \tfrac{112}{9} = 12\tfrac{4}{9}\,\text{cm}$$

# Exercise 8.2

**1.** Write down the area of each of these triangles:

(i)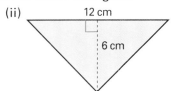

(ii)

(iii)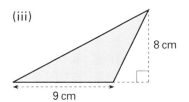

**2.** In the given triangle, $|AB| = 9\,cm$, $|BC| = 12\,cm$ and the perpendicular height from C to [AB] is 8 cm.

Find (i) the area of the triangle ABC
(ii) the perpendicular distance from A to [BC].

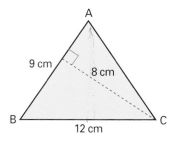

**3.** Find the value of $x$ in each of these triangles:

(i)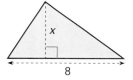

Area = 16 sq. units

(ii)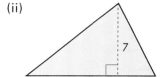

Area = 35 sq. units

(iii)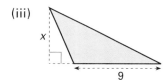

Area = 27 sq. units

**4.** Find the value of $h$ in each of these triangles:

(i)

(ii)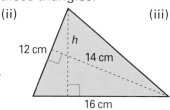

(iii)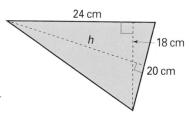

**5.** Find the area of each of these parallelograms:

(i)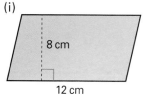

(ii)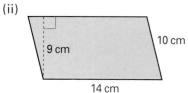

(iii)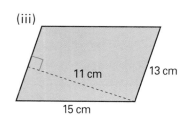

6. Find the area of the given parallelogram ABCD.
   Now find the length of the side [BC].

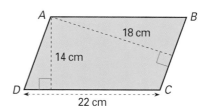

7. ABCD and DCEF are parallelograms.
   Use the diagram to explain why the two
   parallelograms are equal in area.

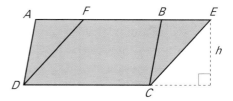

8. The area of the parallelogram ABCD is 40 cm².
   If |DB| = 15 cm, find |AE|, where AE ⊥ DB.

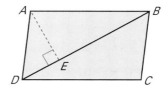

9. ABCD is a parallelogram and angles are marked 1 to 5.
   (i)  Name three pairs of equal angles.
   (ii) Explain why $|\angle 1| + |\angle 2| = 180°$.

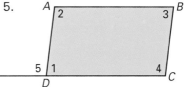

10. ABCD and ADBE are both parallelograms.
    If the area of the triangle DCB = 15 cm², find
    (i)   area of parallelogram ABCD
    (ii)  area of parallelogram ADBE
    (iii) area of the figure ADCE
    (iv)  the perpendicular height from A to [DC],
          if |DC| = 7.5 cm.

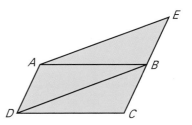

11. ABCD is a parallelogram and M is the midpoint of [AB].
    (i)   Explain why |∠DAM| = |∠MBP|.
    (ii)  Now show that the triangles AMD and MBP
          are congruent.
    (iii) Now show that B is the midpoint of [CP].

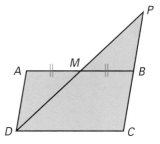

**12.** In the given parallelogram, DE ⊥ AC and BF ⊥ AC. The area of ABCD is 80 cm².

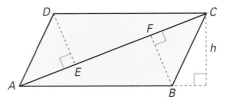

    (i)   If |AC| = 16 cm, find |DE|.

    (ii)  Explain why |DE| = |BF|.

    (iii) If |AB| = 10 cm, find the length of the perpendicular height, *h*.

**13.** ABCD is a parallelogram and E is a point on [AB].

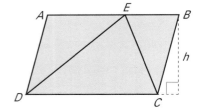

    (i)   Explain why the area of △DCE is equal to half the area of ABCD.

    (ii)  If the area of ABCD is 60 cm² and the area of △ADE is 20 cm², find the area of △ECB.

# SECTION 8.3 Triangles and ratios

## Angles and sides

The triangle ABC on the right is drawn to scale.

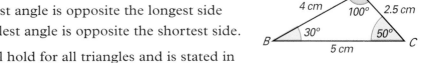

Notice (i)   the largest angle is opposite the longest side

       (ii)  the smallest angle is opposite the shortest side.

These properties will hold for all triangles and is stated in the theorem below.

> **Theorem**
> The angle opposite the greater of two sides is greater than the angle opposite the lesser side.

In the given triangle ABC, we are given the measures of the three angles.

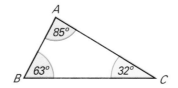

**Converse** means opposite or reversed.

The converse of the theorem above states that [BC] is the longest side because it is opposite the greatest angle and [AB] is the shortest side because it is opposite the smallest angle.

> **Converse of theorem:**
> The side opposite the greater of two angles is longer than the side opposite the lesser angle.

## Triangle inequality

The shortest distance between two points is the line that joins these points.

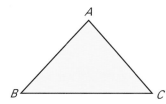

It follows from this that

$$|BA| + |AC| > |BC|$$

Similarly $\quad |AB| + |BC| > |AC|$

and $\quad |BC| + |CA| > |AB|$.

**Theorem**
Two sides of a triangle are together greater than the third side.

## Transversals

In the given diagram, $\ell$, $m$ and $n$ are parallel lines.

The lines $p$ and $q$ are called **transversals**.

For the transversal, $p$, $|AB| = |BC|$.

In this case we say that the parallel lines cut off **equal segments** on the transversal.

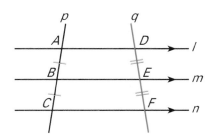

The line, $q$, is another transversal.
It can be shown that the line segments [DE] and [EF] are also equal in length.

The same property also holds for all other transversals.

> **Theorem**
> If three parallel lines cut off equal segments on some transversal line, then they will cut off equal segments on any other transversal.

---

**Example 1**

The diagram shows three parallel lines and two transversal $x$ and $y$.

$$|AB| = |BC|.$$

If $|DE| = 6\,cm$, find $|EF|$

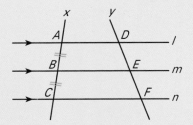

Since the parallel lines cut equal segments on the transversal $x$, they will also cut equal segments on transversal $y$.

$\therefore \quad |DE| = |EF|$

$\therefore \quad |EF| = 6\,cm$

## Line parallel to a side of a triangle

The diagram on the right shows the side [AB] of the triangle divided into three equal parts. If lines are drawn through D and E parallel to BC, then the points X and Y will divide the side [AC] into three equal parts also.

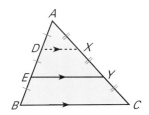

In the given triangle, X divides the side [AB] in the ratio $s:t$.

If XY is parallel to BC, then Y will divide [AC] also in the ratio $s:t$, as shown.

This diagram illustrates a very important and useful geometric result which is given on the right.

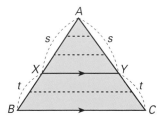

**Theorem**
A line drawn parallel to one side of a triangle divides the other two sides in the same ratio.

---

### Example 2

In the given triangle, the arrows indicate that the lines are parallel. Find the length of the side marked $x$.

$$\frac{3}{4} = \frac{2}{x}$$

$$3x = 8 \qquad \text{...multiply both sides by } 4x$$

$$x = \tfrac{8}{3} = 2\tfrac{2}{3}$$

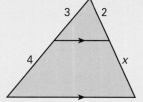

---

## Similar triangles

The triangles ABC and DEF shown below have equal angles.

Notice that the triangles have the same shape but different sizes.
These triangles are said to be **similar** or **equiangular** triangles.

The sides [AB] and [DE] are said to be **corresponding sides,** as they are both opposite the 60° angle.

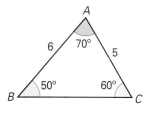

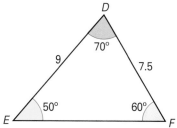

Notice that $|DE| = 1\tfrac{1}{2}|AB|$ and $|DF| = 1\tfrac{1}{2}|AC|$.

Similarly $|EF|$ is $1\tfrac{1}{2}|BC|$.

This illustrates that $\dfrac{|AB|}{|DE|} = \dfrac{|AC|}{|DF|} = \dfrac{|BC|}{|EF|} = \dfrac{6}{9} = \dfrac{2}{3}.$

This important result for similar triangles is stated in the theorem on the right.

**Theorem**
If two triangles ABC and DEF are similar, then their sides are proportional, in order
$$\frac{|AB|}{|DE|} = \frac{|BC|}{|EF|} = \frac{|AC|}{|DF|}$$

---

**Example 3**

(i) Explain why the two given triangles are similar.
(ii) Find the length of the side marked $x$.

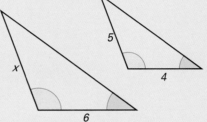

(i) Two angles in one triangle are equal to two angles in the other triangle. Thus the third angles in the triangles are equal.

(ii) $\frac{x}{5} = \frac{6}{4}$

$4x = 30$

$x = \frac{30}{4} = 7\frac{2}{4} = 7\frac{1}{2}$

Two triangles will be similar if 2 angles in one triangle are equal to 2 angles in the other triangle.

---

## Exercise 8.3

1. (i) Which is the longest side in the given triangle ABC?
   (ii) Which is the shortest side?
   (iii) Explain why $|BA| + |AC| > |BC|$.

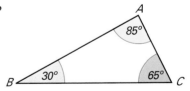

2. In the given triangle XYZ, $|XY| = 7$ cm and $|YZ| = 10$ cm.
   Say if each of the following
   (i) could be true
   (ii) is false
      (a) $|XZ| = 2$ cm
      (b) $|XZ| = 6$ cm
      (c) $|XZ| = 18$ cm.

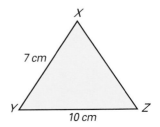

**3.** In the given triangle, |AB| = 5 cm, |BC| = 10 cm and |AC| = 8 cm.

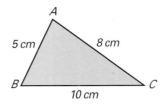

    (i)   Name the largest angle in this triangle. Give a reason for your answer.

    (ii)  Name the smallest angle.

**4.** *a*, *b* and *c* are parallel lines.

*p*, *q* and *r* are three transversals intersecting *a*, *b* and *c*.

|DE| = |EF|, |GH| = 8 cm and |JK| = 7 cm.

Find    (i)  |HI|      (ii)  |GJ|.

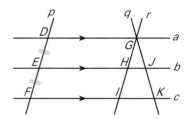

**5.** In the diagram, ℓ, *m* and *n* are parallel lines.
They make intercepts of the indicated lengths
on the lines *j* and *k*.
AB is parallel to *j*.

    (i)   Write down the length of [AB].

    (ii)  Write down the length of [AC].

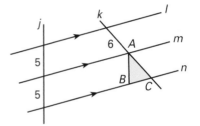

**6.** In each of the following triangles the arrows indicate that the lines are parallel.
Find the length of the line segment marked *x* in each triangle:

    (i)                    (ii)                  (iii)

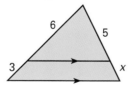 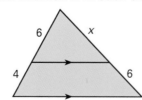 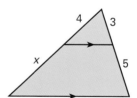

**7.** Find the length of the line segment marked *a* in each of the following triangles where
the arrows indicate parallel lines:

    (i)                    (ii)                  (iii)

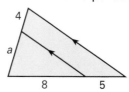 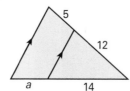 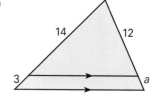

**8.** In the given diagram, DE∥BC.
If $\dfrac{|AD|}{|DB|} = \dfrac{2}{1}$ and $|AE| = 14\,\text{cm}$,
find $|EC|$.

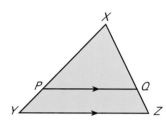

**9.** In the given diagram, PQ∥YZ and $\dfrac{|XQ|}{|QZ|} = \dfrac{5}{3}$.
If $|PY| = 4\,\text{cm}$, find $|PX|$.

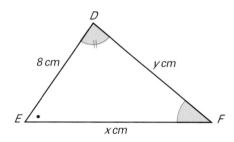

**10.**

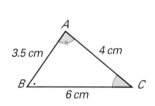

(i)   Explain why the triangles ABC and DEF are similar.
(ii)  Which side of the triangle DEF corresponds to the side [AC]?
(iii) Find the values of $x$ and $y$.

**11.** The two given triangles are similar.
  (i)  Copy and complete this statement:
       'Each side of the bigger triangle is... times
       the length of the corresponding side of
       the smaller triangle'.
  (ii) Find the values of $x$ and $y$.

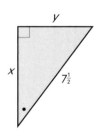

**12.** In the given triangles, the marked angles are equal.
  (i)  Explain why the two triangles are similar.
  (ii) Find the values of $x$ and $y$.

**13.** The triangles ABC and XYZ are similar.

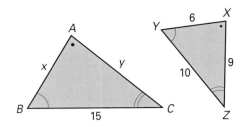

  (i) Which side of the triangle XYZ corresponds to [AB]? Explain your answer.

  (ii) Find the values of x and y.

**14.** Find the value of x and the value of y in the given similar triangles.

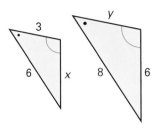

**15.** In the given figure BC∥DE.
Draw the triangles ABC and ADE as separate diagrams.
Mark in the lengths of the known sides in each triangle.

  (i) Explain why the triangles ABC and ADE are similar.

  (ii) Now find |DE|.

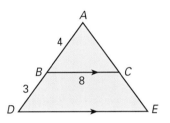

**16.** ABCD is a quadrilateral in which AB∥DC and |∠DAB| = |∠DBC|.

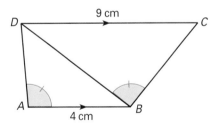

  (i) Name two other equal angles in this figure.

  (ii) Now explain why the triangles ABD and DCB are similar.

  (iii) Which side in the △DCB corresponds to [DB] in the △ABD?

  (iv) Which side in the △ABD corresponds to [BC] in the △BCD?

**17.** In the given triangle DE∥BC,
|AD| = 8,
|DB| = 4 and
|AC| = 9.
Find |AE|.
[Hint: Let |AE| = x ⇒ |EC| = 9 − x.]

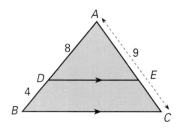

**18.** Explain why the triangles ABC and ADE are similar.

(i) Fill in the missing parts in these ratios:

$$\frac{|AD|}{|AB|} = \frac{|AE|}{\boxed{\phantom{xxx}}} = \frac{|DE|}{\boxed{\phantom{xxx}}}.$$

(ii) Use these ratios to find the values of $x$ and $y$.

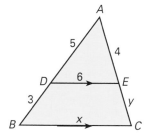

# SECTION 8.4  Circle theorems

In this section we will deal with the geometry of the circle and look at some important mathematical results known as **circle theorems**.

You will have already learned that the angle in a semicircle is a right angle.

In this circle, $|\angle ACB| = 90°$.

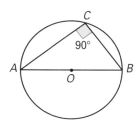

## Tangents and chords

A tangent to a circle is a straight line which meets the circle at one point only.

In the given diagram, $\ell$ is a tangent to the circle.

T is called the **point of contact**.

[AB] and [CD] are **chords** of the circle.

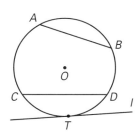

> **Theorem**
> The perpendicular from the centre of a circle to a chord bisects the chord.

In the given diagram, [OM] is perpendicular to the chord [AB].

$|AM| = |MB|$

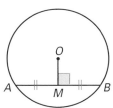

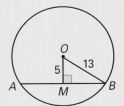

### Example 1

In the given diagram, O is the centre of the circle and [OM] is perpendicular to [AB]. If |OM| = 5 and |OB| = 13, find |AB|.

The triangle OBM is right-angled.

$$\therefore \quad |OB|^2 = |OM|^2 + |MB|^2$$
$$13^2 = 5^2 + |MB|^2$$
$$169 = 25 + |MB|^2$$
$$|MB|^2 + 25 = 169$$
$$|MB|^2 = 169 - 25$$
$$= 144$$
$$|MB| = 12$$

Since M is the midpoint of [AB], |AM| = |MB|.

$$|AB| = |AM| + |MB|$$
$$= 12 + 12$$
$$|AB| = 24$$

The diagram below shows a tangent $PT$ to the circle $k$ with centre O.

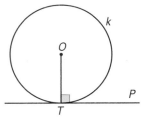

**Theorem (1)**
A tangent is perpendicular to the radius that goes to the point of contact.

T is the point of contact and [OT] is a radius.

$$OT \perp TP$$

**Theorem (2)**
If a point P lies on a circle k, and a line $\ell$ is perpendicular to the radius to P, then $\ell$ is a tangent to k.

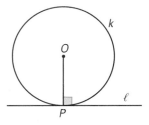

### Example 2

In the given diagram PT is a tangent to the circle and [OT] is a radius.
If $|\angle TOQ| = 120°$, find the measures of the angles marked x and y.

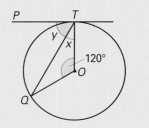

The triangle OTQ is isosceles as $|OT| = |OQ| =$ radius

$$\therefore \quad |\angle OTQ| = |\angle OQT| = x$$
$$\therefore \quad\quad 2x = 180° - 120°$$
$$= 60$$
$$x = 30°$$

Since $OT \perp PT \Rightarrow |\angle OTP| = 90°$

$$\therefore \quad x + y = 90°$$
$$30 + y = 90° \quad ... x = 30°$$
$$y = 90° - 30°$$
$$y = 60°$$

## Corollary

If two circles intersect at one point only, then the two centres and the point of contact are collinear.

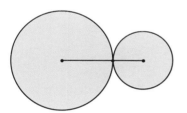
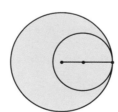

A **corollary** is a statement attached to a theorem which has been proven and follows obviously from it.

## Exercise 8.4

1. Find the measure of the angles marked with letters in the following circles with O as centre:

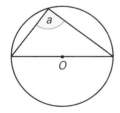
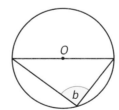
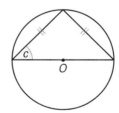

2. In the given circle, O is the centre.
   Explain why △OAC is isosceles.
   Now write down
   (i)   $|\angle OCA|$
   (ii)  $|\angle ACB|$
   (iii) $|\angle OBC|$

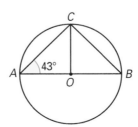

3. Find the measure of the angles marked with letters in the following diagrams, where O is the centre of the circles.

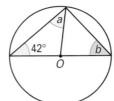 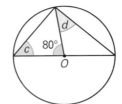 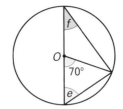

4. In the given diagram, O is the centre of the circle, |AB| = 6 and |OB| = 5.
   (i) Name the right-angled triangle.
   (ii) |OB| = 5.
       Name two other line segments that are 5 units in length.
   (iii) Find |AC|.
   (iv) Find |BC|.
   (v) Find the area of △ABC.

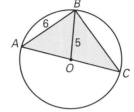

Area of △ is $\frac{1}{2}$ base × ⊥ height

5. In the given figure, O is the centre of the circle and OM ⊥ AB.
   If |OM| = 5 cm and |AB| = 12 cm, find
       (i) |AM|
       (ii) the length of the radius of the circle.

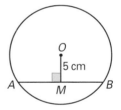

6. In the given diagram, O is the centre of the circle of radius 26 cm.
   OX is perpendicular to CD and |OX| = 10 cm.
   Find |CD|.

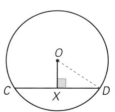

7. ST is a tangent to the given circle with O as centre.
   If |∠PST| = 40°, find
       (i) |∠OST|
       (ii) |∠OSP|
       (iii) |∠OPS|
       (iv) |∠SOP|

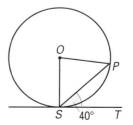

8. In the given diagram, PT is a tangent to the
   circle of centre O and $|\angle BPE| = 55°$.
   Find   (i)  $|\angle EPO|$
           (ii)  $|\angle BPO|$
           (iii)  $|\angle ABP|$
           (iv)  $|\angle BAP|$.

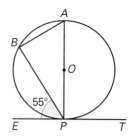

9. In the given figure BX is a tangent to the
   circle with centre O.
   If $|\angle XOD| = 120°$, find $|\angle OBX|$.

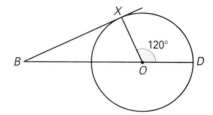

10. In the given diagram PT is a tangent to the
    circle of centre O and radius length 5 cm.
    If $|PQ| = 8$ cm, find $|PT|$.

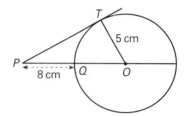

11. In the given diagram, PQ is a tangent to the
    circle of centre O.
    If $|\angle TPO| = 30°$, find
       (i)  $|\angle POT|$
       (ii)  $|\angle TOR|$
       (iii)  $|\angle ORT|$
       (iv)  $|\angle RTO|$.

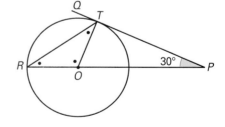

12. PT is a tangent to the circle of centre O.
    If $|\angle POT| = 70°$ and $|\angle PAO| = 40°$,
       find   (i)  $|\angle OPT|$
               (ii)  $|\angle OPA|$.

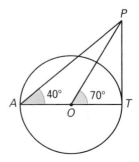

13. In the given diagram, O is the centre of the circle. PA and PB are tangents to the circle.

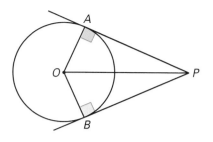

  (i) Explain why the triangles AOP and BOP are congruent.

  (ii) Hence show that |PA| = |PB|.

> The lengths of two tangents from a point to a circle are equal.

14. In the given diagram PA and PT are tangents to the circle of centre O.

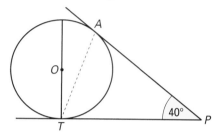

If |∠APT| = 40°, find |∠ATO|.

15. In the given diagram, [AB] is a tangent to the circle and [AD] is a diameter.
   If |∠ABD| = 50° and |AB| = |AE|,
   find
     (i)   |∠EAB|
     (ii)  |∠DAE|
     (iii) |∠ADE|.

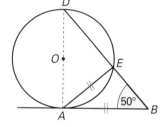

# SECTION 8.5  Formal proofs of theorems

Geometry results or **theorems** are proved in a formal or structured way by using previously established results and axioms to explain the steps that we take. This method of proving geometric results was first used by a Greek mathematician named Euclid about 300 BC.

> An **axiom** is a statement accepted without proof. The angles in a straight line add to 180° is an example of an axiom.

The proofs of numerous theorems are contained in his famous book on geometry called *Elements*. Today, over 2000 years later, we still use Euclid's approach to solve many problems in geometry.

> A **theorem** is a statement that can be shown to be true through the use of axioms and logical argument.

In this section formal proofs of the ten theorems on your course are given. You will not be asked to reproduce these proofs in your examination. They are given here to illustrate the formal steps that are followed in the proof of a geometric theorem.

You will be familiar with the results of these theorems from the earlier sections of this chapter. The various geometrical problems that you solved used the results established in these theorems.

**Theorem 1**  The angle opposite the longer of two sides is greater than the angle opposite the shorter side.

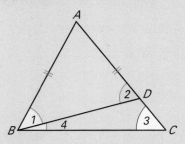

*Given:*  The triangle ABC in which $|AC| > |AB|$

*To Prove:*  $|\angle ABC| > |\angle ACB|$.

*Construction:*  Take the point D on [AC] such that $|AD| = |AB|$. Join BD. Name the angles 1, 2, 3 and 4, as shown.

*Proof:*  $|\angle 1| = |\angle 2|$   ...isosceles triangle
$|\angle 2| > |\angle 3|$   ...exterior angle > interior angle
$\Rightarrow \; |\angle 1| > |\angle 3|$
$\Rightarrow \; |\angle 1| + |\angle 4| > |\angle 3|$
$\Rightarrow \; |\angle ABC| > |\angle ACB|$

**Theorem 2**  The sum of the lengths of any two sides of a triangle is greater than that of the third side.

*Given:*  The triangle ABC.

*To Prove:*  $|BA| + |AC| > |BC|$

*Construction:*  Produce BA to D such that $|AD| = |AC|$. Join DC.

*Proof:*  $|\angle ACD| = |\angle ADC|$   ...($|AD| = |AC|$)
But $|\angle BCD| > |\angle ACD|$
$\Rightarrow \; |\angle BCD| > |\angle ADC|$
In the triangle BCD, $|BD| > |BC|$ ...side opposite greater angle
But $|BD| = |BA| + |AC|$
$\Rightarrow \; |BA| + |AC| > |BC|$.

**Theorem 3**   If three parallel lines make segments of equal length on a transversal, then they will also make segments of equal length on any other transversal.

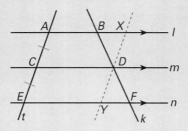

*Given:*   Three parallel lines $\ell$, $m$ and $n$ intersecting the transversal $t$ at the points A, C and E such that $|AC| = |CE|$.
Another transversal $k$ intersects the lines at B, D and F.

*To prove:*   $|BD| = |DF|$.

*Construction:*   Through D draw a line parallel to $t$ intersecting $\ell$ at X and $n$ at Y.

*Proof:*   ACDX and CEYD are parallelograms.
$\Rightarrow$   $|AC| = |XD|$ and $|CE| = |DY|$   ...opposite sides
But   $|AC| = |CE|$.
$\Rightarrow$   $|XD| = |DY|$
In the triangles BDX and YDF,
$\quad\quad |XD| = |DY|$
$\quad |\angle BDX| = |\angle YDF|$   ...vertically opposite
$\quad |\angle DBX| = |\angle DFY|$   ...alternate angles
$\Rightarrow$   the triangles BDX and YDF are congruent
$\Rightarrow$   $|BD| = |DF|$   ...corresponding sides

**Theorem 4**   Let ABC be a triangle. If a line XY is parallel to BC and cuts [AB] in the ratio $s : t$, then it cuts [AC] also in the same ratio.

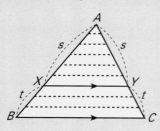

| | |
|---|---|
| *Given:* | The triangle ABC with XY parallel to BC. |
| *To Prove:* | $\dfrac{\lvert AX \rvert}{\lvert XB \rvert} = \dfrac{\lvert AY \rvert}{\lvert YC \rvert}$ |
| *Construction:* | Divide [AX] into $s$ equal parts and [XB] into $t$ equal parts. Draw a line parallel to BC through each point of the division. |
| *Proof:* | The parallel lines make intercepts of equal length along the line [AC]. |

∴   [AY] is divided into $s$ equal intercepts and [YC] is divided into $t$ equal intercepts.

$$\therefore \quad \frac{\lvert AY \rvert}{\lvert YC \rvert} = \frac{s}{t}$$

But $\dfrac{\lvert AX \rvert}{\lvert XB \rvert} = \dfrac{s}{t} \quad \Rightarrow \quad \dfrac{\lvert AX \rvert}{\lvert XB \rvert} = \dfrac{\lvert AY \rvert}{\lvert YC \rvert}$

**Theorem 5**   If two triangles ABC and DEF are similar, then their sides are proportional in order:

$$\frac{\lvert AB \rvert}{\lvert DE \rvert} = \frac{\lvert BC \rvert}{\lvert EF \rvert} = \frac{\lvert AC \rvert}{\lvert DF \rvert}$$

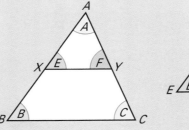 

| | |
|---|---|
| *Given:* | The triangles ABC and DEF in which $\lvert \angle A \rvert = \lvert \angle D \rvert$, $\lvert \angle B \rvert = \lvert \angle E \rvert$ and $\lvert \angle C \rvert = \lvert \angle F \rvert$. |
| *To Prove:* | $\dfrac{\lvert AB \rvert}{\lvert DE \rvert} = \dfrac{\lvert BC \rvert}{\lvert EF \rvert} = \dfrac{\lvert AC \rvert}{\lvert DF \rvert}.$ |
| *Construction:* | Mark the point X on [AB] such that $\lvert AX \rvert = \lvert DE \rvert$. Mark the point Y on [AC] such that $\lvert AY \rvert = \lvert DF \rvert$. Join XY. |

*Proof:*   The triangles AXY and DEF are congruent   ...(SAS)

$\therefore$  $|\angle AXY| = |\angle DEF| = E$   ...corresponding angles

$\therefore$  $|\angle AXY| = |\angle ABC|$

$\therefore$  $XY\|BC$

$\therefore$  $\dfrac{|AB|}{|AX|} = \dfrac{|AC|}{|AY|}$   ...a line parallel to one side divides
the other side in the same ratio

$\therefore$  $\dfrac{|AB|}{|DE|} = \dfrac{|AC|}{|DF|}$

Similarly it can be proved that $\dfrac{|AB|}{|DE|} = \dfrac{|BC|}{|EF|}$.

$\therefore$  $\dfrac{|AB|}{|DE|} = \dfrac{|BC|}{|EF|} = \dfrac{|AC|}{|DF|}$.

---

**Theorem 6**   For a triangle, base times height does not depend on the choice of base.

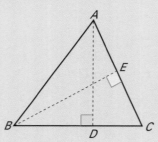

*Given:*   The triangle ABC with AD $\perp$ BC and BE $\perp$ AC.

*To prove:*   $|BC|\cdot|AD| = |AC|\cdot|BE|$.

*Proof:*   In the triangles
ADC and BEC
$|\angle ADC| = |\angle BEC| = 90°$
$\angle ACD$ is common to both
$\Rightarrow$  $|\angle CAD| = |\angle EBC|$
$\Rightarrow$  the triangles ADC
and BEC are similar

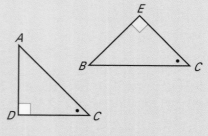

Since the corresponding sides are in the same ratio,

$\Rightarrow$  $\dfrac{|AD|}{|BE|} = \dfrac{|AC|}{|BC|}$

$\Rightarrow$  $|BC|\cdot|AD| = |AC|\cdot|BE|$.

**Theorem 7**   A diagonal bisects the area of a parallelogram.

*Given:*   The parallelogram ABCD and
the diagonal [AC]

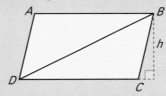

*To prove:*   The diagonal [AC] bisects the
area of ABCD.

*Proof:*   In the triangles ABC and ADC,
|AB| = |DC|   ...opposite sides
|BC| = |AD|   ...opposite sides
|AC| = |AC|
∴   the triangles ABC and ADC are congruent   ...(SSS)
∴   the area of △ABC = area of △ADC
∴   the diagonal [AC] bisects the area of ABCD.

---

**Theorem 8**   The area of a parallelogram is the base by the height.

*Given:*   The parallelogram ABCD with perpendicular height, $h$.

*To Prove:*   The area of ABCD = |DC| × $h$.

*Proof:*   Area of △BCD = $\frac{1}{2}$ base × perpendicular height
= $\frac{1}{2}$ |DC| × $h$
Area of △ABD = area of △BCD
⇒   Area ABCD = $2\left[\frac{1}{2} |DC| \times h\right]$   ...diagonal bisects area
of a parallelogram
Area of ABCD = |DC| × $h$

---

**Theorem 9**   A tangent is perpendicular to the
radius that goes to the point of
contact.

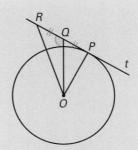

*Given:*   A tangent $t$ to a circle of centre O.
P is the point of contact of the
tangent and circle and [OP] is
the radius to the point of contact.

| | |
|---|---|
| *To prove:* | $OP \perp t$ |
| *Construction:* | Let the perpendicular to the tangent from the centre O meet it at Q. Pick another point R on *t* such that $|PQ| = |QR|$. Join OQ and OR. |
| *Proof:* | In the triangles OPQ and OQR, |

$$|OQ| = |OQ| \quad \text{...common side}$$
$$|PQ| = |QR| \quad \text{...given}$$
$$|\angle OQP| = |\angle OQR| \quad \text{...both } 90°$$
∴ the triangles OPQ amd OQR are congruent
∴ $|OR| = |OP|$ ...both hypotenuses
So R is a second point where *t* meets the circle.
This contradicts the given fact that *t* is a tangent.
Thus *t* must be perpendicular to [OP], i.e., $OP \perp t$.

**Note:** The proof above is an example of proof by contradiction.

| | |
|---|---|
| **Theorem 10** | The perpendicular from the centre of a circle to a chord bisects the chord. |
| *Given:* | A circle k with centre O and a chord [AB]. $OM \perp AB$. |
| *To Prove:* | $|AM| = |MB|$ |
| *Construction:* | Join OA and OB. |
| *Proof:* | In the triangles AOM and BOM, |

$$|OA| = |OB| = \text{radius}$$
$$|OM| = |OM| \quad \text{...common side}$$
$$|\angle OMA| = |\angle OMB| \quad \text{...both} = 90°$$
∴ the triangles AOM and BOM are congruent ...(RHS)
∴ $|AM| = |MB|$.

# TEST YOURSELF 8

1. In the given triangle, marked sides are equal and $|\angle CAE| = 124°$.
   (i) What sort of triangle is ABC?
   (ii) Name two equal angles.
   (iii) Find $|\angle ABC|$.

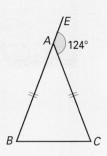

2. ABCD is a parallelogram.
   If $|\angle CAB| = 25°$ and $|\angle BDC| = 55°$, find $|\angle AOD|$.

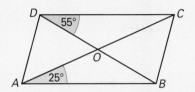

3. Find the area of each of the parallelograms shown below:

   (i)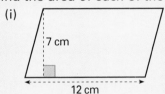
   7 cm
   12 cm

   (ii)
   9 cm
   14 cm

   (iii)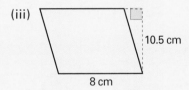
   10.5 cm
   8 cm

4. The area of the given parallelogram is 280 cm².
   (i) Find the value of $h$.
   (ii) If $|AB| = 28$ cm, find the perpendicular height from A to DC.

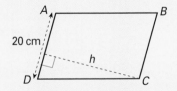

20 cm

5. ABCD and ABDE are both parallelograms.
   (i) Explain why ABCD and ABDE are equal in area.
   (ii) If the area of $\triangle ABC = 24$ cm², find the area of the figure ABCE.

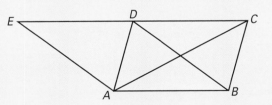

6. In the given figure, BC is a tangent to the circle at B and O is the centre of the circle.
   (i) Explain why $OB \perp BC$.
   (ii) Name two line segments that are equal in length.
   (iii) Find $|\angle BOA|$.

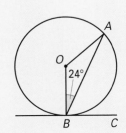

24°

**7.** In the given diagram PT is a tangent to the circle of
centre O and radius 7 cm.

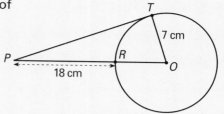

  (i)   What is $|\angle PTO|$?
        Explain your answer.
  (ii)  Write down $|PO|$.
  (iii) Find $|PT|$.

**8.** In the given circle, O is the centre, $|\angle ACD| = 65°$ and $|AB| = |BC|$.

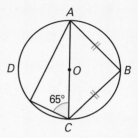

  (i)   Name two right angles in the figure.
  (ii)  Find $|\angle BAD|$.

**9.** In the given circle, O is the centre and the angles $x$ and $y$
are marked.

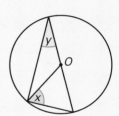

  (i)   Copy this figure and mark in another angle $x$
        and another angle $y$.
  (ii)  Explain why $x + y = 90°$.

**10.** PT is a tangent to the circle at T.
The centre of the circle is O.
$|PT| = 6$ cm and $|ON| = |NP|$.

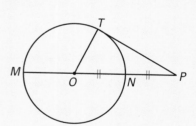

  (i)   What is $|\angle OTP|$?
  (ii)  Find the length of the radius of the circle.

**11.** In the given triangle , $\ell \| k$.
Calculate the value of $x$.

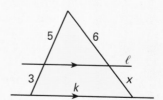

**12.** In the given triangle, $XY \| BC$ and $|AX| : |XB| = 3 : 2$.
If $|YC| = 10$ cm, find $|AY|$.

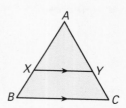

**13.** In the given diagram, DE∥BC.

    (i)   Explain why the triangles ADE and ABC
         are similar.

    (ii)  Find the length of the line segments
         marked x and a.

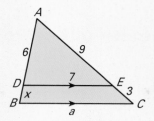

**14.** In the given circle, O is the centre and AD is a tangent at A.
The triangle AOB is equilateral.

    (i)   Name two right angles in the figure.

    (ii)  Find |∠OAB|

    (iii) Find |∠BAD|

    (iv) Find |∠CAO|.

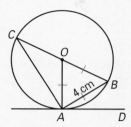

**15.** In the given figure, ∠CAB and ∠ABD are both right angles.
|AC| = 6, |AB| = 8 and |AD| = 17.

    (i)   Find |DB|.

    (ii)  Find the area of ACBD.

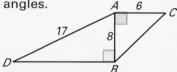

**16.** ABCD, AEBD and AEFC are parallelograms.
The area of △ABE = 12 square units.

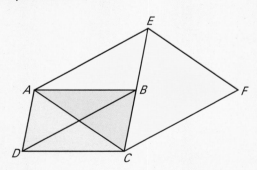

    (i)   Explain why the area of △ABD is also 12 square units.

    (ii)  Explain why the parallelograms ABCD and AEBD are equal in area.

    (iii) Find the area of the figure ADCE.

    (iv) Find the area of the △ABC.

    (v)  Find the area of the △ACE.

    (vi) Find the area of the figure ADCFE.

## Summary of Key Points

1. The sum of the lengths of any two sides of a triangle is greater than the length of the third side.

2. The angle opposite the longer of two sides is greater than the angle opposite the shorter side.

3. For any triangle, base times height does not depend on the choice of base.

4. A diagonal of a parallelogram bisects the area.

5. The area of a parallelogram is the base multiplied by the perpendicular height.

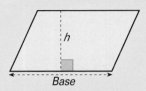

6. If three parallel lines cut off equal segments on some transversal line, then they will cut off equal segments on any other transversal.

7. A line drawn parallel to one side of a triangle divides the other two sides in the same ratio.

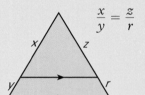

8.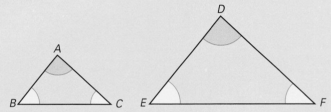

If two triangles ABC and DEF are similar, then their sides are proportional in order,

$$\frac{|AB|}{|DE|} = \frac{|BC|}{|EF|} = \frac{|AC|}{|DF|}.$$

9. The perpendicular from the centre of a circle bisects the chord.

10. A tangent is perpendicular to the radius that goes to the point of contact.

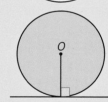

11. If two circles intersect at one point only, then their centres and the point of contact are collinear.

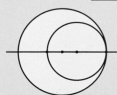
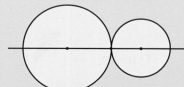

## SECTION 9.1 Enlargements

Here are two photographs.

They are both printed from the same negative.

The dimensions of the photo on the right are twice the dimensions of the photo on the left.

We say that one photo is an **enlargement** of the other.

Since the length and width of the larger photo are twice those of the smaller photo, we say that the **scale factor** of the enlargement is **2**.

In this diagram the rectangle A′B′C′D′ is an enlargement of the rectangle ABCD.

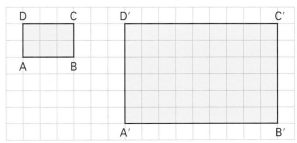

Here      |AB| = 3   and   |A′B′| = 9
          |AD| = 2   and   |A′D′| = 6

The sides of the rectangle A′B′C′D′ are three times as long as the sides of the rectangle ABCD. Here the **scale factor** is **3**.

Now consider the two triangles ABC and A'B'C', shown below.

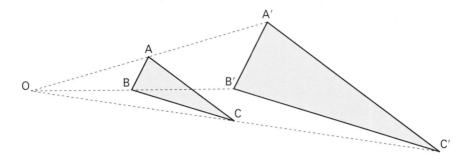

The triangle A'B'C' is an enlargement of the triangle ABC.

The point O is called the **centre of enlargement**.

Since $|OA'| = 2|OA|$, the scale factor is 2.

Since the scale factor is 2,  $|A'B'| = 2|AB|$,  $|A'C'| = 2|AC|$  and  $|B'C'| = 2|BC|$.

The given triangle ABC is called the **object**.

The triangle A'B'C' is called the **image**.

The dotted lines are called guidelines or **rays**.

## Drawing enlargements

To construct the image of a given figure under an enlargement, we need
  (i)   the centre of enlargement
 (ii)   the scale factor of the enlargement.

The diagram below shows a square ABCD and a centre of enlargement O.

We will now enlarge ABCD with O as centre of enlargement and scale factor 3.

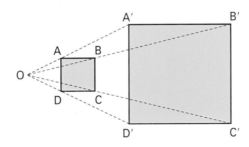

To find the image of A, we join O to A and continue to A' so that $|OA'| = 3|OA|$.

Similarly, join O to B and continue to B' so that $|OB'| = 3|OB|$.

Repeat the process for the points C and D.

The square A'B'C'D' is the image of the square ABCD.

Since the scale factor is 3, $|A'B'| = 3|AB|$ and $|A'D'| = 3|AD|$.

## When a vertex is the centre of enlargement

The diagrams below show how to enlarge the shape ABCD by a scale factor of 2 using A as the centre of enlargement.

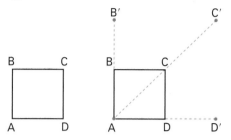 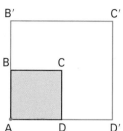

Notice that the centre of enlargement, A, does not move.

In the final figure,  $|AB'| = 2|AB|$,  $|AD'| = 2|AD|$  and  $|AC'| = 2|AC|$.

The diagram on the right shows an enlargement where the centre of enlargement, X, is inside the figure.

In this enlargement, the scale factor is 2.

Draw the line [XA] and extend it so that  $|XA'| = 2|XA|$.

Extend [XB] so that  $|XB'| = 2|XB|$.

Repeat for [XC].

Each side of the enlarged triangle A'B'C' is twice the length of the corresponding side in ABC.

For any enlargement, the scale factor is found by dividing the length of the image side by the length of the corresponding object side.

> The scale factor is
> $$\frac{\text{length of image side}}{\text{length of corresponding object side}}$$

## Enlargements with a Scale Factor less than 1

An enlargement with a scale factor less than 1 produces a smaller figure nearer to the centre of enlargement.

In the figure below, where A'B'C' is the image of ABC under an enlargement where the scale factor is $\frac{1}{2}$.

Thus  $|OA'| = \frac{1}{2}|OA|$  and  $|A'B'| = \frac{1}{2}|AB|$.

> If the scale factor is $k$, then
> (i) if $k > 1$, the figure is enlarged
> (ii) if $k < 1$, the figure is reduced.

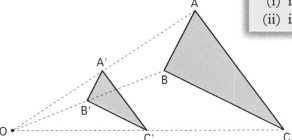

When the scale factor is a positive fraction less than 1, the result is a reduction of the given figure.

## Finding the centre of enlargement

When a figure and its enlargement are given, then the centre of enlargement is found by joining two sets of corresponding points and continuing the lines until the meet.

In the diagram below, A'A and C'C meet at O. The centre of enlargement is this point, O.

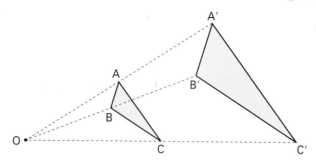

---

### Example 1

In the given figure, AB'C' is an enlargement of the triangle ABC where A is the centre of enlargement.
If $|AC| = 6$, $|CC'| = 9$ and $|B'C'| = 12.5$, find

  (i)   the scale factor of the enlargement

 (ii)  $|BC|$

(iii)  the ratio $|AB| : |AB'|$.

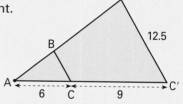

  (i)  It may simplify your work if you draw the two triangles separately.

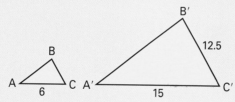

The scale factor $= \dfrac{\text{image length}}{\text{object length}} = \dfrac{|AC'|}{|AC|} = \dfrac{15}{6} = 2.5$

(ii)  Since the scale factor is $2\frac{1}{2}$, $|B'C'| = 2\frac{1}{2}|BC|$

$$|B'C'| = 2\tfrac{1}{2}|BC| \;\Rightarrow\; |BC| = \frac{|B'C'|}{2\frac{1}{2}} = \frac{12.5}{2.5} = 5$$

$\therefore \qquad |BC| = 5$

(iii)  $|AB'| = 2\frac{1}{2}|AB|$

$\therefore \qquad \dfrac{|AB'|}{|AB|} = 2\frac{1}{2} = \dfrac{5}{2}$

$\boxed{\begin{array}{l}\dfrac{x}{y} = \dfrac{3}{4} \\[4pt] \Rightarrow \quad x : y = 3:4\end{array}}$

$\therefore \quad |AB'| : |AB| = 5 : 2$

$\Rightarrow \quad |AB| : |AB'| = 2 : 5$

## Enlargement and area

The given grid shows that one triangle is an enlargement of the other.

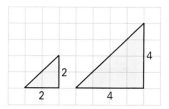

$$\text{Area of smaller triangle} = \tfrac{1}{2}(2)(2)$$
$$= 2 \text{ square units}$$
$$\text{Area of larger triangle} = \tfrac{1}{2}(4)(4)$$
$$= 8 \text{ square units}$$

Notice that the area of the larger triangle is four times the area of the smaller triangle.

Notice also that 4 is (scale factor)$^2$.

If the scale factor is $k$, then

$$\text{Area of image} = k^2 \text{ (Area of object)}.$$

> When a figure is enlarged by a scale factor $k$, the area of the image figure is increased by a scale factor $k^2$.

---

### Example 2

The figure P′Q′R′S′ is an enlargement of the figure PQRS. If the area of PQRS is 12 cm² and the area of P′Q′R′S = 48 cm², find the scale factor of the enlargement.

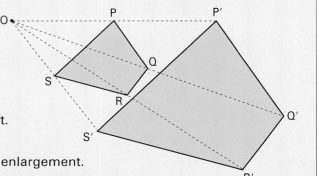

Let $k$ be the scale factor of the enlargement.

$$\text{Area of P'Q'R'S'} = k^2 \text{ (area of PQRS)}$$
$$\Rightarrow \quad 48 = k^2 (12)$$
$$12k^2 = 48$$
$$k^2 = 4$$
$$k = 2$$

∴ the scale factor of the enlargement is 2.

---

In example 2 above, the figure PQRS is enlarged by a scale factor of 2.

If we start with the figure P′Q′R′S′ and enlarge it to get the image PQRS, it is clear that the scale factor is $\frac{1}{2}$.

That is, each side in PQRS will be half the corresponding side in P′Q′R′S.

> If a figure is enlarged by a scale factor $k$, then the scale factor for the inverse enlargement is $\frac{1}{k}$.

Going from the image figure back to the original figure is generally called the **inverse enlargement**.

In the given figure, A is an enlargement of B.
The scale factor $k$ is $1\frac{1}{2}$.

Now if B is an enlargement of A, the scale factor is $\frac{1}{k}$.

$$\frac{1}{k} = \frac{1}{1\frac{1}{2}} = \frac{2}{3}$$

∴ the inverse scale factor $= \frac{2}{3}$.

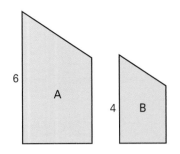

## Exercise 9.1

1. The diagram on the right shows a figure and
   its enlargement.
     (i) Use the grid to write down the scale
         factor of the enlargement.
     (ii) The lengths of two sides are given.
          Find the lengths of the sides marked
          $x$ and $y$.

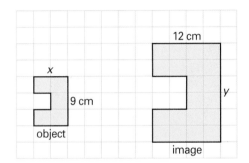

2. In the given diagram, the triangle A′B′C′
   is the image of the triangle ABC under an
   enlargement with centre O and scale factor 2.
   If |BC| = 4, |AC| = 6 and |A′B′| = 10, find
     (i) |B′C′|
     (ii) |A′C′|
     (iii) |AB|.

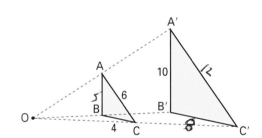

3. Make a copy of the rectangle ABCD, as shown.
   Draw an enlargement of ABCD with A as centre
   of enlargement and scale factor 2.
   Label the image AB′C′D′.
   Which point of the given rectangle remains in its
   original position? A

4. Make a copy of this triangle.
   Now draw an enlargement of this triangle with Z
   as centre of enlargement and scale factor 3.
   Label the image figure X′Y′Z.
   Write down the length of
     (i) [ZY′] 6
     (ii) |ZX′| 9

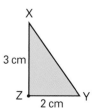

**5.** The given diagram shows the figure ABCD and its enlargement PQRS.

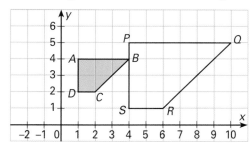

   (i)   Use the grid to write down the scale factor of the enlargement. 2

   (ii)  Describe how you would find the centre of enlargement.

   (iii) Use a straight edge to find the coordinates of the centre of enlargement.

**6.** In the given figure, the triangle marked B is
an enlargement of the triangle marked A.
Use the grid to write down

   (i)   the scale factor of the enlargement

   (ii)  the coordinates of the centre of the
         enlargement.

   (iii) Use the grid to write down the area
         of triangle A and triangle B.

   (iv)  If the scale factor is $k$, verify that
         area of triangle B = $k^2$ times area of
         triangle A.

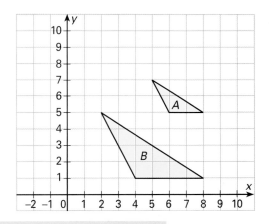

Area of a triangle is half base multiplied by perpendicular height.

**7.** In the given diagram, the triangle ORS is the image
of the triangle OPQ under an enlargement with O as centre.
   $|OP| = 4$, $|PR| = 6$ and $|SR| = 8$.
Draw OPQ and ORS as separate triangles and use
these triangles to write down

   (i)   the scale factor of the enlargement

   (ii)  $|PQ|$

   (iii) the ratio $|OQ| : |OS|$.

If the area of $\triangle OPQ = 4$ square units, find the area of $\triangle ORS$.

**8.** Make a copy of the given triangle PQR.
Now draw an enlargement of the triangle
with A as centre and scale factor 2.

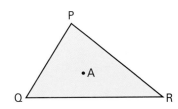

**9.** The triangles A'B'C' and $A_2B_2C_2$ are enlargements of the triangle ABC.

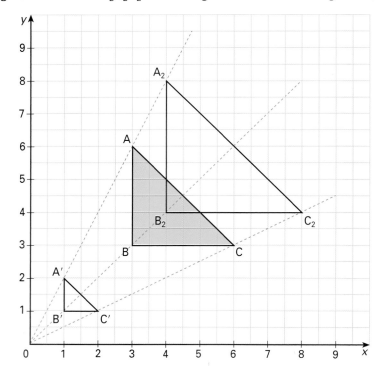

(i)   Which triangle is the result of an enlargement with a scale factor less than 1?

(ii)   Write down the scale factor for
    (a) $\triangle A'B'C'$                     (b) $\triangle A_2B_2C_2$.

(iii)   If $|BC| = 12$ cm find
    (a) $|B'C'|$                          (b) $|B_2C_2|$.

**10.** For each of these pairs of shapes, state whether the larger shape is an enlargement of the smaller shape?
Explain your answer in each case.

**11.** In the given diagram, one figure is an enlargement of the other.

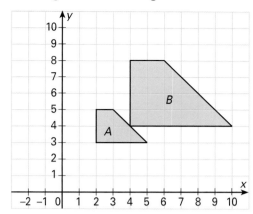

   (i)   Use the grid and a straight edge to write down the coordinates of the centre of enlargement.

  (ii)   If B is an enlargement of A, write down the scale factor.

 (iii)   If A is an enlargement of B, write down the scale factor.

 (iv)   If the area of A = 15 square units, find the area of B.

**12.** In the given figure, AB′C′ is an enlargement of the triangle ABC, where A is the centre of enlargement. If $|AC| = 8$, $|CC'| = 12$ and $|B'C'| = 25$, find

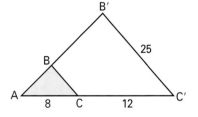

   (i)   the scale factor of the enlargement

  (ii)   $|BC|$      (iii)  the ratio $|AB| : |AB'|$

 (iv)   the area of the $\triangle AB'C'$ if the area of $\triangle ABC$ is 16 square units.

**13.** This diagram is reduced on a photocopier to $\frac{2}{3}$ of its original size.

   (i)   If the height of the original diagram is 156 mm, how high will the reduced diagram be?

  (ii)   If the label on the reduced diagram is 28 mm in height, find the height of the label on the original diagram.

**14.** In the given figure, box B is an enlargement of box A.

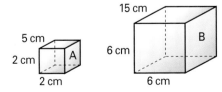

   (i)   Write down the value of $k$, the scale factor of the enlargement.

  (ii)   What is the relationship between $k$ and the scale factor for volume?

**15.** The design on a hardcover book is to be used on the paperback version.
To do this, the design is reduced to $\frac{3}{5}$ of its original size.
How high will the design be on the paperback cover if it is 18 cm high on the hardcover?

**16.** Darren enlarged a diagram by scale factor 2 for a science project. He decided it still wasn't large enough, so he enlarged his enlargement by scale factor 1.5.

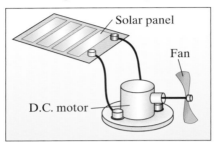

   (i)   What single scale factor could he have used to get the final diagram from the original?
   (ii)  If the dimensions of the double enlargement were 42 cm by 28 cm, what were the dimensions of the original diagram?

**17.** The scale on a map is 1 : 1000.
   Anna enlarges the map by a scale factor 2.
   (i)   What is the scale for the enlarged map?
   (ii)  On the original map, Anna's street is 6 cm long.
         What is the actual length of the street in real life?
         Give your answer in metres.
   Sean borrowed Anna's original map and he enlarged it by a scale factor $\frac{1}{2}$.
   (iii) What is the scale on Sean's enlarged map?
   (iv)  If the distance between two railway stations is 1 km, how far are they apart on Sean's enlarged map?

# SECTION 9.2 Constructions

In your study of constructions for your Junior Certificate you will have learned:
- How to bisect a line segment
- How to bisect an angle
- How to construct various triangles
- How to draw parallel and perpendicular lines

In this section we will deal with six new constructions that are on the Leaving Certificate course as well as the application of these constructions to real-life situations. For these constructions you will need a compass, straight edge and protractor.

> When you use a compass you must leave the construction arcs as evidence that you have used the correct method.

# 1. Constructing an angle of 60°

Each angle in an equilateral triangle is 60°.
We will now use this information to draw
an angle of 60°.

> In an equilateral triangle, all the
> sides are equal in length.

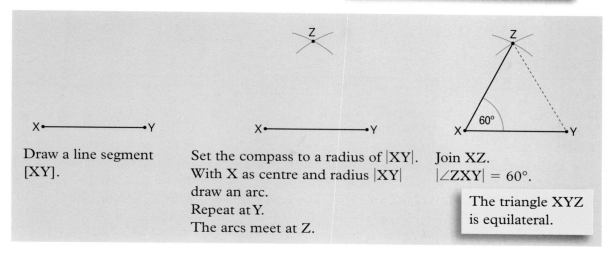

Draw a line segment
[XY].

Set the compass to a radius of |XY|.
With X as centre and radius |XY|
draw an arc.
Repeat at Y.
The arcs meet at Z.

Join XZ.
|∠ZXY| = 60°.

> The triangle XYZ
> is equilateral.

# 2. How to construct a tangent to a circle at a given point on it

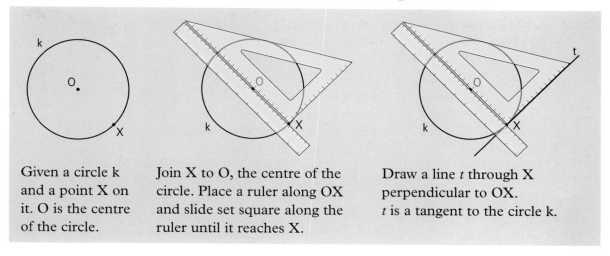

Given a circle k
and a point X on
it. O is the centre
of the circle.

Join X to O, the centre of the
circle. Place a ruler along OX
and slide set square along the
ruler until it reaches X.

Draw a line *t* through X
perpendicular to OX.
*t* is a tangent to the circle k.

# 3. How to construct a parallelogram, given the lengths of the sides and the measures of the angles

The instructions on the following page show how to
construct a parallelogram ABCD where
|AB| = 3.5 cm, |AD| = 4 cm and |∠DAB| = 55°.

We first draw a rough sketch of ABCD.

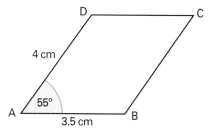

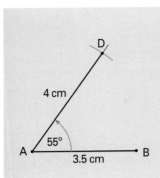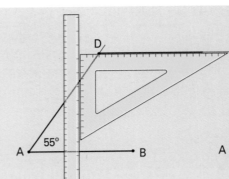

| Draw a horizontal line [AB] = 3.5 cm. Use a protractor to measure an angle of 55° at A. Draw a line through A and measure |AD| = 4 cm. | Place set square along the line AB. Use a ruler to slide the set square up to the point D. Draw a line through D parallel to AB. | Use a compass with a radius of 3.5 cm (the same as |AB|) to draw an arc on the line. |DC| = 3.5 cm. Join BC. ABCD is the required parallelogram. |

## Circles and triangles

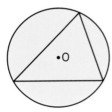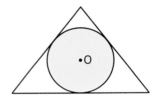

The **circumcircle** of a triangle is the circle which passes through the three vertices, as shown.
The centre, O, of this circle is called the **circumcentre** of the triangle.

A circle inscribed in a triangle such that all three sides touch the circle is called the **incircle** of the triangle. The centre of the incircle is called the **incentre** of the triangle. In the figure above, O is the incentre.

The construction of the circumcircle and incircle of a triangle will involve two constructions that you studied for your Junior Certificate examination.

The diagrams shown below will help you recall the steps involved in doing these constructions.

## The perpendicular bisector of a line segment

## The bisector of an angle

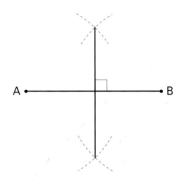

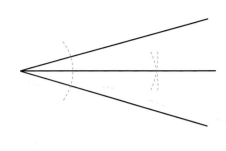

You should practise these constructions before attempting to draw the circumcircle and incircle of a triangle.

## 4. How to construct the circumcircle of a given triangle

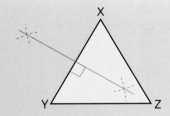

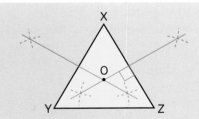

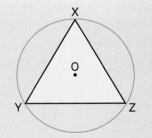

Construct the perpendicular bisector of [XY].

Construct the perpendicular bisector of [XZ]. The two bisectors meet at the point O, as shown. O is the circumcentre.

With O as centre and |OX| as radius, draw a circle through X, Y and Z. This is the circumcircle of the triangle.

## 5. How to construct the incircle of a given triangle

The construction of the incircle of a triangle involves constructing the bisector of an angle which is given on the previous page.

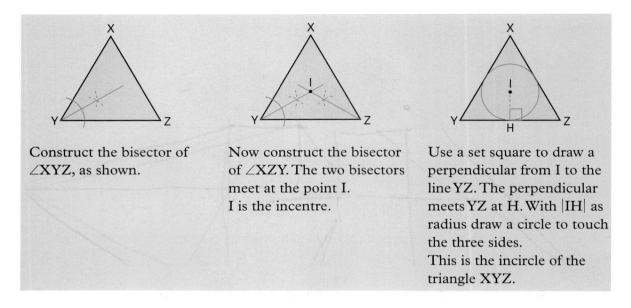

Construct the bisector of ∠XYZ, as shown.

Now construct the bisector of ∠XZY. The two bisectors meet at the point I.
I is the incentre.

Use a set square to draw a perpendicular from I to the line YZ. The perpendicular meets YZ at H. With |IH| as radius draw a circle to touch the three sides.
This is the incircle of the triangle XYZ.

## 6. How to construct the centroid of a triangle

The line segment joining the vertex of a triangle to the midpoint of the opposite side is called a **median**.

In the given triangle [XM] is a median.

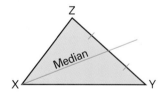

The point of intersection of the three medians of a triangle is called the **centroid** of the triangle.

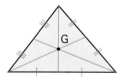

G is the centroid.

To find the midpoint of any line segment, we construct the perpendicular bisector of that line segment, as shown below.

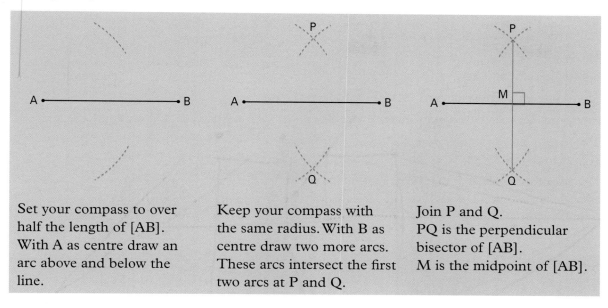

Set your compass to over half the length of [AB]. With A as centre draw an arc above and below the line.

Keep your compass with the same radius. With B as centre draw two more arcs. These arcs intersect the first two arcs at P and Q.

Join P and Q. PQ is the perpendicular bisector of [AB]. M is the midpoint of [AB].

The three diagrams below illustrate the steps to be followed in the construction of the centroid of a triangle.

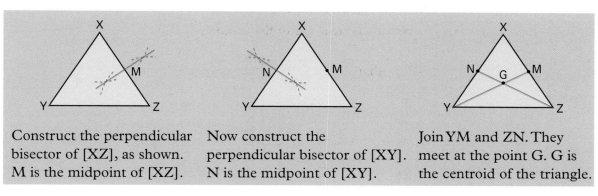

Construct the perpendicular bisector of [XZ], as shown. M is the midpoint of [XZ].

Now construct the perpendicular bisector of [XY]. N is the midpoint of [XY].

Join YM and ZN. They meet at the point G. G is the centroid of the triangle.

## Applications of the given constructions

In the given diagram, the line $\ell$ is the perpendicular bisector of [AB].

Any point on this bisector is the same distance from A and B.

Thus $|AX| = |XB|$.

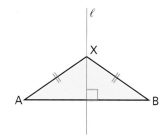

Take any three points X, Y and Z.
How do we find a point that is the same
distance from all three points?

Construct the perpendicular bisectors
of [XY] and [YZ].

Name these lines ℓ and m.

Any point on ℓ is equidistant from X and Y.

Any point on m is equidistant from Y and Z.

The lines ℓ and m intersect at K.
K is equidistant from X, Y and Z.

The **largest circle** that can be drawn inside a
triangle is the **incircle**, that is, the circle that
touches all three sides.

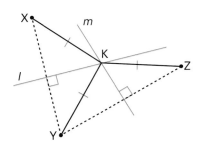

Equidistant means 'the same distance'.

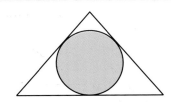

## Exercise 9.2

1. Draw a line 5 cm in length.
   Using a compass and ruler only, construct the perpendicular bisector of the line.

2. Use your protractor to draw an angle of 70°.
   Now use your compass and ruler to construct the bisector of the angle.

3. Construct the triangle ABC with base |BC| = 6 cm, |AB| = 4.5 cm and |∠ABC| = 60°.

4. Using a compass and ruler only, construct an angle of 60°.

5. Construct the parallelogram shown on the right.

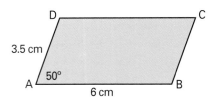

6. Construct a rectangle of length 6 cm and breadth 4 cm.

7. Construct the parallelogram PQRS so that |PQ| = 7 cm, |PS| = 5 cm and |∠QPS| = 55°.
   Measure |PR|.

8. The diagram on the right shows a rough sketch of
   the parallelogram ABCD.
   Construct this parallelogram if its perpendicular
   height is 4 cm.

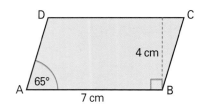

9. Draw the parallelogram ABCD in which the base [AB] = 4.5 cm, |BC| = 3 cm and |AC| = 6 cm. Measure ∠ABC.

10. Draw a triangle of sides 6 cm, 5 cm and 4 cm.
    Now construct the circumcircle of this triangle.
    Show all construction lines.

11. Draw the right-angled triangle, as shown on the right.
    Now construct the circumcircle of this triangle.
    What do you notice about the circumcentre of the triangle?
    Now draw any other right-angled triangle and construct the circumcircle.
    Did you get the same result as you got for the first triangle?
    What conclusion is suggested regarding the circumcentre of a right-angled triangle?

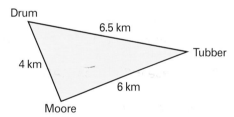

4.5

6

12. The diagram shows three villages, Drum, Moore and Tubber.
    The distances between the villages are shown.

Drum

6.5 km

Tubber

4 km

6 km

Moore

Using the scale 1 cm = 1 km, draw an accurate drawing of the diagram above.
It is planned to build a school that is equidistant from the three villages.
Show on your drawing where the school should be built.

13. Draw a triangle of sides 6.5 cm, 5 cm and 4 cm.
    Use the bisectors of any two angles of the triangle to find the centre of its incircle.
    Now draw the incircle.

14. The line XD is the bisector of ∠AXB.
    K is a point on XD, KZ ⊥ AX and KY ⊥ XB.
    Show that the triangles XKZ and XKY are congruent.
    Hence show that |KZ| = |KY|.
    What conclusion can you come to regarding any point on the bisector of an angle?

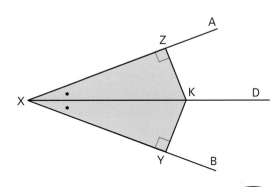

**15.** Construct the triangle shown.
Now construct the medians [AM] and [BN].
The medians intersect at the point G.
Measure |AG| and |GM|.

Now find the ratio $\dfrac{|AG|}{|GM|}$. Find also the ratio $\dfrac{|BG|}{|GN|}$.

Based on the answers you have found, complete this statement:
'The medians of a triangle divide one another in the ratio … : … '.

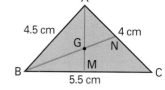

**16.** Three people A, B and C on a shoreline see a boat at sea.
The boat is the same distance from all three people.
Describe how you would locate the position of the boat.

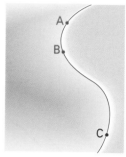

**17.** Draw a circle of radius 3 cm and mark the centre O.
Mark a point X on this circle.
Now use a ruler and set square to draw a tangent to this circle at the point X.

**18.** The given figure shows a circle and two chords [AB] and [CD].
What can you say about the perpendicular bisector of [AB]?
Now describe how these two chords can be used to find
the centre of the circle.

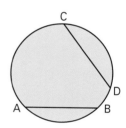

**19.** Draw a circle of radius 3.5 cm. [Do not mark the centre.]
Draw any two chords similar to those in Q18 above.
Use these two chords to locate the centre of the circle.

**20.** In Q19 we used two chords to find the centre of a circle.
The given diagram shows a circle and two points on
the circle.
Describe another way of finding the centre of
this circle using the points X and Y.

**21.** A campsite is in the shape of a triangle with busy roads
running along all three sides of the site.
The sides of the site are 110 m, 150 m and 170 m in length.
   (i)   Using 10 m = 1 cm, draw a scaled diagram of this site.
   (ii)  Show on the diagram the best position to pitch a tent
         so that it is as far away as possible from all three roads.

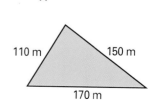

# TEST YOURSELF 9

**1.** In the given diagram, K'L'M'N' is an enlargement of KLMN.

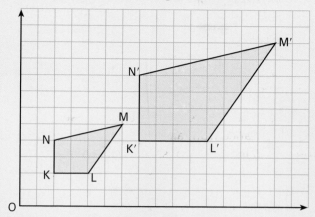

    (i) Use the grid to find the scale factor of the enlargement.

    (ii) If |KN| = 5 cm, find |K'N'|.           (iii) If |N'M'| = 21 cm, find |NM|.

    (iv) Explain why O is the centre of enlargement.     (v) If |ON| = 16 cm, find |ON'|.

**2.** The diagram shows two figures P and Q where one is an enlargement of the other.

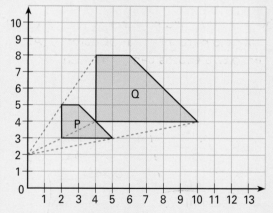

    (i) Write down the coordinates of the centre of enlargement.

    (ii) If Q is an enlargement of P, find the scale factor.

    (iii) If P is an enlargement of Q, find the scale factor.

    (iv) If the area of P is 24 cm², find the area of Q.

**3.** In the given figure, AB'C'D' is an enlargement of ABCD.

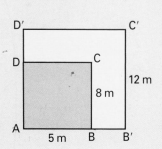

    (i) Name the centre of enlargement.

    (ii) Find the scale factor of the enlargement.

    (iii) Find |D'C'|.

    (iv) If |AC| = 9.4 m, find |AC'|.

    (v) If ABCD is an enlargement of AB'C'D',
        what is the scale factor of the enlargement?

**4.** The triangle AB'C' is an enlargement of the triangle
ABC with A as centre and scale factor 1.5.
If $|AC| = 8$, $|B'C'| = 9$ and $|BB'| = 3$, find
    (i)   $|AC'|$          (ii)   $|BC|$         (iii)   $|AB|$.
If the area of $\triangle ABC = 20$ square units,
find the area of $\triangle AB'C'$.

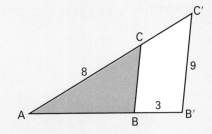

**5.** Construct a triangle of sides 5 cm, 4 cm and 3.5 cm.
Now construct the circumcircle of this triangle.

**6.** Make an accurate construction of the parallelogram
given on the right.
Measure $|AC|$.

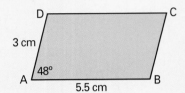

**7.** X, Y and Z are three schools.
The distance from X to Y is 15 km; the distance from Y to Z is
12 km and the distance from X to Z is 18 km.
Make a scale drawing of these distances, using 1 cm = 3 km.
Now construct the location of a sportsfield that is equidistant
from all three schools.

**8.** This diagram was made by enlarging a triangle by a
scale factor of 2.5.
    (i)   Which is the original triangle?
   (ii)   If $|BE| = 4.5$ cm, find $|CD|$.
  (iii)   If the triangle ABE is the image of the triangle
          ACD under an enlargement, what is the scale factor?
  (iv)   If $|\angle AEB| = 28°$, find the size of the angle ADC.
   (v)   If the area of $\triangle ABE = 4.2$ cm², find the area of $\triangle ACD$.

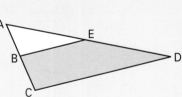

**9.** Shape C has been enlarged to shape C'.

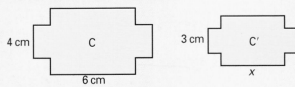

    (i)   What scale factor was used?
   (ii)   What is the length of the side marked $x$ in shape C'?
  (iii)   If the area of C' is 18 cm², find the area of C.

**10.** A group of walkers cannot walk straight from Ashfield to Briarfield, as they usually do. Instead they have to go through Caim to avoid a conservation area.
Caim is 7.2 km from Ashfield and 5.4 km from Briarfield.

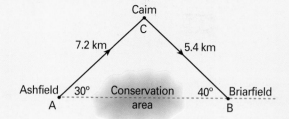

(i)   Construct an accurate scale drawing of the route using 1 cm = 1 km.

(ii)  How much further did the group walk, compared to the direct route from Ashfield to Briarfield?

Give your answer in kilometres, correct to one decimal place.

**11.** The triangle XYZ is an enlargement of the triangle DHG with O as centre.
|DG| = 8, |XZ| = 12 and |XY| = 9.

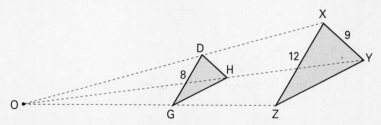

(i)    Find the scale factor of the enlargement.

(ii)   Find |DH|.

(iii)  The area of the triangle XYZ is 27 square units. Find the area of the triangle DHG.

**12.** In each of the two pairs of diagrams shown, shape Q is an enlargement of shape P. For each pair of diagrams, write down

(i)   the scale factor of the enlargement

(ii)  the value of x.

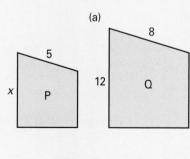

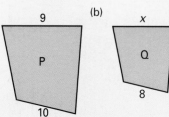

# Summary of Key Points

## Enlargements

When a shape is enlarged

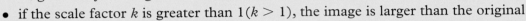

- the object and its image are similar; the size changes but not the shape
- the **scale factor** gives the number of times the length of any line segment has been increased
- if the scale factor $k$ is greater than $1 (k > 1)$, the image is larger than the original
- if the scale factor $k$ is less than $1 (k < 1)$, the image is smaller than the original
- if a figure is enlarged by a scale factor $k$, its area will be increased by a scale factor of $k^2$
- the centre of enlargement is found by drawing lines through two sets of corresponding points. The centre is the point of intersection of these lines.
- if the scale factor for an enlargement is $k$, the scale factor for the inverse enlargement is $\frac{1}{k}$.

## Constructions

### Circumcircle

The centre of the circumcircle is the point of intersection of the perpendicular bisectors of the sides

### Incircle

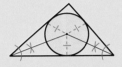

The centre of the incircle is the point of intersection of the bisectors of the angles.

### Centroid

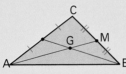

### An angle of 60°

The line AM is called a **median**.
The point G, where the medians meet, is called the **centroid** of the triangle.

### Tangent to a circle

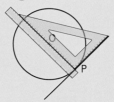

### Parallelograms

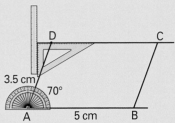

# Answers

## Chapter 1: Collecting Data and Sampling

### Exercise 1.1

1. (i) Discrete    (ii) Discrete
   (iii) Continuous    (iv) Discrete
   (v) Continuous
2. Continuous; time measured on a scale
3. Discrete
4. (i) Discrete    (ii) Continuous
   (iii) Continuous
5. Continuous; discrete
6. (i) Discrete    (ii) Continuous
   (iii) Discrete    (iv) Continuous
   (v) Discrete    (vi) Continuous
   (vii) Discrete

### Exercise 1.2

1. (i) Numerical    (ii) Categorical
   (iii) Numerical    (iv) Categorical
2. (i) Categorical    (ii) Numerical
   (iii) Numerical; number of buttons is discrete
3. (i) No    (ii) Yes
   (iii) Yes    (iv) No
5. (ii) Number of eggs    (iii) Amount of flour
6. Numerical ... Categorical
7. (i) Categorical    (ii) Numerical
   (iii) Numerical
   (iv) Categorical; Shoe-size is discrete;
        Bivariate continous data
8. (i) True    (ii) False
   (iii) False    (iv) False
   (v) True    (vi) False
   (vii) True    (viii) True

### Exercise 1.3

1. (i) Primary    (ii) Secondary
   (iii) Primary    (iv) Secondary
2. (i) Secondary data
   (ii) Roy's; his results are more recent
3. Primary data
5. (i) No    (ii) Primary

### Exercise 1.4

1. (i) (c)    (ii) (a)
   (iii) (b)    (iv) (b)
2. Q(i); Q(ii) is a leading question
3. (i) Too personal    (ii) Too vague
4. (i) Question too personal;
       Response boxes too vague
5. (i) Too personal
   (ii) Leading question
   (iii) Numbers overlapping
6. B and D are leading or biased questions
7. Not suitable – too vague
8. (i) Too personal – may embarrass
9. QA: Too personal; QB: Leading question
10. (i) Too vague
11. (i) Too vague – may embarrass
    (ii) Response boxes should be included
    (iii) Too vague – open to different
          interpretations
15. (i) (a) Too vague ... should provide
            appropriate choice of responses
        (b) Too personal; may cause
            embarrassment

### Exercise 1.5

1. B
2. B
3. People who go to a cinema are already
   interested in cinema
4. Not representative as time frame too limited
   and confined.
5. People at a sports shop are already
   interested in sport and are more likely to
   play some sports
6. Gender biased; only supermarkets
   surveyed; time too limited and so may be
   unrepresentative
7. Method 2; Totally random
11. (i) Not biased
    (ii) Biased
    (iii) Biased
13. 300

## Test yourself 1

1. (i) Numerical   (ii) Categorical
   (iii) Categorical   (iv) Numerical
   (v) Categorical   (vi) Numerical
   (vii) Categorical
2. (i) Discrete   (ii) Discrete
   (iii) Continuous   (iv) Continuous
   (v) Discrete   (vi) Continuous
3. (i) Primary   (ii) Secondary
   (iii) Primary   (iv) Secondary
   (v) Secondary
4. (i) Univariate   (ii) Bivariate
   (iii) Bivariate   (iv) Univariate
   (v) Bivariate
5. (i) A   (ii) A
   (iii) C   (iv) B
   (v) B   (vi) A
   (vii) B   (viii) A
   (ix) A or C   (x) C
6. (i) Leading question
7. (i) B and C   (ii) A and D
10. (i) 219
12. Yes
13. (i) Yes
14. Only B and F are biased

# Chapter 2: Measures of location and spread

## Exercise 2.1

1. (i) 10   (ii) 9   (iii) 8   (iv) 6
2. (a) (i) 8   (ii) 7
   (b) (i) 7   (ii) 7
3. (i) 41 km/hr   (ii) 39.5 km/hr
4. (i) 14   (ii) 14   (iii) 17
5. (i) 6   (ii) 9.5
6. Example: 2, 6, 9, 12, 13, 13, 22
7. (i) 28   (ii) 2
8. 14
9. €7.10
11. (i) $x = 2$   (ii) $k = 17$
12. 17
13. 90 g
14. 4 and 6
15. 6
16. (i) $14\frac{1}{4}$ hours   (ii) $12\frac{1}{4}$ hours
   (iii) Boys: 14.5; Girls: 12
   (iv) Yes

17. $x = 19$
18. (i) 1320 cm   (ii) $165\frac{1}{3}$ cm
19. (i) 195   (ii) 19
20. B − 40
21. (i) Mode   (ii) Mean

## Exercise 2.2

1. (i) 8   (ii) 57   (iii) 11
2. (i) 6   (ii) 8
3. (i) 33   (ii) 29
   (iii) (a) 18.5   (b) 34   (c) 15.5
4. (i) 4   (ii) 11   (iii) 17
5. (i) 13 mins   (ii) 8
   (iii) 15   (iv) 7
6. (i) 5   (ii) 14.5
7. (i) 25   (ii) 50   (iii) 64.5   (iv) 14.5
8. (i) 105 g   (ii) 19 g
9. (i)

| 3 | 5 | 6 | 6 | 7 |
|---|---|---|---|---|

   (ii)

| 4 | 6 | 6 | 7 |
|---|---|---|---|

10. (i) 41 and 47   (ii) 8, 9, 13, 15, 25
11. (i) Football: 13, 13, 4; Hockey: 13.7, 14, 6
   (ii) Football team

## Exercise 2.3

1. (i) Mean   (ii) Mode   (iii) Mean
   (iv) Mode   (v) Median
2. (i) 94 kg
   (ii) $87\frac{4}{9}$ kg; Median best describes data
3. (i) $25\frac{6}{7}$   (ii) 15; Median
4. (i) $30\frac{4}{7}$ °C
   (ii) Closely grouped data (no outliers)
5. (i) $26\frac{6}{11}$
   (ii) Mode (= 37) is not a typical value
6. (i) 8.1   (ii) 6; Median
7. (i) 16   (ii) 16
   (iii) 19.1   (iv) Mode or median
8. (i) €37 667   (ii) €24 500
   (iii) No two salaries the same; Median
9. 330 ml cans

## Exercise 2.4

1. (i) 2 goals   (ii) 3
2. 3
3. (i) 25   (ii) 6 marks   (iii) 5.6
   (iv) 14   (v) 6
4. (i) 4   (ii) 4   (iii) 4.25

**5.** (i) 30    (ii) 7    (iii) 13
    (iv) 13    (v) 13
**6.** (i) 2    (ii) 2    (iii) 5    (iv) 10
**7.** $x = 2$
**8.** $y = 5$
**9.** (ii) 4    (iii) 4.6

## Exercise 2.5

**1.** (i) $(4 - 6)$    (ii) 6.5    (iii) $(4 - 6)$
**2.** (i) $(12 - 14)$    (ii) 14 years    (iii) $(12 - 14)$
**3.** 18.6
**4.** (i) 18 mins    (ii) $(18 - 20)$ interval
**5.** (i) 32 years    (ii) $(30 - 40)$
**6.** (i) $(5 - 9)$    (ii) $(0 - 4)$    (iii) 7

## Exercise 2.6

**1.** $7\frac{5}{6}$
**2.** 14.8
**3.** 73.2%; No distinction
**4.** 6.5%
**5.** 34
**6.** $x = 3$
**7.** Aisling
**8.** Katie

## Exercise 2.7

**1.** (i) 1.9    (ii) 2.4    (iii) 2.8
    (iv) 3.5    (v) 2.7    (vi) 3.9
**3.** (i) 10 is added to each number
    (ii) Same (both $= \sqrt{2}$)
    (iii) equal standard deviations
**4.** 1.6
**5.** 0.84
**6.** 2.3
**7.** Mean $= 4$; $\sigma = \sqrt{10}$
**8.** Mean $= 3$; $\sigma = 1.14$
**9.** (i) 25    (ii) 5.3
    (iii) 30.3; 19.7    (iv) 3
**10.** Mean $= 2$; $\sigma = 1.5$
**11.** 2.3
**12.** (i) 6    (ii) 2
**13.** (i) Route 1 $= 14$; Route 2 $= 15$
    (ii) Route 1 $= 2$; Route 2 $= 2.3$
    (iii) Route 1 recommended

## Test yourself 2

**1.** (i) $x = 2$    (ii) $y = 9$
**2.** (i) 2    (ii) 1, 9    (iii) 8

**3.** (i) 60    (ii) 78
**4.** 2 or 45
**5.** (i) Mean = €67 840; Mode = €4500;
      Median = €45 000
    (ii) Mean
**6.** 5
**7.** (i) 8    (ii) 9    (iii) 5
**8.** (a) False    (b) True
    (c) False    (d) Could be true
**9.** (i) 42    (ii) 42    (iii) 42.5
**10.** (i) $(8 - 12)$    (ii) $(8 - 12)$    (iii) 11.7
**11.** 63%
**12.** 6.5
**13.** (i) 9    (ii) 2.6
**14.** Mean $= 12.6$; $\sigma = 0.9$
**15.** S1; S2
**16.** (i) Rory, 81; Darren, 80
    (ii) Rory, 6; Darren, 9.3; Rory is better
**17.** (a) For group 1; mode $= 46$, median $= 52$,
      mean $= 51.9$
      For group 2; mode $= 39$, median $= 52$,
      mean $= 56.2$
    (b) Group 2 were better

# Chapter 3: Representing data

## Exercise 3.1

**1.** (i) 7    (ii) Brown    (iii) 22
**2.** (i) 25    (ii) 10    (iii) 3
    (iv) 5    (v) 9
**4.** (i) 6    (ii) 16    (iii) Can't tell
**5.** (i) 180    (ii) March and August
    (iii) 36
**6.** Mean $= 12.5$; line too low
**7.** (i) 15    (ii) 1    (iii) 5    (iv) 20%
**8.** (i) Conor    (ii) Barry
    (iii) Dara    (iv) Alan
**9.** (i) Monday    (ii) Saturday    (iii) Saturday
    (iv) Friday    (v) 25
**11.** 88
**12.** (i) 40    (ii) 15; 15%
**13.** 90

## Exercise 3.2

**1.** (ii) 12    (iii) $(20 - 40)$ km
    (iv) 40%
**2.** (i) 10    (ii) $(40 - 50)$ yrs
    (iii) 12    (iv) 60
    (v) $(50 - 60)$ yrs    (vi) $(40 - 50)$ yrs

**3.** (ii) 38     (iii) $(12 - 16)$ mins
(iv) $(12 - 16)$ mins     (v) 30
**4.** (i) 19     (ii) 54
(iii) $(10 - 15)$ secs     (iv) $(10 - 15)$ secs
(v) 20     (vi) 20
**5.** (ii) $(25 - 35)$ mins     (iii) $(25 - 35)$ mins
(iv) $(15 - 25)$ mins     (v) 48
(vi) 29 mins

## Exercise 3.3

**1.** Symmetrical distribution
(i) Normal distribution
(ii) People's heights
**2.** Negative skew
**3.** Positive skew
**4.** (i) (c)     (ii) (a)     (iii) (b)
(iv) (b)     (v) (c)
**5.** Median
**6.** (i) Ⓑ     (ii) Ⓐ
(iii) Normal distribution
**7.** (i) Negatively skewed
(ii) Mode is generally higher when the distribution is negatively skewed
**8.** Negative skew     (i) Mean     (ii) Mode
**9.** (ii) Positively skewed
(iii) Mode $<$ Median $<$ Mean

## Exercise 3.4

**1.** (i) 20   (ii) 5   (iii) 94   (iv) 51   (v) 8
**2.** (i) 4     (ii) 27
(iii) 8     (iv) 36 years old
**4.** (ii) 8     (iii) 16
**5.** (i) 6     (ii) 4.3 secs
(iii) 3.5 secs     (iv) 3.5 secs
**6.** (i) 62   (ii) 47   (iii) 67   (iv) 20
**7.** (ii) 16.5     (iii) 40     (iv) 23.5
**8.** (i) 19     (ii) (a) 66   (b) 49
(iii) 55     (iv) 26
**9.** (i) 37     (ii) 44     (iii) 54
(iv) 16     (v) 26; Brian
**10.** (i) Median = 76; Range = 27
(ii) Median = 68; Range = 38
(iii) The group who did not smoke
**11.** (i) 52 mins
(ii) (a) 52 mins   (b) 69 mins
(iii) (a) 31 mins   (b) 55 mins
**12.** (i) 41     (ii) 41     (iii) 53
**13.** (ii) 55     (iii) 66.5     (iv) English

## Exercise 3.5

**1.** (i) B     (ii) C     (iii) D
**2.** (i) C and F     (ii) A and E     (iii) B and D
(iv) A; Perfect positive correlation
**3.** (i) 6     (ii) 8.2 years
(iii) Weak positive
**4.** (i) Strong positive
(ii) Strong or close relationship
**5.** (i) 100 kg     (ii) 170 cm
(iii) 175 cm, 85 kg     (iv) Weak positive
**6.** (ii) Strong negative correlation; Yes, as you would expect positive correlation
**7.** (ii) Older bikes are cheaper
(iii) Strong negative
**9.** (i) B     (ii) C     (iii) A     (iv) D
**10.** (i) Strong negative     (ii) Strong positive
(iii) No correlation     (iv) Strong negative
(v) Strong positive

## Exercise 3.6

**1.** Strong positive; 0.7
**2.** A: 0.1; B: $-1$; C: $-0.4$; D: 0.8
**4.** $-0.9$
**5.** $-0.8$
**6.** $-1$
**7.** 0.1
**8.** (i) 0.9     (ii) $-0.8$     (iii) 0
(iv) $-1$     (v) $-0.1$     (vi) 0.2

## Exercise 3.7

**1.** (i), (ii), (v) and (vi)
**2.** (i) 39 000 km
(ii) Strong positive correlation
(iii) Yes (Older implies more kms travelled)
(iv) 2 years, 40 000 km
**3.** (i) Strong negative correlation
(ii) Yes; Older implies less value
**4.** (ii) Strong positive correlation
(iii) Yes; Sunshine causes higher temperatures
**5.** (ii) Strong negative correlation
(iii) No

## Test yourself 3

**1.** (i) 47   (ii) 38   (iii) 29   (iv) 47   (v) 18
**2.** (i) 49   (ii) 30   (iii) 54   (iv) 24
**3.** (i) 32   (ii) €48   (iii) €25   (iv) €29
(v) Males spent more

**4.** (i) €850  (ii) €300  (iii) €500  (iv) €150
**5.** (ii) Strong negative correlation
**6.** (i) D  (ii) C  (iii) A
   (iv) (a) B  (b) D  (c) C  (d) A
**7.** (i) Positive  (ii) Positive
   (iii) No correlation  (iv) Positive
   (v) Positive
**8.** (i) Bar chart or pie chart
   (ii) Scatter graph
   (iii) Back-to-back stem and leaf diagram
   (iv) Bar chart or pie chart
   (v) Pie chart or bar chart
   (vi) Scatter graph
**9.** (i) Symmetrical (or normal) distribution
**10.** (i) Higher concentration of values at lower end (or start) of the distribution
   (ii) Positively skewed
   (iii) Ages at which people learn to read
**11.** (i) Negatively skewed
   (ii) Ages at which people become grandparents
**12.** (i) 13  (ii) (a) 62  (b) 78
   (iii) 53  (iv) women

# Chapter 4: Probability

## Exercise 4.1

**1.** (i) Impossible (ii) Evens  (iii) Certain
   (iv) Evens  (v) Impossible
**2.** (i) Impossible  (ii) Very likely
   (iii) Very unlikely  (iv) Very unlikely
   (v) Evens  (vi) Certain
   (vii) Unlikely
**3.** (i) Bigger than 5  (ii) Yes
**5.** (i) B  (ii) C  (iii) C
   (iv) A  (v) B  (vi) C
**6.** (i) 6  (ii) 4  (iii) 0  (iv) 2
**7.** (i) 6  (ii) 8  (iii) 2

## Exercise 4.2

**1.** (i) $\frac{1}{6}$  (ii) $\frac{1}{3}$  (iii) $\frac{1}{2}$  (iv) $\frac{1}{2}$  (v) $\frac{1}{3}$  (vi) $\frac{1}{2}$
**2.** (i) $\frac{1}{4}$  (ii) $\frac{3}{8}$  (iii) $\frac{1}{4}$  (iv) $\frac{1}{8}$  (v) $\frac{3}{8}$
**3.** (i) $\frac{1}{8}$  (ii) $\frac{1}{4}$  (iii) $\frac{3}{8}$
**4.** (i) $\frac{1}{4}$  (ii) $\frac{3}{4}$  (iii) $\frac{1}{4}$; $\frac{3}{4}$
**5.** (i) $\frac{1}{2}$  (ii) $\frac{1}{4}$  (iii) $\frac{1}{13}$  (iv) $\frac{1}{26}$
**6.** (i) $\frac{5}{12}$  (ii) $\frac{1}{4}$  (iii) $\frac{3}{4}$  (iv) $\frac{2}{3}$
**7.** (i) $\frac{1}{4}$  (ii) $\frac{3}{8}$  (iii) $\frac{5}{8}$  (iv) $\frac{1}{4}$
**8.** (i) $\frac{1}{5}$  (ii) $\frac{1}{5}$  (iii) $\frac{2}{5}$  (iv) $\frac{1}{2}$

**9.** (i) $\frac{1}{7}$  (ii) $\frac{2}{7}$  (iii) $\frac{2}{7}$
**10.** (i) $\frac{1}{6}$  (ii) $\frac{1}{3}$
**11.** (i) $\frac{1}{5}$  (ii) $\frac{1}{21}$  (iii) 0
**12.** (i) $\frac{2}{15}$  (ii) $\frac{2}{5}$  (iii) $\frac{2}{3}$
**13.** (i) (a) $\frac{1}{4}$  (b) $\frac{1}{6}$  (ii) (a) $\frac{1}{4}$  (b) $\frac{5}{12}$
**14.** (i) $\frac{2}{5}$  (ii) $\frac{3}{10}$  (iii) $\frac{11}{25}$; $\frac{1}{6}$
**15.** $\frac{2}{5}$
**16.** (i) $\frac{1}{2}$  (ii) $\frac{8}{25}$  (iii) $\frac{8}{25}$
**17.** (i) $\frac{2}{5}$  (ii) $\frac{3}{5}$  (iii) $\frac{4}{25}$  (iv) $\frac{4}{15}$  (v) $\frac{2}{5}$
**18.** (i) $\frac{1}{7}$  (ii) 5 fours
**19.** (i) $\frac{3}{49}$  (ii) $\frac{12}{49}$
**20.**

## Exercise 4.3

**1.** (i) $\frac{1}{12}$  (ii) $\frac{1}{4}$  (iii) $\frac{1}{3}$  (iv) $\frac{1}{6}$
**2.** (i) $\frac{1}{9}$  (ii) $\frac{1}{12}$  (iii) $\frac{1}{12}$  (iv) $\frac{5}{36}$
**3.** (i) $\frac{1}{8}$  (ii) $\frac{1}{8}$  (iii) $\frac{3}{8}$
**4.** (i) $\frac{1}{12}$  (ii) $\frac{1}{6}$  (iii) $\frac{1}{2}$; 9 most often; $\frac{1}{4}$
**5.** BBR, RBB; $\frac{2}{3}$
**6.** (i) (1, 5), (1, 6), (1, 7), (2, 5), (2, 6), (2, 7), (3, 5), (3, 6), (3, 7), (4, 5), (4, 6), (4, 7)
   (ii) 12
   (iii) (a) $\frac{1}{3}$  (b) $\frac{1}{6}$  (c) $\frac{1}{4}$
**7.** ABC, ACB, BAC, BCA, CAB, CBA;
   (i) $\frac{1}{6}$  (ii) $\frac{1}{3}$
**8.** (i) $\frac{1}{6}$  (ii) $\frac{2}{3}$  (iii) $\frac{1}{4}$
**9.** (i) $\frac{1}{8}$  (ii) $\frac{3}{8}$  (iii) $\frac{1}{8}$  (iv) $\frac{7}{8}$

## Exercise 4.4

**1.** 50
**2.** (i) 10  (ii) 10  (iii) 20
**3.** (i) 50  (ii) 150
**4.** (i) $\frac{13}{20}$  (ii) 100  (iii) Yes
**5.** (i) $\frac{1}{12}$  (ii) $\frac{1}{6}$  (iii) $\frac{1}{4}$
**6.** (i) (a) $\frac{1}{5}$  (b) $\frac{2}{15}$
   (ii) (a) $\frac{1}{6}$  (b) $\frac{1}{6}$
   (iii) No
**7.** If fair – 6 times; No
**8.** $\frac{7}{10}$

9. (i) 0.15    (ii) '1'    (iii) 50
10. Ben's; Joe's
11. (i) $x = 0.1$    (ii) 0.6    (iii) 200
12. (i) Ciara    (ii) 0.4, 0.3, 0.2, 0.1 (1, 2, 3, 4)
   (iii) Yes
13. Red dice is fair
14. (i) Bill's    (ii) Biased spinner
   (iii) $\frac{63}{290}$
15. (ii) 1    (iii) Yes
   (iv) Extremely unlikely    (v) Mint

## Exercise 4.5

1. (i) $\frac{1}{6}$    (ii) $\frac{1}{2}$    (iii) $\frac{2}{3}$
2. (i) $\frac{1}{2}$    (ii) $\frac{1}{4}$    (iii) $\frac{3}{4}$
3. (i) $\frac{4}{9}$    (ii) $\frac{2}{9}$    (iii) $\frac{2}{3}$
4. (i) $\frac{1}{4}$    (ii) $\frac{3}{26}$    (iii) $\frac{19}{52}$
5. (i) $\frac{1}{2}$    (ii) $\frac{1}{3}$    (iii) $\frac{2}{3}$
6. (i) $\frac{1}{4}$    (ii) $\frac{1}{13}$    (iii) $\frac{4}{13}$
   (iv) $\frac{1}{2}$    (v) $\frac{1}{13}$    (vi) $\frac{7}{13}$
7. (i) $\frac{1}{36}$    (ii) $\frac{1}{6}$    (iii) $\frac{1}{6}$
8. (i) yellow 3 included twice    (ii) $\frac{3}{5}$
9. (ii) Yes   (iii) No   (iv) No   (v) Yes

## Exercise 4.6

1. (i) $\frac{11}{20}$ (ii) $\frac{3}{10}$ (iii) $\frac{3}{40}$ (iv) $\frac{3}{8}$
2. (i) 35 (ii) $\frac{4}{7}$ (iii) $\frac{8}{35}$ (iv) $\frac{1}{5}$ (v) $\frac{6}{35}$ (vi) $\frac{4}{5}$
3. (i) $\frac{13}{41}$ (ii) $\frac{6}{41}$ (iii) $\frac{13}{41}$ (iv) $\frac{26}{41}$ (v) $\frac{15}{41}$
4. (i) 12 (ii) $\frac{3}{5}$ (iii) $\frac{1}{10}$ (iv) $\frac{21}{25}$ (v) $\frac{37}{50}$
5. (ii) $\frac{1}{5}$ (iii) $\frac{4}{15}$ (iv) $\frac{7}{15}$ (v) $\frac{8}{15}$
6. (i) $\frac{19}{30}$ (ii) $\frac{3}{10}$ (iii) $\frac{9}{10}$ (iv) $\frac{1}{15}$ (v) $\frac{1}{10}$ (vi) $\frac{14}{15}$
7. (i) 24
   (ii) They like both chocolate and ice-cream
   (iii) $\frac{3}{20}$    (iv) $\frac{3}{4}$

## Exercise 4.7

1. (i) $\frac{1}{4}$    (ii) $\frac{1}{4}$
2. (i) $\frac{1}{12}$    (ii) $\frac{1}{4}$    (iii) $\frac{1}{6}$
3. (i) $\frac{1}{36}$    (ii) $\frac{1}{4}$    (iii) $\frac{1}{9}$
4. (i) $\frac{25}{81}$    (ii) $\frac{20}{81}$    (iii) $\frac{20}{81}$
5. (i) $\frac{1}{24}$    (ii) $\frac{1}{4}$    (iii) $\frac{1}{12}$
6. (i) $\frac{4}{49}$    (ii) $\frac{1}{49}$    (iii) $\frac{1}{49}$    (iv) $\frac{9}{49}$
7. (i) $\frac{1}{4}$    (ii) $\frac{1}{2}$    (iii) $\frac{1}{16}$    (iv) $\frac{1}{8}$
8. (i) $\frac{1}{5}$    (ii) (a) $\frac{1}{25}$    (b) $\frac{1}{5}$

9. (i) $\frac{2}{5}$ (ii) $\frac{2}{25}$ (iii) $\frac{4}{25}$ (iv) $\frac{8}{25}$
10. (i) $\frac{1}{7}$ (ii) $\frac{1}{49}$ (iii) $\frac{4}{49}$
11. (i) $\frac{1}{4}$ (ii) $\frac{1}{8}$
12. (i) $\frac{1}{6}$ (ii) $\frac{25}{216}$
13. (i) $\frac{8}{27}$ (ii) (a) $\frac{2}{9}$ (b) $\frac{2}{27}$
14. (i) $\frac{1}{64}$ (ii) $\frac{9}{16}$ (iii) $\frac{9}{64}$
15. (i) $\frac{2}{5}$ (ii) $\frac{18}{125}$
16. (i) $\frac{4}{25}$ (ii) $\frac{4}{125}$ (iii) $\frac{1}{125}$
17. (i) $\frac{7}{10}$ (ii) $\frac{9}{100}$ (iii) $\frac{147}{1000}$
18. (i) $\frac{1}{3}$ (ii) $\frac{2}{9}$ (iii) $\frac{2}{27}$
19. (i) $\frac{1}{4}$ (ii) $\frac{9}{64}$ (iii) $\frac{27}{64}$
20. (i) $\frac{1}{8}$ (ii) $\frac{3}{8}$ (iii) $\frac{3}{8}$
21. (i) $\frac{1}{5}$ (ii) $\frac{9}{50}$ (iii) $\frac{2}{25}$ (iv) $\frac{3}{25}$
22. (i) $\frac{1}{6}$ (ii) $\frac{1}{6}$ (iii) $\frac{1}{36}$
   (iv) 6, 6, 6, or 5, 6, 5 or 5, 5, 6    (v) $\frac{1}{72}$

## Exercise 4.8

1. 12    **2.** 12    **3.** 504    **4.** 20
5. 12    **6.** 54    **7.** 20    **8.** 27
9. 90    **10.** 120    **11.** 336

## Exercise 4.9

1. 120
2. 720; (i) 240    (ii) 48
3. 24
4. 60; (i) 12    (ii) 24
5. 720; (i) 240    (ii) 24    (iii) 48
6. 120
7. (i) 720    (ii) 120
8. 720; (i) 120    (ii) 360    (iii) 144
9. 96
10. 120; 48
11. 720; 240
12. 24; (i) 12    (ii) $\frac{1}{2}$
13. (i) 24    (ii) DABC, CABD, DBAC, CBAD
   (iii) $\frac{1}{6}$
14. (i) 120    (ii) 24    (iii) 6
15. (i) 120    (ii) 5040    (iii) 120    (iv) 144
16. (i) No    (ii) No
17. (i) 8(7!)    (ii) 56(6!)
18. $k = 11$

## Exercise 4.10

1. (i) 10    (ii) 35    (iii) 70
   (iv) 120    (v) 120    (vi) 120
3. 210

**4.** 190

**5.** (i) 924 (ii) 462

**6.** (i) 330 (ii) 210

**7.** 28

**8.** 15; 10

**9.** 252; (i) 120 (ii) 60

**10.** (i) 21 (ii) 15 (iii) 10

**11.** (i) 330 (ii) 150

**12.** 21

**13.** (i) 126 (ii) 20 (iii) 60

**14.** (i) $n = 8$ (ii) $n = 11$

**15.** (i) 2925 (ii) 1260

**16.** (i) 330 (ii) 120 (iii) 150 (iv) $\frac{1}{22}$

## Test yourself 4

**1.** (i) $\frac{1}{4}$ (ii) $\frac{3}{4}$ (iii) $\frac{3}{8}$
(iv) 0 (v) 1

**2.** (i) 50 times (ii) 150 times

**3.** (i) $\frac{1}{7}$ (ii) $\frac{4}{7}$

**4.** (i) $\frac{1}{6}$ (ii) $\frac{1}{3}$ (iii) $\frac{1}{2}$ (iv) $\frac{1}{2}$

**5.** (i) $\frac{1}{4}$ (ii) Lose money
(iii) $\frac{19}{20}$ (iv) 60 times

**6.** (i) $\frac{11}{20}$ (ii) $\frac{1}{4}$ (iii) 18

**7.** 90

**8.** (i) $\frac{1}{12}$ (ii) $\frac{1}{36}$ (iii) $\frac{5}{18}$ (iv) $\frac{1}{6}$

**9.** $\frac{3}{8}$

**10.** $\frac{1}{6}$

**11.** (i) $\frac{1}{2}$ (ii) $\frac{1}{4}$

**12.** (i) $\frac{2}{7}$ (ii) $\frac{1}{2}$ (iii) $\frac{3}{4}$ (iv) $\frac{5}{7}$

**13.** (i) (a) 0.52 (b) Yes

**14.** (i) $\frac{1}{9}$ (ii) $\frac{2}{27}$

**15.** (i) $x = 0.25$ (ii) 60

**16.** (i) (a) (ii) $\frac{11}{15}$

**17.** (i) $\frac{1}{3}$ (ii) $\frac{1}{9}$ (iii) $\frac{4}{27}$

**18.** Yes

**19.** 60; (i) 12 (ii) 36

**20.** 5040; (i) 720 (ii) $\frac{1}{7}$

**21.** (i) $\frac{1}{72}$ (ii) $\frac{1}{24}$ (iii) $\frac{1}{24}$

**22.** (i) $P(1) = \frac{1}{10}$; $P(2) = \frac{7}{50}$; $P(3) = \frac{4}{25}$; $P(4) = \frac{1}{4}$;
$P(5) = \frac{7}{20}$
(ii) 40 (iii) No

**23.** (i) $\frac{1}{3}$ (ii) $\frac{1}{3}$
(iii) (a) {3, 4, 5} or {5, 4, 3}, or {2, 6, 4} or...
(b) 11
(iv) (a) 3 (b) $\frac{1}{216}$

# Chapter 5:
# Coordinate Geometry: The Line

## Exercise 5.1

**1.** A = (5, 4), B = (6, 1), C = (3, 2), D = (−4, 3),
E = (−4, 0), F = (−3, −3), G = (0, −2),
H = (4, −2), I = (3, 0)

**3.** (i) First (ii) Third (iii) Fourth
(iv) Second (v) Fourth (vi) Third

**4.** (i) x-axis (ii) x-axis (iii) y-axis
(iv) y-axis (v) Both axes/origin

**5.** (i) A(4, 2), B(−3, 2), C(−5, −2), D(5, −3)
(ii) 1.3 km (iii) 1.3 km

**6.** (i) (0, 8), (9, −1) (ii) (4, 11), (0, 15)
(iii) (7, 1), (−3, 11), (10, −2)

## Exercise 5.2

**1.** (i) $\sqrt{34}$ (ii) $\sqrt{50}$ (iii) $\sqrt{53}$; No

**2.** (i) |FE| = 6, |ED| = 3 (ii) $\sqrt{45}$

**3.** (i) $\sqrt{10}$ (ii) $\sqrt{5}$ (iii) $\sqrt{13}$
(iv) $\sqrt{89}$ (v) $\sqrt{53}$ (vi) 5

**4.** (i) $\sqrt{26}$ (ii) $\sqrt{8}$
(iii) $\sqrt{10}$ (iv) $\sqrt{8}$

**6.** |XY| = $\sqrt{65}$; |XZ| = $\sqrt{65}$; |YZ| = $\sqrt{26}$;
|XY| = |XZ| $\Rightarrow$ $\triangle$XYZ is isosceles

**7.** A(2, 0); B(6, 7); C(10, 0); D(6, 0); $2\sqrt{65}$ units

**8.** $\sqrt{53}$

**9.** (i) $\sqrt{18}$ (ii) $\sqrt{34}$; No

**10.** $k = 1$ or $k = 3$

**11.** $k = 5$ or $k = -1$

**12.** $\sqrt{26}$ km

## Exercise 5.3

**1.** (i) (4, 3) (ii) (1, 3) (iii) (3, 1)
(iv) (1, 1) (v) (1, −2) (vi) (−2, 0)

**2.** $\left(0, \frac{11}{2}\right)$; y-axis

**3.** (2, 4)

**4.** $\left(1, \frac{1}{2}\right)$

**5.** (−1, −1)

**6.** (−1, 6)

## Exercise 5.4

**1.** (i) a + c (ii) b + d

**2.** (i) b (ii) $\frac{2}{3}$ (iii) 2

**3.** Line is falling from left to right; $-\frac{1}{2}$

**4.** (i) 1 (ii) $-\frac{3}{2}$ (iii) 8
(iv) 1 (v) 1 (vi) $\frac{2}{3}$

5. They are parallel
6. Yes, parallel
8. $a = \frac{1}{2}$, b = 1, c = 2
9. (i) $\frac{3}{4}$      (ii) $-\frac{4}{3}$
10. (i) $-\frac{3}{2}$      (ii) $-\frac{5}{4}$      (iii) $\frac{4}{3}$
    (iv) $\frac{5}{2}$      (v) 2
11. (i) 1      (ii) −1
12. (i) −1      (ii) 1
13. $k = 5$
14. $k = -\frac{8}{3}$
15. (i) $\frac{1}{2}$      (ii) $\frac{2}{k-1}$      (iii) 5
16. (i) Each line is falling from left to right
    (ii) $\ell = -2$, $m = -1$, $n = -\frac{1}{2}$, $k = 0$

## Exercise 5.5

1. (i) $2x - y - 2 = 0$      (ii) $4x - y + 1 = 0$
    (iii) $5x - y + 13 = 0$      (iv) $3x + y + 6 = 0$
    (v) $5x + y + 17 = 0$      (vi) $2x - 3y - 9 = 0$
2. (i) $3x - 4y - 19 = 0$      (ii) $3x - 5y + 22 = 0$
3. (i) $4x - y + 11 = 0$      (ii) $2x + y + 1 = 0$
    (iii) $3x - 4y + 18 = 0$      (iv) $2x + 3y - 5 = 0$
4. $3x + y = 0$
5. (i) $3x - y = 0$      (ii) $5x + y = 0$
    (iii) $x - 3y = 0$      (iv) $3x + 2y = 0$
6. $-3$; $3x + y - 5 = 0$
7. (i) $3x - 2y = 0$      (ii) $2x + y = 0$
    (iii) $x + 6y - 1 = 0$      (iv) $4x + 5y - 7 = 0$
    (v) $x - y + 5 = 0$      (vi) $2x - y + 1 = 0$
8. $5x + 4y - 2 = 0$
9. (i) A = (4, 3), B = (7, 5), C = (10, 3)
    (ii) $\frac{2}{3}$      (iii) $2x - 3y + 1 = 0$

## Exercise 5.6

1. (i) $y = -x + 4$; −1    (ii) $y = -3x + 5$; −3
    (iii) $y = -\frac{2}{3}x + \frac{7}{3}$; $-\frac{2}{3}$
    (iv) $y = \frac{5}{2}x + \frac{3}{2}$; $\frac{5}{2}$
    (v) $y = -\frac{3}{4}x + \frac{1}{2}$; $-\frac{3}{4}$
    (vi) $y = \frac{3}{4}x + \frac{3}{2}$; $\frac{3}{4}$
2. $y = -\frac{2}{3}x + \frac{7}{3}$
    (i) $-\frac{2}{3}$      (ii) $-\frac{2}{3}$      (iii) $\frac{3}{2}$
3. $-2$
5. (i) $y = 3x + 6$      (ii) $y = -\frac{1}{3}x + 11$
6. Yes; parallel
7. (i) 3      (ii) (0, −2)
8. (i) $a + f$      (ii) $a + e$ or $b + d$
    (iii) e      (iv) a

9. $x - 2y + 2 = 0$ or $y = \frac{1}{2}x + 1$
10. $k = 4$
11. $k = 2$
12. $k = 6$

## Exercise 5.7

1. $-2$; $2x + y - 8 = 0$
2. $3x - y - 9 = 0$
3. $\frac{2}{3}$; $-\frac{3}{2}$; $3x + 2y - 10 = 0$
4. $2x - 3y + 7 == 0$
5. $3x - y + 12 = 0$
6. $x + 3y = 0$
7. P(2, 4); $5x - y - 6 = 0$
8. $2x + y - 5 = 0$
9. $x + 4y - 28 = 0$
10. C
11. $x + 2y - 10 = 0$
12. (i) $\frac{5}{3}$      (ii) (b) $3x + 5y = 2$

## Exercise 5.8

1. a: $y = 1$; b: $y = 3$; c: $x = 3$; d: $x = -1$
3. (i) $x = 3$      (ii) (0, 6)      (iii) 4
    (iv) 1      (v) 9 sq. units
4. x-axis; (6, 0); y-axis; (0, −3)
6. x-axis: (5, 0); y-axis: $\left(0, -\frac{5}{2}\right)$
7. 9 sq. units
9. (i) A      (ii) B
    (iii) Not perpendicular
    (iv) 7.5 sq. units
11. (i) d    (ii) c    (iii) a    (iv) b
12. (iv) Not on line
14. $k = -6$
15. $k = 3$
16. (i) $k = 2$      (ii) $t = 5$

## Exercise 5.9

1. (4, 1)     2. (1, 4)     3. (2, 3)
4. (3, 1)     5. (−2, 1)     6. (−3, 1)
7. (−2, 3)     8. (−3, −1)     9. (−1, −2)
10. (3, −4)     11. (−2, 5)

## Exercise 5.10

1. (i) $\frac{5}{2}$ sq. units      (ii) $\frac{27}{2}$ sq. units
    (iii) $\frac{5}{2}$ sq. units      (iv) 5 sq. units
    (v) 3 sq. units      (vi) 9 sq. units
2. B′ = (−7, −2); C′ = (1, −2); 8 sq. units

**3.** (i) $\frac{9}{2}$ sq. units    (ii) $\frac{33}{2}$ sq. units

   (iii) 15 sq. units    (iv) 4 sq. units

**4.** 14 sq. units; 14 sq. units

**5.** 14 sq. units

**6.** 14 sq. units

**7.** 4 sq. units

**8.** Not a triangle, i.e. a straight line

**9.** $k = 1$

## Test yourself 5

**1.** (i) $\sqrt{10}$      (ii) $\frac{1}{3}$

**2.** (ii) $-\frac{4}{3}$     (iii) $4x + 3y - 10 = 0$

**3.** (i) 2      (ii) $(0, -4)$

   (iii) $(2, 0)$     (iv) $-\frac{1}{2}$

**4.** (ii) $k = 3$

**5.** (i) $(0, 5)$; $y$-axis    (ii) $\frac{4}{3}$

   (iii) $-\frac{3}{4}$       (iv) $3x + 4y = 0$

**6.** $\frac{1}{2}$; $y = \frac{1}{2}x + 1$

**7.** (i) $-2$      (iii) $(0, 4)$

**8.** (ii) $\frac{1}{2}$      (iii) $2x + y - 10 = 0$

**9.** (i) $k = 2$

   (ii) $A(3, 0)$, $B(0, 2)$; 3 sq. units

**10.** (i) $3x + y - 6 = 0$   (ii) 6 m

   (iii) 6.3 m

**11.** $(2, 2)$

**12.** (i) $2x + y - 12 = 0$

   (ii) $x$-axis: $(6, 0)$; $y$-axis: $(0, 12)$

   (iii) 36 sq. units

**13.** (i) $2x - y + 1 = 0$

**14.** (i) b and c      (ii) 2

   (iii) D, a; E, b; F, c

**15.** (i) $c = -7$     (ii) $3x + 2y - 4 = 0$

**16.** (iii) 10 sq. units

**17.** (i) 95°F     (ii) 58°F

   (iii) 10°C     (iv) 38°C; $5x - 9y - 160 = 0$

## Chapter 6: Coordinate Geometry: The Circle

### Exercise 6.1

**1.** (i) $x^2 + y^2 = 4$    (ii) $x^2 + y^2 = 9$

   (iii) $x^2 + y^2 = 1$   (iv) $x^2 + y^2 = 25$

   (iv) $x^2 + y^2 = 2$

**2.** (i) $x^2 + y^2 = 8$    (ii) $x^2 + y^2 = 8$

   (iii) $x^2 + y^2 = 18$   (iv) $x^2 + y^2 = \frac{4}{9}$

   (v) $x^2 + y^2 = \frac{16}{9}$

**3.** 5; $x^2 + y^2 = 25$

**4.** (i) $x^2 + y^2 = 13$   (ii) $x^2 + y^2 = 5$

   (iii) $x^2 + y^2 = 25$   (iv) $x^2 + y^2 = 16$

**5.** (i) $x^2 + y^2 = 25$   (ii) $x^2 + y^2 = 9$

   (iii) $(0, 5)$, $(0, -5)$   (iv) $(3, 0)$, $(-3, 0)$

**7.** $36\pi$

**8.** (i) 3      (ii) 7      (iii) 1

   (iv) $2\sqrt{3}$    (v) $3\sqrt{3}$    (vi) $\sqrt{5}$

**9.** (i) $x^2 + y^2 = \frac{9}{4}$; $\frac{3}{2}$   (ii) $x^2 + y^2 = \frac{25}{9}$; $\frac{5}{3}$

   (iii) $x^2 + y^2 = \frac{49}{4}$; $\frac{7}{2}$

**10.** (i) $(0, 0)$   (ii) 5     (iii) $x^2 + y^2 = 25$

**11.** 18

**12.** $x^2 + y^2 = 20$

**13.** (i) $x^2 + y^2 = 6$    (ii) $x^2 + y^2 = 24$

   (iii) $x^2 + y^2 = 18$   (iv) $x^2 + y^2 = 12$

   (v) $x^2 + y^2 = 45$

**14.** $x^2 + y^2 = 36$

### Exercise 6.2

**2.** Outside

**3.** $(5, 0)$, $(-5, 0)$; $(0, 5)$, $(0, -5)$

**5.** (i) Outside     (ii) On

   (iii) Outside    (iv) Inside

**6.** (iii)

**7.** (i) $P(0, 4)$, $Q(0, -4)$   (ii) 8

**8.** $k = 2$

### Exercise 6.3

**1.** (i) $(x - 3)^2 + (y - 1)^2 = 4$

   (ii) $(x - 3)^2 + (y - 4)^2 = 9$

   (iii) $(x - 1)^2 + (y + 4)^2 = 25$

   (iv) $(x + 3)^2 + (y - 5)^2 = 16$

   (v) $(x + 3)^2 + (y + 2)^2 = 1$

   (vi) $(x - 3)^2 + y^2 = 36$

   (vii) $(x + 3)^2 + (y + 5)^2 = 10$

   (viii) $x^2 + (y + 2)^2 = 8$

**2.** (i) $\sqrt{10}$

   (ii) $(x - 2)^2 + (y - 4)^2 = 10$

**3.** $(x - 5)^2 + (y + 2)^2 = 85$

**4.** $(x - 2)^2 + (y - 2)^2 = 10$

**5.** (i) $(1, 3)$     (ii) $\sqrt{8}$

   (iii) $(x - 1)^2 + (y - 3)^2 = 8$

**6.** $(2, 3)$; 4

**7.** $(4, -3)$; 3

**8.** $(-2, -5)$; 8

**9.** $(-5, 1)$; 9

**10.** $(0, 4)$; 5

**11.** $(3, 0)$; 3

**12.** $(1, -5)$; $\frac{4}{3}$

**13.** $(0, 2)$; $2\sqrt{3}$

**14.** $(3, 3)$; $(x - 3)^2 + (y - 3)^2 = 9$

**15.** (i) (4, 0)   (ii) $(x - 4)^2 + y^2 = 16$
(iii) 2   (iv) (4, 2)
(v) $(x - 4)^2 + (y - 2)^2 = 4$   (vi) (4, 4)

**16.** (i) 2   (ii) (4, −4)
(iii) $(x - 4)^2 + (y + 4)^2 = 4$   (iv) $k_4$

**17.** (2, 3); $(x - 2)^2 + (y - 3)^2 = 10$

**18.** (i) 3   (ii) $(x - 4)^2 + (y - 3)^2 = 9$

**19.** (i) (4, 0)   (ii) $(x - 4)^2 + y^2 = 4$
(iii) $(x - 4)^2 + y^2 = 36$   (iv) Yes, equal

**20.** (i) $(x - 1)^2 + y^2 = 1$   (ii) (2, 1)
(iii) $(x - 2)^2 + (y - 1)^2 = 1$
(iv) $2 - \frac{\pi}{2}$ sq. units

## Exercise 6.4

**1.** (i) (−2, −3), (3, 2)   (ii) (3, 1), (1, 3)
(iii) (5, 0), (−3, −4)   (iv) (4, 2), (−2, 4)

**2.** (2, −1)

**3.** (i) (1, 1)   (ii) (1, −3)   (iii) (2, −1)

**4.** (3, 0), (0, −3); No; Two points of intersection

**5.** (4, 2), (−4, −2)

**6.** $x^2 + y^2 = 10$; (−1, −3), (−3, −1)

**7.** $x + y - 3 = 0$; (2, 1), (1, 2)

**8.** Point of contact = (−2, 4)

**9.** (i) (3, 3)   (ii) $(x - 3)^2 + (y - 3)^2 = 9$
(iii) $y = 6$   (iv) $x = 6$   (v) (6, 6)

## Exercise 6.5

**1.** (i) (2, 0), (−2, 0)   (ii) (5, 0), (−5, 0)
(iii) (9, 0), (−9, 0)

**2.** (0, 7), (0, −7)

**3.** (i) (2, 0), (8, 0)   (ii) (6, 0), (−2, 0)

**4.** (0, 1), (0, −7)

**6.** (−4, 1); 3

**7.** Outside

**8.** $(x + 3)^2 + y^2 = 10$; 2

**9.** (i) 4   (ii) $(x + 2)^2 + (y - 4)^2 = 16$

## Test yourself 6

**1.** (i) (0, 0); $r = 7$

**2.** $x^2 + y^2 = 25$; (5, 0), (−5, 0)

**3.** (i) 6   (ii) $x^2 + y^2 = 144$

**4.** $(x - 2)^2 + (y + 3)^2 = 16$

**5.** (i) (3, 4); radius = 5

**6.** Point of intersection = (1, −3)

**7.** (i) 6   (iii) (0, 6), (0, −6)

**8.** (i) A(−9, 0), C(9, 0)
(ii) a: $(x + 9)^2 + y^2 = 36$  c: $(x - 9)^2 + y^2 = 36$
(iii) $y = 6, y = -6$

**9.** (i) A(2, 6), B(6, −2)

**10.** (i) (1, −2); $r = \sqrt{5}$   (ii) $(x - 1)^2 + (y + 2)^2 = 5$

**11.** (i) C(2, 0); $r = 3$   (ii) $(x - 2)^2 + y^2 = 9$
(iii) $t_1$; $y = 3$; $t_2$: $y = -3$

**12.** (i) A = (3, 1), B = (−3, −1)

**13.** (3, 4); $r = 2\sqrt{5}$; A = (1, 0), B = (5, 0); $|AB| = 4$

**14.** (i) (4, −1); $r = 4$
(ii) $(x - 4)^2 + (y + 1)^2 = 16$
(iii) $\frac{5}{4}$; AE ⊥ EB (angle in a semicircle)

**15.** (i) (−2, 3); $r = 5$   (iii) P = (−7, 3), Q = (3, 3)
(iv) $x = -7, x = 3$   (v) $(x + 2)^2 + y^2 = 25$

**17.** $k_1$: $x^2 + (y - 2)^2 = 4$; $k_2$: $x^2 + (y + 2)^2 = 4$;
$k_3$: $x^2 + y^2 = 16$; $y = 4$

**18.** (i) (−4, 3); $r = 6$   (ii) (−10, 3)

**19.** $(x + 1)^2 + (y - 2)^2 = 25$

# Chapter 7: Trigonometry

## Exercise 7.1

**1.** 12 cm²   **2.** 31 cm²   **3.** Yes

**4.** $a = 3.6$ cm,   $b = 9.2$ cm,   $c = 9.5$ cm,
$d = 4.5$ cm,   $e = 15$ cm,   $f = 12$ cm,
$g = 9.4$ cm,   $h = 6.4$ cm,   $i = 8.9$ cm

**5.** 12.8 cm   **6.** 8.1

**7.** 2.6 m   **8.** 6.4 cm

**9.** (i) 3 cm   (ii) 5.8 cm

**10.** $c = 10$ cm, $d = 24$ cm

**11.** 25 cm   **12.** 25.7 m

## Exercise 7.2

**1.** (i) tan A   (ii) cos A   (iii) sin A

**2.** $\frac{3}{5}, \frac{4}{5}, \frac{3}{4}, \frac{5}{13}, \frac{12}{13}, \frac{5}{12}, \frac{\sqrt{3}}{2}, \frac{1}{2}, \sqrt{3}$

**3.** 5; (i) $\frac{5}{13}$   (ii) $\frac{12}{13}$   (iii) $\frac{5}{12}$

**4.** 2; $\frac{3}{\sqrt{13}}$   (ii) $\frac{2}{\sqrt{13}}$   (iii) $\frac{3}{2}$

**5.** (i) tan θ   (ii) sin θ   (iii) cos θ

**6.** $\sin B = \frac{12}{13}, \tan B = \frac{12}{5}$

**7.** (i) $\frac{1}{\sqrt{5}}$   (ii) $\frac{\sqrt{21}}{2}$

**8.** $\sin C = \frac{1}{2}, \cos C = \frac{\sqrt{3}}{2}$

**9.** 1

**10.** (i) 1   (ii) 1

## Exercise 7.3

**1.** (i) 0.7431   (ii) 0.2756
(iii) 0.2679   (iv) 0.9511
(v) 0.8788

**2.** (i) 0.5344      (ii) 0.7266
   (iii) 0.5914     (iv) 0.2773
**3.** (i) 48°       (ii) 69°
   (iii) 55°     (iv) 78°
   (v) 42°     (vi) 12°
**4.** (i) 36.9°     (ii) 41.1°
   (iii) 75.4°    (iv) 74.2°
**5.** (i) 42°      (ii) 53°
   (iii) 41°     (iv) 24°
   (v) 29°     (vi) 12°
   (vii) 35°    (viii) 58°
**6.** $A = 56.7°$; $\sin A = 0.84$
**7.** $A = 37°$; $B = 68°$; $C = 39°$

## Exercise 7.4

**1.** (i) cosine   (ii) tangent   (iii) cosine
**2.** $x = 3.8$, $y = 10.0$, $z = 10.2$
**3.** (i) 3.3     (ii) 16.7     (iii) 13.5
**4.** (i) 37°     (ii) 46°     (iii) 23°
**5.** $p = 67°$, $q = 24°$, $r = 37°$
**6.** $x = 9.4$
**7.** (i) 12.0     (ii) 15.9     (iii) 18.8
**8.** $x = 15$, $y = 20$
**9.** (i) 13.9     (ii) 44°
**10.** 12.5 cm
**11.** (i) 13 cm     (ii) 11°
**12.** (i) 4.2 cm     (ii) 25°
**13.** 20 m
**14.** 21 m
**15.** 40 m
**16.** (i) 4.0 m     (ii) 12.7 m
**17.** (i) 25°     (ii) 107 m
   (iii) 118 m    (iv) 355 m
**18.** Yes
**19.** (i) 37°     (ii) $|BC| = 6$ m, $|DC| = 4$ m
**20.** 3 cm

## Exercise 7.5

**1.** (i) 24.1 cm²   (ii) 7.4 cm²   (iii) 11.4 cm²
**2.** (i) 12 cm²     (ii) 49 cm²     (iii) 85 cm²
**3.** 87 sq. units
**4.** 338 cm²
**5.** 139 cm²
**6.** $A = 75°$, $B = 22°$
**7.** 8.3
**8.** 10 cm
**9.** $\sin A = \frac{3}{5}$; 168 sq. units
**10.** 153 m
**11.** (ii) 90°     (iii) Four times
**12.** (i) $\frac{\sqrt{24}}{5}$     (ii) $6\sqrt{6}$; $k = 6$

## Exercise 7.6

**1.** (i) 15.3     (ii) 11.3     (iii) 11.0
**2.** (i) $A = 34°$   (ii) $B = 51°$   (iii) 75°
**3.** (i) 40°     (ii) 22 cm
**4.** (i) 29      (ii) 302 sq. units
**5.** (i) 19.2 m     (ii) 15.3 m
**6.** (i) 94 m     (ii) 81 m
**7.** (i) 47°     (ii) 98 km
**8.** (i) 8 cm     (ii) 33 cm²
**9.** (i) 37 m     (ii) 23 m
**10.** (i) 60°     (ii) 74 m     (iii) 1899 m²

## Exercise 7.7

**1.** $a = 4.4$, $b = 11.1$, $a = 14.7$
**2.** $a = 6$, $b = 21$, $c = 9$
**3.** $A = 49°$, $B = 43°$, $C = 29°$
**4.** 29°
**5.** 45°
**6.** 66 m
**7.** (i) 13 m     (ii) 72°
**8.** 101 cm
**9.** 21 km
**10.** (i) 9 cm     (ii) 16.1 cm
**11.** (i) 23 cm     (ii) 39°
**12.** (i) 7.39     (ii) 10.61
**13.** 9 m
**14.** (i) 30 m     (ii) 177 m
**15.** (i) 13.7 cm     (ii) 69°
**16.** (i) 386 m     (ii) 363 m
**17.** (i) 37 m
**18.** (i) 58°     (ii) 79°

## Exercise 7.8

**1.** $\frac{1}{2}$   **2.** 1   **3.** $\frac{1}{2}$   **4.** $\frac{1}{\sqrt{2}}$   **5.** $\frac{1}{4}$
**6.** $\frac{\sqrt{3}}{2}$   **7.** $\frac{\sqrt{3}}{2}$   **8.** $\frac{1}{2}$   **9.** $\frac{3}{4}$   **10.** $\frac{1}{3}$
**12.** $x = 3$, $y = 3\sqrt{3}$
**13.** $x = 3$, $y = 4$
**14.** $x = 4\sqrt{3}$, $y = 4$, $z = \frac{8}{\sqrt{3}}$ $\left(\text{or } \frac{8\sqrt{3}}{3}\right)$
**15.** $400\sqrt{3}$

## Exercise 7.9

**1.** (i) 34 cm²   (ii) 127 cm²   (iii) 44 cm²
**2.** (i) 8.4 cm   (ii) 23.0 cm   (iii) 17.5 cm
**3.** (i) 410.5 cm²   (ii) 58.6 cm
**4.** (i) 24 cm     (ii) 212 cm²
**5.** 14 cm       **6.** 15 cm
**7.** 115 m       **8.** 5.9 km²

**9.** (i) 170 cm$^2$    (ii) 54 cm
**10.** (i) 25 cm    (ii) 23 cm    (iii) 226 cm$^2$
    (iv) 160 cm$^2$    (v) 66 cm$^2$
**11.** (i) 106°    (ii) 18.5 m

## Exercise 7.10

**1.** (i) 0.7660    (ii) −0.7660
   (iii) 0.6428    (iv) −0.6428
**2.** (i) 0.6691    (ii) −0.8480
   (iii) −0.9004    (iv) −0.9336
   (v) 0.2309    (vi) −0.8290
   (vii) 0.7314    (viii) 3.4874
**3.** (i) sin 50°    (ii) −cos 65°
   (iii) −tan 20°    (iv) −cos 40°
   (v) −sin 70°    (vi) −tan 60°
**4.** (i) $\frac{\sqrt{3}}{2}$    (ii) $-\frac{1}{\sqrt{2}}$    (iii) $-\frac{\sqrt{3}}{2}$

   (iv) $-\frac{1}{2}$    (v) $\frac{\sqrt{3}}{2}$    (vi) 1

   (vii) $-\frac{\sqrt{3}}{2}$    (viii) $-\frac{\sqrt{3}}{2}$    (ix) $-\frac{1}{\sqrt{3}}$
**5.** 13° and 167°
**6.** (i) 147° and 213°    (ii) 129° and 309°
**7.** 30° and 150°
**8.** 1 and −1
**9.** $\frac{\sqrt{3}}{2}$ and $-\frac{\sqrt{3}}{2}$
**10.** $\frac{1}{2}$ and $-\frac{1}{2}$
**11.** 233°
**12.** $-\frac{3}{4}$
**13.** $-\frac{\sqrt{3}}{2}$
**14.** $-\frac{1}{\sqrt{5}}$

## Test yourself 7

**1.** (i) $\frac{3}{5}$    (ii) $\frac{3}{4}$; $A = 37°$
**2.** $x = 12$;    (i) $\frac{5}{12}$    (ii) $\frac{12}{13}$
**3.** 17.8 cm
**4.** (i) 8 cm    (ii) 22°
**5.** (i) 16 cm$^2$    (ii) 6 cm    (iii) 41°
**6.** (i) 4.2 cm    (ii) 25°
**7.** (i) 32.0°    (ii) 43°
**8.** (i) 41 cm$^2$    (ii) 11.6 cm
**9.** (i) 15 m    (ii) 9.6 m
**10.** (i) 22.3 cm$^2$    (ii) 6.0 cm$^2$
**11.** (i) 22 cm    (ii) 27 cm
**12.** (i) 240° and 300°    (ii) $\frac{3}{2}$

**13.** (i) 15 cm    (ii) 148 cm$^2$
**14.** 12.7 m
**15.** (i) 13.1 cm    (ii) 39°
**16.** (i) 20 cm$^2$    (ii) 18 cm
**17.** 9.1 cm; 50°
**18.** (i) Radar A    (ii) Radar A
**19.** (i) 150° and 210°    (ii) $a = 2\sqrt{2}$, $b = \sqrt{6}$
**20.** 6.0 km$^2$

# Chapter 8: Geometry 1
## Exercise 8.1

**1.** $a = 32°$, $b = 148°$, $c = 46°$, $d = 134°$, $e = 60°$,
   $f = 120°$, $g = 110°$, $h = 70°$, $j = 140°$, $\ell = 80°$,
   $m = 100°$
**2.** $a = 50°$, $b = 86°$, $c = 111°$, $d = 74°$, $e = 48°$,
   $f = 112°$
**3.** $a = 65°$, $b = 40°$, $c = 52.5°$, $d = 60°$, $e = 30°$
**4.** $x = 65°$, $y = 50°$
**5.** $a = 62°$, $b = 110°$, $c = 55°$, $d = 34°$
**6.** 25°
**7.** (i) 55°    (ii) 45°
**8.** (i) 76°    (ii) 52°
**9.** $a = 95°$, $b = 115°$, $c = 39°$, $d = 85°$
**10.** (i) $x = 116°$, $y = 52°$
   (ii) $x = 20°$, $y = 140°$
   (iii) $x = 80°$, $y = 30°$
**11.** $x = 10$, $y = 5$, $z = 8$
**12.** $|AB| = 6$;  Area = 13.5 sq. units
**13.** (i) 5    (ii) 13
**14.** (i) $\sqrt{76}$    (ii) $\sqrt{32}$    (iii) $\sqrt{44}$
**15.** $x = 5$, $y = 12$
**16.** RHS
**17.** SSS or SAS
**18.** SAS
**19.** $x = 10$, $y = 8$

## Exercise 8.2

**1.** (i) 30 cm$^2$    (ii) 36 cm$^2$    (iii) 36 cm$^2$
**2.** (i) 36 cm$^2$    (ii) 6 cm
**3.** (i) 4    (ii) 10    (iii) 6
**4.** (i) $4\frac{4}{5}$ cm    (ii) $10\frac{1}{2}$ cm    (iii) $21\frac{3}{5}$ cm
**5.** (i) 96 cm$^2$    (ii) 126 cm$^2$    (iii) 143 cm$^2$
**6.** 308 cm$^2$; $|BC| = 17\frac{1}{9}$ cm
**7.** $|DC| \times h$ is area of each
**8.** $2\frac{2}{3}$ cm
**9.** (i) (1, 3), (2, 4), (2, 5), (4, 5)
   (ii) Interior angles or supplementary angles

**10.** (i) 30 cm²    (ii) 30 cm²
    (iii) 45 cm²    (iv) 4 cm
**11.** (i) Alternate angles      (ii) ASA
**12.** (i) 5 cm      (iii) 8 cm
**13.** (i) $\frac{1}{2}|DC| \times h : |DC| \times h$      (ii) 10 cm²

## Exercise 8.3

**1.** (i) [BC]      (ii) [AC]
**2.** (a) (i)      (b) (i)      (c) (ii)
**3.** (i) ∠BAC      (ii) ∠ACB
**4.** (i) 8 cm      (ii) 7 cm
**5.** (i) 5      (ii) 6
**6.** (i) 2.5      (ii) 9      (iii) $6\frac{2}{3}$
**7.** (i) $6\frac{2}{5}$      (ii) $5\frac{5}{6}$      (iii) $2\frac{4}{7}$
**8.** 7
**9.** $6\frac{2}{3}$
**10.** (i) equal angles      (ii) [DF]
    (iii) $x = 12$ cm, $y = 7$ cm
**11.** (i) $1\frac{1}{2}$ times      (ii) $x = 6$, $y = 4.5$
**12.** (ii) $x = 9$, $y = 10\frac{1}{2}$
**13.** (i) [XY]      (ii) $x = 10$, $y = 16\frac{2}{3}$
**14.** $x = 4.5$, $y = 4$
**15.** (ii) 14
**16.** (i) ∠ABD + ∠BDC      (iii) [DC]
    (iv) [AD]
**17.** 6
**18.** (i) $\frac{|AE|}{|AC|} = \frac{|DE|}{|BC|}$      (ii) $x = \frac{48}{5}$, $y = \frac{12}{5}$

## Exercise 8.4

**1.** $a = 90°$, $b = 90°$, $c = 45°$
**2.** As $|AO| = |OC| =$ radius;
    (i) 43°    (ii) 90°    (iii) 47°
**3.** $a = 42°$, $b = 48°$, $c = 50°$, $d = 40°$, $e = 55°$,
    $f = 35°$
**4.** (i) △ABC      (ii) [AO] + [OC]
    (iii) 10      (iv) 8
    (v) 24 sq. units
**5.** (i) 6 cm    (ii) $\sqrt{61}$ cm
**6.** 48 cm
**7.** (i) 90°    (ii) 50°    (iii) 50°    (iv) 80
**8.** (i) 90°    (ii) 35°    (iii) 90°    (iv) 55°
**9.** 30°
**10.** 12 cm
**11.** (i) 60°    (ii) 120°    (iii) 30°    (iv) 30°
**12.** (i) 20°    (ii) 30°

**14.** 20°
**15.** (i) 80°    (ii) 10°    (iii) 80°

## Test yourself 8

**1.** (i) Isosceles      (ii) ∠ABC + ∠ACB
    (iii) 62°
**2.** 80°
**3.** (i) 84 cm²    (ii) 126 cm²    (iii) 84 cm²
**14.** (i) 14 cm    (ii) 10 cm
**5.** (ii) 72 cm²
**6.** (ii) |OB| = |OA|      (iii) 132°
**7.** (i) 90°    (ii) 25 cm    (iii) 24 cm
**8.** (i) ∠ADC + ∠ABC      (ii) 70°
**9.** Angle in a semicircle
**10.** (i) 90°      (ii) $2\sqrt{3}$
**11.** $3\frac{3}{5}$
**12.** 15 cm
**13.** $x = 2$, $a = 9\frac{1}{3}$
**14.** (i) ∠CAB + ∠AOD      (ii) 60°
    (iii) 30°      (iv) 30°
**15.** (i) 15      (ii) 92 sq. units
**16.** (iii) 36 sq. units
    (iv) 24 sq. units
    (v) 60 sq. units

# Chapter 9: Geometry 2: Enlargements and Constructions

## Exercise 9.1

**1.** (i) 2      (ii) $x = 6$ cm, $y = 18$ cm
**2.** (i) 8      (ii) 12      (iii) 5
**3.** The point A
**4.** (i) 6 cm      (ii) 9 cm
**5.** (i) 2      (iii) (−2, 3)
**6.** (i) 2      (ii) (8, 9)
    (iii) A = 2 sq units, B = 8 sq. units
**7.** (i) 2.5      (ii) 3.2
    (iii) 2 : 5;  25 sq. units
**9.** (i) A'B'C'
    (ii) (a) $\frac{1}{3}$    (b) $\frac{4}{3}$
        (c) (a) 4 cm    (b) 16 cm
**10.** Yes;  No
**11.** (i) (0, 2)      (ii) 2
    (iii) $\frac{1}{2}$      (iv) 60 sq. units
**12.** (i) 2.5      (ii) 10
    (iii) 2 : 5      (iv) 100 sq. units
**13.** (i) 104 mm      (ii) 42 mm

**14.** (i) 3
  (ii) Volume of image $= k^3$ times vol. of object
**15.** 10.8 cm
**16.** (i) 3  (ii) 14 cm by $9\frac{1}{3}$ cm
**17.** (i) 1:500  (ii) 60 m
  (iii) 1:2000  (iv) 50 cm

## Exercise 9.2

**7.** 10.7 cm
**9.** 105°
**11.** Yes, same result
**14.** Point is equidistant from the two lines which form the angle
**15.** $|AG|:|GM| = 2:1$; $|BG|:|GN| = 2:1$; $2:1$
**16.** Point of intersection of perpendicular bisectors of [AB] and [BC]

## Test yourself 9

**1.** (i) 2  (ii) 10 cm  (iii) 10.5 cm
  (iv) N'N and L'L intersect at O
  (v) 32 cm
**2.** (i) (0, 2)  (ii) 2  (iii) $\frac{1}{2}$  (iv) 96 cm$^2$
**3.** (i) A  (ii) $\frac{3}{2}$  (iii) 7.5 m  (iv) 14.1 m
  (v) $\frac{2}{3}$
**4.** (i) 12  (ii) 6  (iii) 6; 45 sq. units
**6.** 7.8 cm
**7.** Sports field at circumcentre
**8.** (i) △ABE  (ii) 11.25 cm  (iii) $\frac{2}{5}$
  (iv) 28°  (v) 26.25 cm$^2$
**9.** (i) $\frac{3}{4}$  (ii) 4.5 cm  (iii) 32 cm$^2$
**10.** (ii) 2.2 km
**11.** (i) 1.5  (ii) 6  (iii) 12 sq. units
**12.** (i) (a) $\frac{8}{5}$  (b) $\frac{4}{5}$  (ii) (a) 7.5  (b) 7.2